INTRODUCTION TO

Comparative Entomology

Reinhold Books in the Biological Sciences

CONSULTING EDITOR: PROFESSOR PETER GRAY

Department of Biological Sciences
University of Pittsburgh
Pittsburgh, Pennsylvania

The Encyclopedia of the Biological Sciences, edited by Peter Gray

Biophysics: Concepts and Mechanisms, by E. J. Casey
Cell Function, by L. L. Langley
Chordate Morphology, by Malcolm Jollie
Concepts of Forest Entomology, by Kenneth Graham
Cytology, by G. B. Wilson and John H. Morrison
Ecology of Inland Waters and Estuaries, by George K. Reid
Evolution: Process and Product, Revised Edition, by Edward O. Dodson
Management of Artificial Lakes and Ponds, by George W. Bennett
Manual of Insect Morphology, by E. Melville DuPorte
Natural History, by Richard A. Pimentel
Paramedical Microbiology, by Stanley E. Wedberg
The Plant Community, by Herbert C. Hanson and Ethan D. Churchill
Principles in Mammalogy, by David E. Davis and Frank B. Golley

Consulting Editor's Statement

The Foxes bring to the writing of a textbook in entomology a combined background of unusual breadth. As a husband-wife team they have, at various stages of their joint career, engaged in museum taxonomy, college teaching, the analysis of a civic water supply in the Rocky Mountains, medical entomology in tropical Africa and even in a search for useful drugs among the West African tribes. This wealth of experience has enabled them to bring to what is often a hackneyed subject a vigorous new approach.

A teacher of entomology will find no aspect of his subject lacking and will benefit from a presentation by experienced teachers. The systematist will find not only a deep understanding of the insects themselves but also a thorough appreciation of the importance of placing the insects in relation to the other arthropod groups. The field worker will be relieved that neither the pedagogy nor the taxonomy is presented from the restricted viewpoint of the armchair specialist.

This new addition to REINHOLD BOOKS IN THE BIOLOGICAL SCIENCES, though primarily designed as a textbook, can be warmly recommended to any student of the insects or of the Arthropoda in general.

PETER GRAY

ARGYNNIS DIANA (Lepidoptera) from Virginia, upper sides. Top, male; bottom, female. *By courtesy of the Journal of Research on the Lepidoptera, Dr. William Hovanitz, editor.*

INTRODUCTION TO

Comparative Entomology

RICHARD M. FOX

Associate Curator of Insects and Spiders
Carnegie Museum
Adjunct Professor of Zoology
Graduate School, University of Pittsburgh
Pittsburgh, Pennsylvania

JEAN WALKER FOX

Entomologist, Section of Insects and Spiders
Carnegie Museum
Pittsburgh, Pennsylvania

NEW YORK
REINHOLD PUBLISHING CORPORATION
CHAPMAN AND HALL, LTD., LONDON

We had a colleague, teacher
and valued personal friend in
Doctor Walter R. Sweadner,
late Curator of Insects and Spiders,
Carnegie Museum.
Since he could not help us write
this book—a project into which
he would have entered with
characteristic enthusiasm and
to which he would have contributed
a remarkable fund of knowledge—
we dedicate it to his memory.

P R E F A C E

This is a book about insects, myriapods and arachnoids written for zoologists. It is intended primarily to serve the needs of those who teach or study entomology as an academic subject and it assumes that the student using it has previously completed at least one full course in general zoology or general biology.

Because its concern is with insects, myriapods and arachnoids as animals, this book emphasizes information often given little attention in introductory entomology texts: comparative morphology, physiology, embryology and evolution. We believe this is the information needed by the zoologist who may study only one course in entomology. At the same time, it represents a sound foundation for further work, including that of the future professional entomologist.

Conversely, certain information commonly included in entomology textbooks has been deliberately omitted from this one. There are no keys to the identification of anything; should the need to identify arise during the term, as it certainly will, there are excellent keys available in many books and research papers—that is why colleges have libraries. There is no discussion of the chemistry or use of insecticides; there is no instruction on controlling, collecting or preserving insects, myriapods or arachnoids. We believe this information has a very low priority in an introductory course in entomology, though these matters can and should be touched upon in the laboratory; serious study of such topics properly belongs in advanced courses for specialists.

Myriapods and arachnoids have long been inquilines in the nest of entomology. Their structures, functions, development and habits are decidedly relevant to understanding insects and vice versa. We have treated these three great arthropod classes comparatively, and to that extent the title on the cover is suitable. The word *entomology* is less so since, strictly speaking, it refers only to insects. There is, however, no single, convenient word in our language to comprise the three kinds of arthropods discussed:

vii

coining one (*entomyriapodarachnology?*) would serve no useful end. Of necessity we use *entomology* in a broader if less pure context.

Prefaces often state, in effect, that the textbook to follow is a compendium of the consensus of opinion on what is and is not fact. While facts are facts and as such do not change, interpretation of facts is subject to evolution. Too, science has its fads and fancies. We do not agree that proposition X is true *merely* because it is defended and advocated by Professor Z, a venerated member of the Academy. Proposition X must be re-examined: it may or may not be found true. We would like students to have the same attitude. A basic purpose of the liberal arts program is to produce educated persons with enquiring and sometimes skeptical minds. Progress is generated by controversy, not by conformity or security—intellectual or otherwise. Accordingly we have not hesitated to hold up controversial matter for the student to examine and we view without alarm the possibility that in doing so we may have taken unpopular positions.

There is a surprising—and healthy—lack of unanimity among our colleagues on a wide range of things within the purview of entomology. Parts of the manuscript were read by two eminent entomologists. Their comments revealed diametrically opposite viewpoints on many topics. We are aware that every entomologist using this book will find points with which he disagrees. We can only hope that such departures will be relatively minor and we are under no illusion that our work is free of error.

By electing to treat insects, myriapods and arachnoids together on a broad zoological basis, we ran head-on into a difficult problem—that of vocabulary. *Larva,* for example, does not imply exactly the same thing to a student of myriapods or to a student of arachnoids as it implies to a student of insects, and the same is true of *nymph.* In general zoological terms, the early instars of the grasshopper or the termite are *larvae,* while only the last immature instar is a *nymph.* Similarly, the acarologist expects the larval tick to become a nymphal tick before becoming adult. But to American entomologists an immature insect must be *either* a larva or a nymph; the one cannot become the other. To tell him that *all* insects have both larval and nymphal stages only confuses or annoys him. How, then, can we use such conflicting vocabularies to discuss and compare life cycles? Such a problem confronted us at every turn (what is *segmentation?* what is a *trochanter?*) We can only trust that we have had some measure of success in collating the diverse vocabularies employed by the various specialists and that some contribution has been made to arriving at common denominators in the use of certain terms.

We are not persuaded that "one picture is worth a thousand words," but we believe that carefully selected illustrations help the reader to understand difficult concepts and to relate them to observations in the laboratory. To this end we have selected the illustrations. While many of the figures are original, it has seemed fruitless to try to devise an original figure to elucidate an idea which has been previously expounded with the utmost clarity in a published drawing. We have, therefore, quoted liberally from the works of our predecessors and colleagues in the matter of illustrations, though all borrowed figures have been redrawn and sometimes reinterpreted. The source of every figure is acknowledged in the legend and is fully cited in the bibliography. In most cases these original sources contain useful amplification of the subject matter illustrated and can be profitably consulted. We are grateful for the generous courtesies accorded us by the vast majority of copyright owners and for their willingness to allow us to draw upon the work of others in order to help train another generation.

We gratefully acknowledge the unstinting cooperation of Carnegie Museum. Director M. Graham Netting gave us every possible assistance in the arduous task of producing this book, freeing our time and making available every facility required. Mrs. Anna R. Tauber, the Museum Librarian, located books we needed and expedited numerous interlibrary loans. Dr. George E. Wallace, Curator of Insects and Spiders, helped us greatly with his knowledge of entomology and entomological literature, found specimens for dissection or for illustration and took more than a routine interest in our bibliography.

Special mention must be made of our "staff." Richard T. Satterwhite was our assisting artist and prepared most of the final ink drawings. Joseph Y. Quil spent long hours typing and retyping manuscript.

This book owes its existence to Dr. Peter Gray, who persuaded us (with minimal difficulty, to be sure) to dust off some notes we had long ago filed away and almost forgotten and to develop them into a book for Reinhold. At the moment of writing this preface we probably are less grateful to him than we should be for his unerring faith in our ability to write a useful book—for the past eighteen months we have read, written and drawn to the almost total exclusion of every other activity. When we have recovered from writer's cramp, we undoubtedly will thank Dr. Gray for his assistance, guidance and constant encouragement.

J. Gordon Edwards reviewed the entire manuscript, giving us the benefit of his scholarship as an entomologist and his experience as a teacher. Thanks to his comments and suggestions, numerous errors were eliminated and the entire presentation was improved.

Having Reinhold as the midwife for our brain child has turned out to be a pleasurable experience. Jim Ross, Murray Chastain and Leonard Roberts have worked on the theory—by no means universal among editors —that a book should be what the authors want it to be. But the R.N. on duty has been Elisabeth Belfer; we must record our grateful appreciation of her competent cooperation at every stage of our labor.

Finally, particular mention should be made of Sir Tipsy, Lord Whiskers, F.P., F.R.C.C., who for eighteen months has kept us on an even keel by making us laugh before breakfast.

October 1963   R. M. AND J. W. FOX

CONTENTS

A Balance Sheet

A Hair perhaps divides the False and True.
RUBÁIYÁT OF OMAR KHAYYÁM

Why bother with bugs? Most of them are small and some of them are smaller than that. How can such creatures be of any importance?

A legitimate question worth investigating!

There are so many different kinds of arthropods living in and around man's chosen habitat that it is inevitable for some of them to be harmful to him, others helpful. They have a large potential for destroying crops, goods or even man himself; some of them produce useful and valuable materials. Not always appreciated are the subtler influences exerted by insects and their relatives upon the world's economy—influences difficult to organize into statistics but which are, even by the measure of money, the most important of all.

It is not easy to be fair when considering the role played by terrestrial arthropods. That any small, repulsive and altogether inferior thing should have the effrontery to give us malaria, to eat up our corn patch or put holes in our best winter clothes beclouds our judgment. On the other hand, we sometimes so overflow with profuse admiration for the ant's tireless labors or the bee's cleverness in storing honey that good sense flies out the window.

Whether it injures or benefits man is a matter of total indifference to the insect. In every case it is living the only life it knows and is just trying to get along. All too often an animal becomes pestiferous because man himself upsets the natural balance of things—sometimes of necessity, often through ignorance. Nor do the beneficial species perform wonders merely for man to behold. Silk and honey are made solely for the benefit of the insect itself; man has learned to utilize the fruits of the insect's labor.

IN RED INK

Injury inflicted by various terrestrial arthropods falls into two categories: (a) damage to useful plants, especially crop plants, or to stored foods or goods; (b) damage to animals, including man, either directly or in the transmission of disease pathogens.

INJURY TO PLANTS

It has been estimated that during 1957 insects and acarids in the United States destroyed more than $2 billion worth of crops—field, garden, orchard and forest—about ten per cent of the total planted. This estimate does not take into account the money and effort expended on control measures, without which the loss would have been much higher. In the same year $500 million worth of stored grain and another $350 million worth of household goods and packaged foods were also destroyed. The story is the same, year after year. And what of the roses and radishes in the backyard? How shall their loss be measured? In 1961 householders in the United States and Canada spent more than $83 million just on aerosol sprays to use against insects.

Any insect that feeds on any part of a living plant is potentially a pest; into this category fall hundreds of species of Lepidoptera, Coleoptera, Hemiptera and Thysanoptera, many Hymenoptera and orthopteroids, a few termites and other insects. The majority of the Acarida and some myriapods are plant feeders. The total number of species with a pest potential runs to six figures; that all are not regarded as pests is because conditions favor only a comparative few.

To be a certified pest, an insect must attack a plant in which man has an economic or aesthetic interest, and it must be present in sufficient numbers that its depredations are appreciable. In its natural, undisturbed habitat hardly any insect is likely to be a pest because inherent environmental factors—food supply, climate, weather and natural enemies—limit its numbers. Natural enemies are of four kinds: macropredators, micropredators, parasites and pathogens. Macropredators comprise the numerous insect-feeding vertebrates. While it is true that a robin or a sparrow or a toad will consume quite a few insects, the contribution macropredators thereby make to natural control is relatively insignificant; were enough robins, sparrows or toads present to make any substantial inroad on an insect species, they, not the insect, would be the pest. Micropredators—beetles, wasps, spiders, mantids, centipedes—likewise make a definite contribution to pest control, and they are much more important than macropredators because they can hunt more systematically and because they are more numerous. Parasites such as certain wasps and flies probably account for an even larger portion of pest mortality, and they are able to find their hosts in situations inaccessible to predators. In recent years there has been more and more evidence that pathogens—bacteria, viruses, protozoa and fungi—may prove to be the most important factors in natural control under certain conditions.

When a phytophagous species is transplanted to a new habitat it is likely to become pestiferous in the absence of its natural enemies. A list of such examples would include the gypsy moth, the brown-tail moth and the cabbage butterfly (*Pieris rapae* (Linné)), all imported from Europe, the fire ant from South America and San José scale from China. In the same way, America has contributed pest species to Europe, Japan, Australia and elsewhere, including our Colorado potato beetle, grape phylloxeran and most of our pests of stored grain and fruits.

The Japanese beetle (*Popillia japonica* Newman) was accidentally imported into the United States in 1916 on nursery stock. It readily became established in New Jersey, spreading out until today it is present nearly everywhere east of the Mississippi River. Adults are fruit and leaf feeders, and larvae eat the roots of grass and most other kinds of plants, destroying lawns, shrubbery and some crops. This beetle has become a very serious pest in America, yet in its native Japan it was never a problem. Neither our predators and parasites nor our traps and sprays coped effectively with it. In the end, measures which proved to be of the greatest value have been: (a) importation from Japan of several species of parasitic wasps and (b) propagation and wide distribution of a bacterium, *Bacillus popillae,* the pathogen of "milky disease" in the grubs.

An unanticipated side effect of the general use of chlorinated hydrocarbon sprays (DDT and others) in recent years has been that spider mites and other phytophagous Acarida have become increasingly abundant. These sprays effectively kill nearly all insects, the good with the bad, but do not affect mites; thus the natural insect predators of mites are destroyed but not their prey.

The other general procedure for converting a species into a pest is to increase its food supply. If a previously natural area is plowed and planted to a crop—wheat, for example—the indigenous insect fauna suffers one of two fates. The many species that cannot feed on wheat will be eliminated from the area, whereas those that can eat wheat stems, leaves, flowers, fruit or roots will increase rapidly in the face of this new abundance—some are likely to become pestiferous if their natural enemies do not keep pace with the multiplication. Furthermore, when the grain is stored, the many species that had previously eked out an existence on scattered wild seeds will quickly move into the storage bins and cause considerable damage. Such phenomena are inevitable consequences of large-scale agriculture—which is not to imply that agriculture should therefore cease.

This principle in reverse has been usefully applied by the rubber industry. *Hevea* rubber plantations in Central and South America are difficult to make profitable because of the many insect enemies of the tree in its native habitat. The *Hevea* tree has been carefully transplanted to Liberia, West Africa, where it grows magnificently and profitably, free of the insects that attack it in the Americas.

Not all insect damage is the simple result of chewing, boring, sucking or egg laying. Some 200 serious plant diseases are transmitted by insects, the pathogens being mostly viruses, but some fungi, bacteria and protozoa are included. Several bark beetles (Scolytidae) attack dead wood in elms and, while not intrinsically causing much damage, transmit the fungus pathogen of "Dutch elm disease," which has nearly wiped out American elms in the northeastern states. Another disastrous fungus, also carried by beetles, has made the native chestnut tree a curiosity. Piercing and sucking species, especially leafhoppers and aphids (Hemiptera), thrips (Thysanoptera) and mites (Acarida), are the major agents in the transmission to plants of virus diseases—mosaics, wilts, yellows, curly-top and the like. Although the insect vectors themselves are not always obviously injurious, the diseases they carry are serious. Nectar-feeding and nectar-gathering species—the honeybee is one of the most important—transmit the virulent bacterial disease "fire blight" from fruit tree to fruit tree. Many other examples could be mentioned.

For more detailed information on the long list of plant pests, the student should consult various State and Federal government publications (many are available without cost) and any of the excellent entomology texts emphasizing the economic aspect (see page 413).

INJURY TO GOODS

The ravages of insects that damage stored foods, woolens or carpets are all too familiar. Bugs in the oatmeal! Ants in the sugar! Moths in the clothes press! Sound "General Quarters" and man your battle stations, mama's mad!

But let the housewife take what comfort she may from knowing that the presence of insects is not necessarily the sign of poor housekeeping. The pests may have entered by routes over which she has little control. Once they're in, however, she'd best do something about them.

Certain species of ants can establish nests within a house, but most come in from outdoors. They will get into uncovered food and pollute it, but frequently they are in the sink to drink water. They are rarely seriously damaging, though certainly annoying. Cockroaches often enter homes by way of cardboard cartons from stores. They will eat almost anything and can be damaging. Both ants and cockroaches may distribute disease pathogens.

There are three species of clothes moths, all small and brownish in the adult stage; they tend to fly away from light and always fold their wings over their abdomens like shut fans when not flying. The larvae primarily feed on woolens, but may also attack other animal products like feathers, fur, bristles and leather. Carpet beetles attack everything the clothes moths do, plus a few more: dried meat, grain, cotton goods, specimens in museum collections and even emulsions on photographs. The larvae are less than a quarter of an inch long, reddish brown and hairy. In a home they may maintain a colony by feeding on the lint that collects between floor boards or behind baseboards. The adults are black or variegated and ovoid, the commonest species about three-sixteenths of an inch long. These two pests are not only troublesome in homes, but they are a major problem in warehouses and department stores, where extraordinary precautions are taken against them.

Stored grains are attacked by a dozen different kinds of beetles and four or five different moths. From the moment the farmer harvests, through every step that grain and grain products take in order to get on the kitchen shelf, these insects may become established. Despite careful and costly measures used by everyone along the line, small colonies of one of these animals are sometimes found in packaged flour, cereal or cake mix. Dried peas, beans, fruit, tobacco products, red pepper, meats and cheese all have pests which find their way into the pantry. In the home the simplest solution is to throw away 29¢ worth of the infected groceries, wash the shelves thoroughly and spray lightly with an appropriate insecticide. It is a different story with the millers and wholesalers; such insects cause them a direct loss of more than $600 million yearly, not counting control, which requires lengthy fumigation of warehouses and costs thousands of dollars a treatment.

Termites, powder post beetles and to a lesser degree various other wood-boring beetles extensively damage timbers in buildings as well as being a constant problem wherever lumber is stored. In many parts of the country these insects provide steady work for professional exterminators trained to deal with them and the damage they do; the total bill is well over $100 million a year.

INJURY TO ANIMALS

As is the case with plant pests, arthropods may be injurious to animals, including man, in one or both of two ways: by reason of direct attack or because a disease is transmitted. These injurious species may be grouped into four categories according to their mode of attack: (1) **obligatory ectoparasites,** which spend all or a greater part of their lives on the surface of their hosts; (2) **obligatory endoparasites,** which must pass a part of their life cycles *within* their hosts; (3) **intermittent ectoparasites,** which visit their hosts only at intervals, generally only to feed; (4) **venomous species,** which employ their protective armament to inflict damage but are not parasites. Many injurious species may correctly belong simultaneously to several of these categories.

Obligatory ectoparasites include three important orders of insects (Anoplura, Mallophaga, Siphonaptera), several families of Diptera (Hippoboscidae, Nycteribiidae, Streblidae) and Hemiptera and some of the Acarida. Mallophaga feed on feathers, fur, dried blood and bits of dead skin; all the others feed entirely or mainly on the host's blood. At the least, these parasites cause annoyance to the host; when the infestation is heavy, their irritation causes extreme nervousness and reduced efficiency. Many also transmit disease (Table 1.1).

Only a few ectoparasites have man as the only host, and some others either attack man as an alternative host or only accidentally. Of the Anoplura, *Pediculus humanus* Linné (head and body louse) and *Phthirus pubis* (Linné) (crab louse) are parasites on man only; the pig louse, *Haematopinus suis* (Linné), sometimes attacks man when circumstances are favorable. Of the Siphonaptera, only *Pulex irritans* Linné (human flea) prefers man, but about a dozen other species, primarily parasites of rats, ground squirrels or birds, are quite willing to take human blood if given the opportunity; among these is *Tunga penetrans* (Linné) (jigger flea), whose female burrows into the skin and causes severe irritations and sometimes secondary bacterial infection. One of the few true ectoparasites of man among the acarids is *Demodex folliculorum* (Simon), a tiny species that lives in the skin pores, especially around the nose and eyes; most people are unaware that they harbor the parasite and it seems to do no harm.

Nycteribiidae and Streblidae confine their attentions to bats and may be involved in spreading rabies among them. Hippoboscidae infest birds or mammals, including domestic animals (sheep keds are hippoboscids). Mallophaga parasitize birds and some mammals; the most important are those infecting domestic fowl. A number of mallophagan species attack chickens, ducks, geese and pigeons. They are sometimes present in great numbers, irritating the birds, reducing egg production and growth, increasing susceptibility to disease and sometimes killing young chicks. Anoplura and Siphonaptera not only are troublesome to domestic animals but also transmit disease to them (see Table 1.1).

Gasterophilidae and Oestridae (warble and bot flies, Diptera) are obligatory endoparasites in their larval stages in mammals. Warble flies deposit young larvae on the host's skin and development is subcutaneous; secondary infection and ulceration may follow. Bot flies develop within the host—in nasal or sinus passages, the lining of the stomach or intestine or, more rarely, other passages. Occasionally the bot larvae find their way to vital organs with very serious consequences. The larvipositing female flies, although they do not sting, are much feared by domestic animals which make extraordinary efforts to avoid them. A few tropical species attack man especially. The female oestrid *Dermatobia hominis*, of tropical America, glues an egg to the ventral side of the abdomen of a female mosquito; when the mosquito feeds upon a warm-blooded animal (sometimes man) body heat stimulates the larva to leave the egg and bore into the skin where it develops as a warble.

In temperate regions **myiasis**, as infestation of vertebrates by fly larvae is called, in man is accidental but not infrequent; nevertheless, several hundred different species of flies have been identified in human myiasis throughout the world.

A third category of attack on man and other vertebrates, intermittent ectoparasitism, results from the blood-feeding habits of many Diptera, the ticks (Ixodidae: Acarida), the bedbug (*Cimex*: Hemiptera), the kissing bugs (*Triatoma, Rhodnius*: Hemiptera) and a few others. Some, like horseflies and deerflies (Tabanidae), inflict a truly spectatular bite, comparable to the effect of an old rusty hypodermic needle in the hands of an eager tyro. Others, like black flies, midges or mosquitoes, may be so numerous and persistent that life in the great outdoors is made miserable; they have chased many a would-be weekend pioneer back to civilization, all thought of conquering the mighty trout abandoned. The bedbug haunts human habitations, emerging from cracks and crannies at night to feed. Most ticks and kissing bugs take a blood meal to enable them to molt, leaving the host as soon as their mission is accomplished, but a few ticks remain on their hosts throughout their life cycle.

A fourth category of "attack"—really self-defense—is inflicted by venomous scorpions and spiders, urticating (itch-making) caterpillars, blistering beetles, stinging wasps, bees and the like. Stings from wasps, hornets and bees involve small quantities of irritating toxic secretion.

One or only a few such stings are, for most people, a passing annoyance involving momentary localized pain, a little swelling and itching, gone the next day or sooner. Sometimes a number of insects will coordinate their efforts, inflicting a great many stings, or the person attacked may have a rare allergy to the toxin; in such cases the results may be serious or, most exceptionally, fatal. On the whole these stings, bites and itches are the consequence of one's own efforts, accidentally or otherwise. The scorpions, spiders or insects cannot be blamed for protecting themselves; they are animals that almost never attack without provocation. Of the same nature are the bites, pinches, blisters or stings inflicted by beetles, ants or other creatures that one might try to pick up. Less obviously acting in self-defense are the harvest mites; harvest hands working in grain fields may get large numbers of them on their bodies, with a skin rash, severe itching and even fever resulting. These mites feed on small arthropods and would much prefer to be allowed to remain on the grain stalks.

Of the above categories, the endoparasitic oestrid larvae are intrinsically dangerous, though they very rarely cause as much damage as they might. Ectoparasites and blood feeders, as such, cause annoyance or even severe discomfort, but they are basically no more than minor irritations. Toxic arthropods can be avoided—at least in principle, though often it is easier said than done, for the victim may be unaware that he seems to threaten a scorpion, spider or hornet.

Transmission of infectious disease is an entirely different matter and occurs especially in connection with the first and third of the foregoing types of attack on animals. Pathogenic organisms may be biologically transmitted by a blood-feeding species—whether an obligatory or an intermittent ectoparasite—when it takes a meal, or transported mechanically by an insect's feet, mouthparts, feces, regurgitation or crushed body.

The notorious housefly (Muscoidae) transmits disease mechanically. Houseflies are attracted to all sorts of unsavory things such as feces, sputum, latrines, decaying flesh, sores, ulcers, wounds—and they also are attracted to food, dishes, cutlery and table tops and are prone to explore areas of exposed skin. In its ubiquitous busyness a housefly is quite likely to walk through a culture of pathogens, or to sample one for flavor. A little later the same fly may march across the uncovered butter dish, defecate on a slice of bread or alight on your nose—with obvious results: pathogenic organisms have been given a free ticket to a new home. In this manner houseflies are *known* to transmit bacillary dysentery and are suspected of carrying typhoid fever, diarrhea, amoebic dysentery, cholera, parasitic worms, poliomyelitis and many others. The various domestic cockroaches are similarly implicated as *possible* carriers of typhoid, tuberculosis, the dysenteries, cholera, leprosy and other diseases—though conclusive proof is wanting. Many muscoid flies feed on ulcers and sores and in the process may spread such skin diseases as Oriental Sore and yaws. Some of the Chloropidae (Diptera) are attracted to eyes, where they feed on lachrymal secretions. These "eye flies" or "eye gnats" disseminate diseases like pink eye and trachoma, as well as dermatitis. Anthrax, tularemia and other blood diseases may be carried by blood-feeding Diptera only as a matter of mechanical transmission, since the pathogen is not really adjusted to the fly and survives for only a short time.

Many very serious diseases are disseminated only by **biological transmission.** As contrasted to mechanical transmission, a highly specific relationship must exist between vector and vertebrate host, and the pathogen must be dependent on each for a phase of its life cycle. This means, in short, that the vector arthropod is essential to the pathogen and that the latter cannot normally be transported in any other way. After being ingested by the vector, the pathogen must **incubate**—complete a part of its life cycle—before it can effectively be inoculated into another victim. Having reached a suitable vertebrate host—sometimes only one species will serve, as is the case in human malaria—the pathogen multiplies, then it invades and destroys host tissue. At some point during this last period it may be ingested by another vector.

Based on what happens during incubation, Huff (1931) recognized three kinds of pathogen-vector relationships: (1) in the **propagative** type, incubation is marked only by simple multiplication, and apparently this is what occurs during the incubation of all bacterial, rickettsial and viral pathogens; (2) protozoal pathogens are **cyclo-propagative,** and during incubation the pathogen passes through a part of its life cycle involving the production of recognizably different stages along with multiplication; (3) many of the tapeworms, flukes and other helminth pathogens are **cyclo-developmental** in that they change in size, shape or both, but do not multiply during incubation. This classification of relationships also reflects the systematic position of the pathogen.

Malaria serves as an excellent example of the cyclo-propagative relationship, the most complex of the three. Generically it is a disease of amphibians, reptiles, birds and mammals, including buffalo, antelopes, bats, squirrels, monkeys, apes and man. The pathogens are sporozoon Protozoa belonging to several related genera; each species is limited to one or to a few closely related vertebrate hosts. Four species are found in man, each causing a slightly different kind of malaria: *Plasmodium malariae, P. vivax, P. ovale* and *Laverania falciparum*. Upon inoculation into a human host, the pathogen undergoes a complex cycle of proliferation in the spleen and other tissues, during which there are no clinical symptoms of the disease. In from six to sixty or more days—depending upon the species of pathogen and other factors—the parasites appear in large numbers in the peripheral blood where they attack and destroy erythrocytes; the patient now experiences chills, fevers and such overt symptoms. Meanwhile, the pathogen becomes established in the liver where a slower multiplication occurs (**exoerythrocytic cycle**) (Bray, 1963); the three species of *Plasmodium* potentially may continue the exoerythrocytic cycle for many years and occasionally break out into the peripheral bloodstream, causing relapses. Such relapses can be more or less annual or may occur several years apart. The exoerythrocytic cycle of *Laverania falciparum*,[1] on the other hand, is abortive, ending with or soon after the first clinical attack. While this type of malaria is the most severe and the most likely to be fatal, relapses do not occur.

One of the end results of the parasite's cycle in peripheral blood is the production of gametes. If a vector mosquito takes a blood meal from a patient when the gametes are present—and only at that time—the pathogen begins another phase of its cycle in the vector. Ingested male and female gametes fuse (fertilization) in the midgut into the zygote which forms a cyst (**oöcyst**) in the gut wall and proceeds to divide repeatedly. Each oöcyst produces hundreds of spindle-shaped **sporozoites** which migrate to the mosquito's salivary glands. When the mosquito feeds again, she (males feed on flower pollen and nectar) first injects a bit of salivary secretion into the wound, preventing the blood from clotting too rapidly and thus clogging her mouthparts. If sporozoites are present in the salivary glands, they enter the host's blood with the salivary secretion, and malaria results.

The vectors of these four malarias are certain mosquitoes of the genus *Anopheles*. Although many species of other mosquito genera feed on man, they do not transmit malaria and not every anopheline species is a vector; physiological conditions prevent the development of the pathogens in the midgut of the nonvector species. However, *Culex, Aedes* and other genera of mosquitoes play a parallel role in transmission of other malaria pathogens to other vertebrate hosts.

In most cases the arthropod vector of a disease picks up the pathogen only by feeding on an infective vertebrate host. There are, however, some

[1] Because of difference in both life cycles and morphology, this pathogen is now placed in a separate genus (Bray, 1958, 1963).

notable exceptions in which the infected female vector passes the pathogens on to her progeny, a situation which obviously complicates control
of the disease. **Transovarian transmission** (sometimes called "hereditary")
occurs mainly in various Acarida (ticks, mites) serving as vectors for
such diseases as Rocky Mountain spotted fever and Texas cattle fever.
Insect vectors having transovarian transmission are not usual, but it is
known to occur in kissing bugs (Hemiptera) for Chagas disease and
in the sand flies (*Phlebotomus:* Diptera) for the several pathogenic
Leishmania (Protozoa). Transovarian transmission is a vector-pathogen
relationship of a different sort than those classified by Huff; it is found in
most vector acarids and a few vector insects, while the pathogens may
be protozoa, bacteria or viruses. A biologically similar situation occurs
when a pregnant human mother infects her unborn child with malaria.

Arthropod-borne diseases generally are serious; they have been and
often still are difficult to control despite medical advances. Their historical role has been important. There is some reason to believe that
malaria contributed to the decline of the Golden Age in Greece and
later to the fall and disintegration of the Roman Empire. The "Black
Death" (bubonic plague) was disastrously epidemic in medieval Europe.
Endemic fevers—malaria, typhus, yellow fever, sleeping sickness, Chagas
disease—have slowed or dammed the economic development of vast
regions of tropical America and Africa. Despite a tremendous amount of
research, the accumulation of a large body of knowledge and some
dramatic progress, there still are more problems unsolved than solved.

Arthropod-borne diseases are not merely exotic problems of foreign
climes or historical phenomena. Many of these diseases are here and now,
and modern transportation has complicated the situation. An airline pilot
or an international traveler may be hospitalized in his home town with
a disease he contracted a few days ago thousands of miles away. Can his
family physician recognize the pathogen heretofore confined to an island
group on the other side of the world? Almost any of the "tropical" diseases
may be accidentally imported to temperate regions.

Some of them are not at all exotic. Bubonic plague, the "Black Death"
of the Middle Ages, is firmly entrenched in the rat and ground squirrel
populations of the western third of North America. Only constant
vigilance prevents the possibility of a serious outbreak. Texas cattle fever
daily threatens to cross the border from Mexico and decimate our herds.
Yellow fever has recently erupted in Central America. Rocky Mountain
spotted fever is present in nearly every state in the Union. Several out-
breaks of encephalitis have occurred in recent years in eastern or central
states.

Table 1.1 Some of the diseases of man and other animals which are biologically transmitted by arthropods, with the systematic position of vectors and pathogens indicated, the vertebrate host of the pathogen and the geographic distribution of the disease. The systematic position of *Rickettsia* is uncertain. Information compiled from various sources.

Vector	Pathogen and Disease	Vertebrate Host(s)	Geographic Distribution
Anoplura			
Pediculus humanus, the human louse	*Pasteurella tularensis* (Bacteria); tularemia	Rabbits, ground squirrels, man	Temperate North America, Eurasia
	Borrelia recurrentis (Spirochaeta); relapsing fever	Man, rats, mice	World-wide
	Rickettsia prowazeki; epidemic typhus	Man	Temperate North America, Eurasia
	Rickettsia quintana; trench fever	Man	Europe
Hemiptera			
Reduviidae: *Triatoma* and *Rhodnius* spp.	*Trypanosoma cruzi* (Protozoa); Chagas disease	Man, armadillos, rodents, others	Rural tropical America north to Texas and southern California
Diptera			
Psychodidae: *Phlebotomus* spp.	*Leishmania tropica* (Protozoa); Oriental sore, cutaneous leishmaniasis	Man, dogs	Mediterranean countries, India, Africa
	Leishmania brasiliensis (Protozoa); Espundia, mucacutaneous leishmaniasis	Man, dogs	Tropical America
	Leishmania donovani (Protozoa); Kala-azar, visceral leishmaniasis	Man, dogs, cats	Mediterranean countries, Asia, South America
Culicidae: *Anopheles* spp. only	*Plasmodium malariae, vivax, ovale, Laverania falciparum* (Protozoa); human malaria	Man	Potentially everywhere between summer isotherms of 16° C (60° F)
Anopheles and *Culex* spp., other genera rarely	*Wuchereria bancrofti, W. malayi* (Nematoda); elephantiasis	Man	Tropics and subtropics
Culex, Aedes, other genera, many spp.	*Plasmodium gallinaceum* and other spp., avian malaria	Birds	World-wide
Aedes, Haemagogus sp.	A virus; yellow fever, jungle fever	Man, monkeys, rodents, other mammals	Tropical and subtropical America and Africa
Aedes spp.	A virus; dengue fever	Man	Most warm countries
Aedes, Culex sp., others	Four or more virus strains; encephalitis	Man, birds, horses	Asia, Europe, the Americas
Simulidae: *Simulium* sp.	*Onchocerca volvulus* (Nemathelminthes); onchocerciasis	Man	Central America, tropical Africa

Tabanidae: *Chrysops* spp.	*Leucocytozoon* spp. (Protozoa); a serious bird malaria	Ducks, turkeys	Northern and eastern United States
	Loa loa (Nemathelminthes); African eye worm	Man	Tropical Africa
	Pasteurella tularensis (Bacteria); tularemia	Rabbits, ground squirrels, man	Western United States
Glossinidae: *Glossina* spp.	*Trypanosoma gambiense* and *rhodesiense* (Protozoa); African sleeping sickness	Man, monkeys, cattle, wild ungulates	Tropical Africa
	Trypanosoma brucei (Protozoa); Nagana, animal sleeping sickness	Dogs, cattle, sheep, goats, wild animals	Tropical Africa
Siphonaptera			
Xenopsylla spp., rat fleas	*Pasteurella pestis* (Bacteria); plague, bubonic and others	Man, rodents	World-wide
Xenopsylla and other fleas	*Rickettsia typhi;* endemic or murine typhus	Man, rodents	World-wide
Acarida			
Argasidae: *Argas persicus*	*Borrelia anserina* (Bacteria); fowl spirochaetosis	Fowl	North America, Brazil, India, Egypt, Australia
Ornithodoros spp.	*Borrelia recurruntis* strains (Bacteria); relapsing fever	Man, rodents	Africa, southern Eurasia, the Americas
Ixodidae: *Ixodes* spp.	Several virus strains; encephalitis	Man, rodents	World-wide
Ixodes and others	*Rickettsia burneti;* Q fever	Man, cattle	Australia, United States
Amblyomma and others	*Rickettsia* sp.; Sao Paulo fever	Man, rodents	South America
Dermacentor spp. and possibly others	*Rickettsia rickettsi;* Rocky Mountain spotted fever	Man, rodents	Everywhere in North America
Dermacentor spp.	A virus; Colorado tick fever	Man, rodents	Rocky Mountain region
Many genera and spp.	*Pasteurella tularensis* (Bacteria); tularemia	Man, rodents, birds	North America, Europe, Japan
Haemophysalis spp.	*Rickettsia* spp.; African tick fever	Man, rodents	Africa
Boophilus annulatus	*Babesia bigemina* (Protozoa); Texas cattle fever	Cattle	Central and South America, South Africa, Philippines, Europe; formerly southern U.S.
Trombiculidae: *Trombicula* spp. and others, chiggers	*Rickettsia tsutsugamushi;* scrub typhus (tsutsugamushi fever)	Man, rodents	Australia, Asia, Pacific islands
Bdellonyssus spp., rat mite	*Rickettsia typhi;* endemic typhus	Man, rodents	World-wide

13

Recent developments in our knowledge of arthropod-borne diseases require a revision of some of our classic concepts. Rabies has been found maintained in some of our native bats; this discovery focuses a new interest on the arthropod ectoparasites of bats. On the other hand, advances in knowledge of treatment and control of malaria are diminishing the importance of that disease; once a major killer, it can become a minor problem if current knowledge is utilized effectively.

There seems to be no end to the problem of vector arthropods. As one vector diminishes in importance, another rears its head. The cost in suffering, in money and in man-hours lost through incapacity is very great indeed, quite aside from the deaths.

Table 1.1 presents information on some of the important diseases for which terrestrial arthropods serve as vectors. Space does not permit discussing them in detail. Further information will be found in references listed in the bibliography.

IN BLACK INK

Contributions made by insects beneficial to man's economy outweigh the injuries inflicted, incredible though it may seem. Most obviously useful are insects or insect products having commercial value, but of far greater importance is the maintenance of biological balance, in which every species, even an overtly destructive one, is an essential factor to a greater or less degree.

A third category is the contribution insects have made to experimental studies. Probably half the learned papers on genetics include in their titles the word *"Drosophila"*; the fruit fly has been a major factor in developing our knowledge of inheritance, of populations and of the gene. A great many insects, because of their short life cycles and ready adaptation to laboratory conditions, have been and are of the greatest value as experimental animals in research. The cockroach, the *Habrobracon* wasp, the moth *Ephestia,* the kissing bug *Rhodnius,* the silkworm, various mosquitoes and muscoid flies and many others are in this category.

INDUSTRIAL PRODUCTS

Bombyx mori (Linné), a moth native to China, has been cultivated for at least 5000 years according to written records. Since the discovery of the usefulness of silk was ascribed to the Empress Lotzu of Kwang-Ti, we may be sure that the actual discovery was made somewhat before her gracious majesty lent her name to the project. Silkworms were introduced into Europe in the sixth century, ending China's ancient monopoly, and by the nineteenth century silk was a major industry in southern Europe. Louis Pasteur, at that time locally respected for his research on micro-organisms affecting the beer and wine industries, ensured his national reputation as a scientist when he identified the pathogen of pebrine, a disease of silkworms, as the protozoan *Nosema bombycis* Nägeli and demonstrated a method for avoiding infections.

Commercial production of silk requires cheap labor and is therefore impractical in the United States. In Japan, China, India and southern Europe, where hand labor is available, about 60 million pounds of raw silk are produced each year with a value of about $500 million. Despite the inroads made by synthetic textiles on the demand for silk, it remains the material *par excellence* for certain uses and for the luxury trade. Silk threads have a tensile strength equivalent to that of steel, an elasticity of twenty per cent and a diameter of forty-six to eighty-four micra. They are produced by the labial glands of the prepupa in forming a cocoon. A number of other species have been used locally or experimentally for silk production, but only *B. mori* responds well to cultivation and has a cocoon that can be easily unwound.

The use of honey as food must have originated during mankind's infancy; perhaps it was a gastronomic delicacy retained from the habits of the homonoid ancestor. Prehistoric cave paintings in Spain depict people gathering wild honey. Nearly all aboriginal peoples everywhere esteem the product of local social bees. More or less successful efforts to cultivate various meliponid bees have been made by primitive people in such diverse places as Central America, Paraguay, Java and Africa. The one bee that best lends itself to cultivation and has the largest hive is *Apis mellifera* Linné, apparently a native of the Orient. Its culture had reached the Near East early enough to be the subject of records in Egyptian hieroglyphics and Assyrian cuneiform. It was brought to North America in the seventeenth century by the early settlers from Europe.

Today beekeeping is a very general, important small business as well as a major backyard hobby. According to the Department of Commerce, the value of honey and beeswax produced in the United States in 1957 was a little more than $48 million. Beeswax is used in small quantities in many different industrial products—cosmetics, carbon paper, shaving cream, electrical and electronic materials, to name a few. Aside from the honey and wax produced, bees are valuable as major pollinating agents for fruit trees, clover, alfalfa, coffee, cotton and other crops. An interesting, increasingly important side line for beekeepers is renting hives to farmers during a crop's blossoming season to ensure higher yield. Where insecticides are indiscriminately used, as in dusting from an airplane, the indigenous populations of pollinators are destroyed and renting beehives to correct the damage becomes necessary.

The third insect of major commercial importance is *Laccifer lacca* (Kern), a scale insect (Coccoidea: Hemiptera) that secretes a thick layer of resinous substance around itself as a protective coat while it feeds on its host plant, various species of figs. The resin is collected, processed and refined. Dissolved, it is shellac, used not only in the white or orange form but also as an ingredient in lacquer, varnish, some paints and other products. No suitable synthetic substitute has been developed. The insect is a native of India and Burma where the wild resin is collected, and the scale insects are cultivated in other tropical countries. About 15,000 insects produce a pound of lac; up to 90 million pounds reach the market every year, the United States using about $20 million worth each year.

The Aztecs of Mexico discovered how to prepare a brilliant red dye from the dried and powdered bodies of *Dactylopius coccus* Costa, a scale insect feeding on the prickly pear cactus. The dye, cochineal, was of major commercial importance until it was supplanted in the textile industry by more readily available aniline dyes. It is still used in cosmetics and, because it is not toxic, in food coloring and cooking. The insect is cultivated in Mexico, Peru, Honduras, the Canary Islands, Spain, Algeria and South Africa, principally as a household industry.

The silk of certain spiders is much finer than that produced by moths and is of a uniform diameter; it is used for cross hairs in optical instruments such as telescopes and bombsights.

Some plant galls are used by local populations or by primitive people as a source of dyes, and others have a limited application in the manufacture of permanent inks.

Sterile maggots of certain muscoid flies (*Phormia* and *Lucilla* species) are used in medicine to clean deep wounds and bone infections. In certain situations they are more efficient than surgical methods or drug treatment. The maggots normally attack only necrotic tissue and do a thorough job of removing it; they destroy harmful bacteria during digestion and their excrement is rich in the substance *allantoin*, which facilitates healing from within. Although allantoin can be manufactured synthetically and is available, some kinds of wounds and infections are better treated directly by the maggots.

The pharmacopoeias of tribal and folk medicine include many different insects and insect products, but in general such materials are either definitely harmful or, if harmless, of doubtful value. "Spanish fly," the pulverized bodies of the beetle *Lytta vesicatoria* (Linné), is high in *cantharadin,* a drug with some dangerous effects and very limited useful application. Honey and vinegar, as well as "royal bee jelly," have recently been promoted as being highly beneficial: the benefits probably accrue more to producers than to users.

BALANCE OF NATURE

In a given place at a given time the balance of nature may be likened to an extremely complex organic molecule. As every chemist knows, minor displacements or substitutions of components in the molecule may drastically alter the characteristics of the whole. In an ecological community every species performs some function related to the total natural balance, so that all species depend on all other species, not only for existence but for the degree to which each exists in that particular community. Any significant increase or decrease in numbers of a member species affects all other members and changes the entire character of the community. When such disturbances occur, they are followed by periods of flux which terminate only when a new balance is achieved.

The main fault in comparing an ecologic community with an organic molecule is that the molecule, no matter how complex it is, is *relatively* simple, measurable and predictable. Ecologic factors are subtler, difficult to measure and often unpredictable. We tend to take for granted familiar things; we rarely try to measure them. Although most of us are as aware of the existing balance of nature as we are of the progress of civilization we are unprepared to evaluate imbalances in our natural environment when they occur. We are horrified when the game fish disappear from our streams, yet we accept with reluctance the obvious agent, industrial pollution, preferring to bemoan the poor fishing instead of requiring industry to avoid contamination. Probably it is this sort of familiarity without understanding that makes so difficult the measurement of ecologic factors. It is psychologically much easier for us to measure atoms and molecules.

One of the major contributions insects make is in pollinating plants. A large number of angiosperm plants are insect pollinated, including some important crops: clover, alfalfa, cotton, tobacco, nearly all fruit, berries, beans, peas, tomatoes, melons and numerous ornamental plants. As a general rule, a plant requiring insect pollination may be recognized by its colorful flower and strong scent. Clearly, insects that pollinate plants make a very important contribution, yet only a part of this service can be expressed in a way resembling a measurement. In 1957, insect-pollinated crops in the United States were valued at over $4.5 billion. To this must be added the value of insect-pollinated plants growing wild, not therefore of immediate concern to agricultural statisticians. Such plants are probably more valuable than all agricultural products put together; they provide surface cover, preventing erosion and helping to maintain the water table; they provide forage and shelter for game and a host of "lesser" life.

Pollinating insects comprise virtually all flower-haunting species. Some are more efficient than others; those with hairy bodies and a tendency to move restlessly from blossom to blossom do the best job. Prominent among such insects are bees, wasps, ants, nearly all butterflies and moths, many flies and a few beetles. Some of these are injurious during larval stages—the Lepidoptera, for example—so that their activity in pollination only partly balances their destructiveness.

Honeybees are generally considered the most important of pollinating insects: they collect both pollen and nectar and they are active in large numbers from early spring to late autumn. Because they are readily cultured and controlled, they afford opportunity to increase crop yields by placing hives in fields or orchards during the flowering season. Between 1945 and 1955 the production of alfalfa seed in California was increased from an average of 215 to 450 pounds to the acre by this method. Similar results have been recorded for many kinds of fruit and vegetable production.

Certain plants, however, are not well served by the honeybee. Bumblebees, with their longer tongues, are more efficient in pollinating the deep flowers of red clover. Some years ago Australian sheep men started to grow red clover to improve the grass range, but got no clover seeds until they also imported bumblebees. The intimate relationship between the edible fig and the fig wasp is classical (see page 407). There are many other examples of specific insects acting as the sole pollinators of specific plants: the Spanish bayonet *Yucca filamentosa* is pollinated only by the moth *Tegeticula yuccasella* (Riley); certain orchids can be pollinated only by hawkmoths (Sphingidae) with unusually long tongues.

Were the pollinating insects to be totally eliminated, all plants depending upon them for fertilization would disappear in a few years for want of replacement by their seeds. This is not to say that all plant life would disappear, for wind-pollinated and self-pollinated plants—a large number of species including, among our crops, the grains and some nuts— would still be present. Whether or not the disappearance of insect-pollinated plants would serve to upset the natural balance in such a way that remaining plants would indirectly suffer is impossible to predict; certainly the world would be a very different place and man would have many very large adjustments to make, especially in diet. It would be difficult, in the resultant economy, to provide even a minimum food supply.

Perhaps one of the most important contributions made by insects is their activity in destroying the dead animals and plants that fall to the ground and in returning this organic material to the soil for re-use. True, this service would, in time, be at least partially performed by bacteria and other micro-organisms, but insects speed the process, thus materially reducing the total organic material tied up in the form of dead branches, debris and carrion. Important among scavenger insects are ants, termites, many fly larvae, many beetles and, to a lesser degree, all species that bore into dead wood. Termites are primarily scavengers of dead wood. They become injurious only because they cannot discriminate between woody litter and wood being used by man. In forested regions, especially in warm climates, termites attack every fallen branch or dead tree. Everywhere in tropical rain forests flat piles of brown dust, the remnants of recent termite work, may be seen, and one is apt to find that any apparent stick or log is in fact a mere shell. In temperate regions termites are present but less ubiquitous. Here a greater contribution probably is made by ants and boring larvae, their tunnels allowing fungus and rot to penetrate more rapidly. Without these insects the litter on the ground would become impenetrable. A pity none feeds on tin cans!

Credit for removing offal and dead animals, great and small, must be divided among beetles, ants and fly maggots, primarily because they are incalculably numerous. These groups usually are on the job at once. The harm done by adult flies as disease transmitters does not reduce the importance of the work of their maggots as scavengers. Ants are everywhere active and effective. Lesser contributions are made by beetles and arachnoids, scavengers which feed principally on dead arthropods, annelids and mollusks. Honors for ingenuity go to sexton beetles and dung beetles. A team of sexton beetles can bury a dead mouse in a short time by industriously excavating the soil under it until it sinks out of sight. Dung-rolling scarabs prepare balls of excrement and cache them in burrows where they serve as a food supply for both adults and larvae. In tropical Africa the dreaded driver ant—by no means the only species useful there in this respect—is a major factor in keeping the jungle clear of decaying animal matter.

Not only do insects police the ground, disposing of many loathsome and often unhealthful objects, but the substance of the debris is transformed to a less obnoxious form and deposited on or in the ground where it becomes one of the most important sources of plant food. Soil is further improved by the action of all sorts of burrowing forms. White grubs may burrow as deep as five feet below the surface and immature cicadas ten feet. A vast number of species, many with large numbers of individuals present, contribute to aeration of the soil and to increasing the depth of useful topsoil. Insect and arachnoid activity in this respect is similar to that of earthworms and may be more important because the former are more numerous.

Men eat fish, fish eat mosquito larvae, adult mosquitoes feed on human blood. This is one of the simpler food cycles. A diagram of all such cycles present in an ecologic community would be a bewildering collection of wheels within wheels within wheels. The size of an animal relative to its food determines whether we refer to "predator and prey" or "parasite and host"; the principle is the same in either case. Plants also enter into these food cycles. The organic matter in the soil on which plants thrive had part of its recent origin in the bodies of dead animals or in animal excrement. In the natural scheme of things, every species of animal or plant serves as the food for certain other species.

Arthropods are the primary diet of a large number of vertebrates. The presence of insects, the preponderant class of terrestrial arthropods, is therefore essential to the presence of the insect-feeding mammals, birds, reptiles and amphibians. Aquatic larvae of insects are a major dietary item for fish, and thus a keystone in maintaining a healthy fresh-water stream. Insects are more important to the survival of songbirds than song-birds are to the control of insects. It should be noted that the feeding animal almost never eliminates the species fed upon: a species with such a tendency would eat itself into starvation and thus in turn be exterminated. "Live and let live" is not the natural rule. It is, rather, "Let enough live to provide for tomorrow."

Man's aversion to eating insects can be mainly attributed to civilization. It will be recalled that in Biblical times locusts (grasshoppers) and wild honey were considered a feast. Protein deficiency characterizes the diet of most primitive peoples who must therefore utilize food from every possible source. In the Congo basin some tribes hunt grasshoppers with specially pronged arrows. Beetle grubs and termites are very generally eaten. In the West African rain forest we have seen the tribal people gathering swarming termites, which are then de-alated and fried in palm oil. The result is nutritious and palatable if one likes the flavor of palm oil. Tihon (1945, *fide* Bodenheimer, 1951) analyzed the fried termites sold in native markets in Leopoldville and found that each 100 grams was 44.4 per cent fat, 36 per cent protein and included available calcium, sulfur and iron; the caloric value was 561. By comparison, 100 grams of peanuts has 559 calories and 100 grams of beef has 319. Primitive groups in Australia and Polynesia prize the caterpillar of the "Bugong" (*Euxoa infusca* (Boisduval)), a larval noctuid moth, and also the "witchetty," a grub of one of the longicorn beetles found in roots of the Eucalyptus tree. Indian tribes in western United States used a variety of insects as food, a practice not confined solely to primitive groups. It is recorded that during the grasshopper plague of 1885, when hordes of the insects destroyed the local vegetation, the white settlers in Utah and the Dakotas utilized them in their diet. The U. S. Department of Agriculture has issued a bulletin urging human utilization of locusts in disaster years and explaining how to prepare them. In China and Japan restaurants serve grasshoppers, silkworm pupae and water beetles; some of these items are available in oriental stores and gourmet counters in supermarkets. Canned "Gusanos de 'Maguey," the larvae of a skipper butterfly (Hesperiidae), are sold in many an epicurean shop. The writers have been served chocolate-covered grasshoppers at cocktail parties and found them inoffensive.

When an animal feeds on another animal small enough to be overpowered and consumed, the former is a **predator**. Almost all arachnoids, all chilopods and a great many insects are predatory. Their total collective body volume and weight certainly are many times greater than the total volume and weight of all existing predatory vertebrates! Arthropods must be considered the most important of the terrestrial predators, not only because of their vast numbers, but also because, being small, they can hunt their prey in crannies and burrows inaccessible to larger animals.

A predator cannot be counted as being directly beneficial to man just because it is a predator. Aside from the intangible importance of any species to the biological balance, predators are overtly beneficial only to the extent that they attack injurious species. Many predators eat anything they can catch—the good with the bad. The praying mantis is one of the many that feed on any small living thing coming readily to hand. It is quite misleading to put a mantis (or a robin) in the midst of a lot of cutworms and solemnly conclude that the mantis is a beneficial predator that feeds on cutworms; the experiment merely demonstrates that the mantis will eat cutworms if they are easy to get. Madame mantis is just as efficient in destroying beneficial insects if *they* get within reach.

Some predators are specialists. The carabid beetles, with long neck-like prothoraces, feed principally on snails and slugs. Dragonflies (Odonata) and robber flies (Diptera: Asilidae) use their agility in flight to catch mosquitoes, gnats, flies and other insects on the wing. Many species of ladybugs or ladybird beetles (Coleoptera: Coccinellidae) are rapacious predators of aphids, bollworms, scale insects and mealy bugs—most of which are agricultural pests. A minor industry has developed in parts of California and Arizona where native ladybugs are common in certain remote areas; about 135 million are collected each year and shipped to farmers who put them out to control injurious species on which they prey. One of the ladybugs, *Rodolia cardinalis* (Mulsant), imported from Australia by citrus growers, proved to be completely effective in the control of *Icerya purchasi* Maskell, a scale insect (Hemiptera) quite injurious to the trees.

The normal housewife views with alarm any arthropod invasion of her domain, but reserves particular horror for spiders and thousand-leggers, not appreciating that both are most helpful to her as active predators on silverfish, cockroaches, termites, ants and flies.

A parasite feeds on or within an animal, called the host, much larger than itself. Most parasites attack only members of one species or a limited group of related species. Ectoparasites infest the external surfaces of their hosts, as their designation implies. Normally, the host is inconvenienced but rarely destroyed by external parasites, which therefore contribute little to control. Endoparasites, on the other hand, are of very great importance in control because the host is so often killed. Microparasites (pathogens) outside the scope of this book—bacteria, viruses, fungi and the like—causing disease in insects, especially during the larval stages, have not yet been fully explored in pest control or as factors in ecologic equilibrium. Eventually the role of micro-organisms undoubtedly will prove to be far greater than we now appreciate. However, insect parasites are of known importance and frequently have been utilized in pest control. Every injurious species is attacked by several endoparasites, among which certain Hymenoptera are of major importance. The female wasp deposits her egg within the host during the latter's egg, larval or pupal stage. The hatched wasp feeds on host tissues, either destroying the host or making it reproductively sterile. Capacity for destruction, along with the characteristic host specificity, offers useful possibilities in pest control by propagating the parasites in the laboratory and releasing them where needed. Released, there is little chance that the parasite will itself become a nuisance, for when the host population is reduced, so also is that of the parasite. As a rule, no alternative host is possible and no beneficial species will be attacked (although exceptions occur). Parasitic wasps and some parasitic flies (Tachinidae) have been used in this way to help control the gypsy moth, the brown-tailed moth, the Japanese beetle and many other pests. Host-parasite relationships are especially important when a foreign species is accidentally imported and becomes injurious. The introduction of parasitic species associated with the pest in its natural habitat helps to restore a natural population balance.

Not more than twenty-five per cent reduction in the population of a host species can be expected from the efforts of parasites in a fully balanced environment—one in which all existing factors have reached an equilibrium through the years. It is estimated that endemic parasites of the cotton boll weevil reduce its population only by sixteen per cent each year. Laboratory breeding and release of parasites create a useful imbalance. No estimates on the populational control exerted by predators are available, but it is certainly far less than that of parasites—perhaps of the order of one to five per cent at most. A great many parasites are viewed as being injurious; some attack beneficial species while others (hyperparasites) parasitize parasites of injurious species.

A further technique in biological control is the use of insects against certain noxious plants, employed with outstanding success in two classic cases and with promising results in many others. The prickly pear (*Opuntia inermis*) became established as an ornamental in Australia about 1840. In its new home it thrived much better than in its native South America, grew higher and overran the grasslands with impenetrable spiny thickets; it eventually made nearly 60 million acres useless for agriculture or grazing. Many of the South American insects that feed on the prickly pear were experimentally introduced to Australia in an effort to control the weed. The trick was turned by a boring moth (*Cactoblastis cactorum* (Berg)), whose larvae reduce the plants to a dry shell easily disposed of. The cactus now occupies only about one per cent of the area it infested when the moth was introduced in 1925. In recent years the Klamath weed —St. John's wort of England and Australia—spread out over the California grazing country, almost wiping out native grasses and forage. The weed has little nutritive value and tends to weaken the cattle that feed on it. *Chrysomela gemellata*, a European species related to the Colorado potato beetle (Coleoptera: Chrysomelidae), attacks only Klamath weed, feeding on nothing else, and has turned the tide of the weed's advance. This imported beetle is reared in insectaries and released in large numbers.

CONTROL

The control of pests has developed into an essential technique in agriculture, one that has very greatly increased the production of food. It is an important factor contributing to our present economic abundance. Control techniques will become more and more essential as the human population of the world approaches the saturation point. Similarly, control of vector arthropods has dramatically reduced the incidence of most of the diseases they transmit and has thus prevented immeasurable human suffering.

Chemical insecticides are of real value in the control both of agricultural pests and of vectors; effective control depends upon their use. Natural predators, parasites and pathogens serve only to mitigate pests, not to eliminate them. Except under unusual circumstances their services must be supplemented by insecticides.

The resources of man and machine are marshaled in campaigns against pests and vectors. A small army of trained men are dedicated to the work. The excellent results obtained are a return on a large investment of time and money by Federal and State governments, as well as by private industry. There can be no question as to the value of control, nor of the benefits derived from it.

Yet dissenting voices are heard suggesting a moratorium on using all insecticides. We hear that if spraying and dusting continue, the honeybees and other pollinators will be destroyed, the streams will become barren ditches, all our food will be contaminated and the birds will sing no more. The argument, in brief, is that insecticides upset the "balance of nature."

One of the difficulties lies in that general phrase, "balance of nature," which does not mean the same thing to all people. To some it implies the *original* state of nature, the land primeval before man interfered by developing his agriculture, his industries and his cities. To others it implies vaguely the "Great Outdoors" or something of the sort—Walden Pond in contrast to Times Square.

To still others—and in foregoing paragraphs we have used the phrase in this context—"balance of nature" implies an *ecologic equilibrium,* the totality of complex interplay among all the innumerable factors (including man himself) present in an environment. Both Walden Pond and Times Square are, in their respective ways, natural balances of all ecologic factors concerned in each situation.

If "balance of nature" is thus defined, upsetting it is not necessarily an undesirable process but simply the result of introducing new factors into the balanced environment. A new balance will be reached after a period of adjustment. Whether upsetting the present balance is good or bad depends entirely upon whether the new balance is good or bad.

Upsetting the balance of nature is something like cutting off a finger; once done it is too late to change your mind. A lot of careful thought should go into the problem *before* taking irreversible action. It cannot be assumed with safety to our future that because an insect *is* an insect it is therefore undesirable or that its elimination is a step forward—the exact opposite may be true. Control programs should be preceded by scientific study of the biologic consequences, but such studies have not always been undertaken when needed.

While Chief of the Federal Division of Entomology, Leland O. Howard wrote in the *American Magazine* for March, 1928, an article called "The Greatest War of All Time—Man Against the Insects," in which he stated that, "If human beings are to continue to exist they must first gain mastery over insects." This statement has been taken as the keynote for economic entomology. It is probable that Howard himself understood that *mastery* does not mean extermination, though others make that mistake. True mastery of insects requires a thorough knowledge of ecologic communities, a knowledge not yet fully developed. Plenty of money has always been available to the chemist who seeks to devise more devastating insecticides, to the physiologist who studies the way an insecticide kills and its effect on man, bird and furry animal and to the engineer who can invent a better way to spray or dust more acres more cheaply. Scientific analysis of ecologic communities has been harder to finance, but it remains a "must" and becomes of greater and greater importance as our own weapons in the "war against insects" improve.

There are, of course, economic pressures to destroy pests. Protagonists of extermination do not necessarily know or care what happens to the balance of nature, just so the pests are killed. There are, on the other hand, sound reasons for going cautiously in matters of control. Advocates of caution do not always think in terms of crops or dollars or disease. Torn between the extremes are the bystanders, people who want good crops, who don't want to get sick and who enjoy hearing the birds sing. Whom shall they believe? Those who continually, hysterically talk about "Our Insect Enemies" and "Our War of Survival"? Or those who just as continually and hysterically cry "We Will All Die of DDT Poisoning" and "Look What THEY Are Doing to Our Feathered Friends"?

There is reasonable middle ground. By all means, let us not hesitate to upset the balance of nature if we are sure the new balance will be better for us—but let us be sure. Let us not take toward insecticides the attitude taken by the wild tribes of Africa toward medicine: that if a medicine cures one disease it will cure all of them. Insecticides and the techniques of control must be used intelligently, not indiscriminately, in order to do the job intended—the control of pests—rather than to reach an end nobody wants—a disastrous capsizing of nature.

In summary: There are some very destructive and even dangerous insects that cause a vast amount of suffering and waste our resources. We would be better off without them. There are some very useful and even essential insects. We must preserve them. Many, many insects are partly good and partly bad.

Before we can get rid of bad insects and keep good ones, we must learn to know the one from the other—not necessarily an easy matter in every case. The first step is to know what insects and arachnoids and myriapods *are*.

CHAPTER TWO

The Skeleton

My skeleton is so protected
  It can hardly be detected,
But there is no slightest doubt
  Most creatures wear it inside out.

J. W. F.

A skeleton of some sort is necessary to every animal more complex than a mere blob of protoplasm. The skeleton gives an animal its distinctive shape and provides support for the body and attachment for the muscles concerned with motion. But there are different kinds of skeletons.

In the parlor game of word association, "color" usually evokes the response "red," and the word "skeleton" evokes "bone" or "skull." In the animal kingdom, however, a bony skeleton or a skull is a rarity found only in one small phylum, the Chordata. **Skeleton** is not defined as something composed of bones; it is defined as the system of supporting structures to which the muscles that move the body are attached.

The phylum Arthropoda may be concisely defined as comprising those animals with bilaterally symmetrical, metameric, exoskeletal bodies set off into several regions and provided with articulating appendages. In this chapter the characteristics, principles and some of the major variations of the skeleton of certain arthropods—myriapods, insects and arachnoids—will be discussed.

THE EXOSKELETON

An essential characteristic of an **exoskeleton,** as distinguished from an **endoskeleton,** is its position relative to the **somatic muscles**—those involved primarily in body movements. As its name implies, an exoskeleton is external, with the somatic muscles attached to its inner (**entad**) side

(Fig. 2.1B). An endoskeleton, such as we ourselves share with the other chordates, reverses this relationship so that the somatic muscles lie outside (**ectad**) of the skeletal elements (Fig. 2.1A). In either kind of skeleton the same mechanical principles apply to the action of a muscle moving a skeletal part. A distal limb segment articulates on the end of a proximal limb segment, for example, with the articulation between the segments serving as the fulcrum of a lever. A muscle attached to the proximal seg-

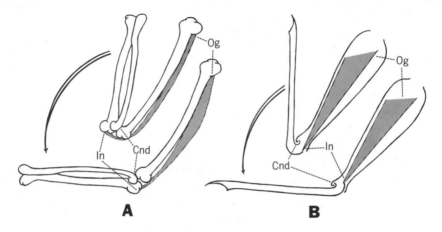

A   **B**

Figure 2.1. Relationship between a somatic muscle and the skeleton of an appendage, illustrating extension in (A) an endoskeletal vertebrate and (B) an exoskeletal arthropod. *Cnd,* fulcrum; *In,* insertion of extensor muscle on the distal segment; *Og,* origin of extensor muscle on proximal segment.

ment applies force at its point of insertion through its ability to contract, the angle of momentum being determined by the distance between the fulcrum and the point where force is applied. Study of Figure 2.1 shows that both systems obtain results and basically in the same way. Furthermore, vertebrate muscle and insect muscle do not differ substantially in such measurable characteristics as absolute power and chronaxie. How, then, can the ant lift and lug objects many times its own size? Or the grasshopper leap many times its own height and length? Equivalent prowess in man would enable him singlehandedly to hoist his car to the grease rack and would completely eliminate the need for stairways. At least two factors contribute to this relatively greater "strength" in insects. First, since the absolute power of a muscle is proportional to its diameter, and since insects are small, their muscles have a higher ratio between absolute muscular power and body weight. Second, the angle of momentum at articulations is often more favorable in insects; this is particularly true of the mechanism of flight, for which see Chapter Four.

Another requirement of the skeleton, that of giving support to the body, is met by the arthropod exoskeleton as well as or better than by the vertebrate endoskeleton. Furthermore, the arthropod skeleton afforts protection for the entire body and its vital systems, not just for the central nervous system as does the vertebrate skeleton.

The exoskeletal scheme of arranging the hard parts outside the soft parts of the body has many advantages, and it is a mistake to think of the arthropod skeleton as being inferior to that of vertebrates.

A serious disadvantage inherent in the exoskeleton is, however, presented by the requirements of growth. The vertebrate endoskeleton, composed as it is of living cellular material, grows with the rest of the body and represents a nearly ideal solution to the growth problem. The exoskeleton is composed of noncellular material secreted by the **hypodermis** (the outermost layer of cells) and called the **cuticle.** The cuticle is composed of firm plates (**sclerites**) connected by flexible bands or areas (**conjunctivae**). The hard sclerites cannot increase in size, and the conjunctivae have limits to their elasticity. The arthropod is therefore seemingly limited in its growth by the volume made available by the enclosing skeleton. There is a solution, and while it is not a wholly happy one, it appears to be the only one possible.

When the body has reached the limits permitted by its exoskeleton, the cuticle is loosened from the hypodermis and a new, larger cuticle is secreted under the old one. The old skeleton then is split, almost always along the dorsal midline, and is sloughed off. The new cuticle gradually hardens upon contact with air or water, as the case may be, and a new period of internal growth is made possible within the increased limits of the larger skeleton. The serious drawback to this process lies in the temporary vulnerability of the individual while the old cuticle is being cast off and before the new cuticle hardens sufficiently to afford adequate protection and efficient muscular activity. This skeleton-shedding process, known as **ecdysis,** must occur repeatedly until the animal reaches adult size. The process is characteristic of all arthropods. As will be seen from analyzing life histories (Chapter Eight), arthropods typically spend these periodically recurring periods of vulnerability in some protected situation.

THE INTEGUMENT

The arthropod integument (Fig. 2.2) is composed of (1) the **hypodermis** (epidermis), a single layer of cells derived from the embryonic ectoderm and lying closely packed with little or no intracellular material;

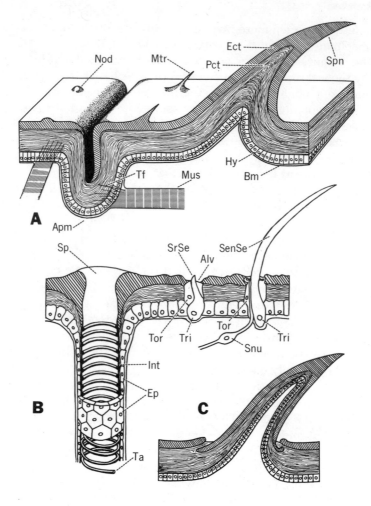

Figure 2.2. Structure and apophyses of the skeletal integument. Sections through (A) an apodeme and a spine, showing muscle attachments and fixed apophyses; (B) a spiracle, showing integumental modifications in a trachea and two kinds of setae; (C) a spur. *Alv,* alveolus; *Apd,* apodeme; *Bm,* basement membrane; *Ect,* epicuticle; *Ep,* epithelium; *Hy,* hypodermis; *Int,* intima; *Mtr,* microtrichia; *Mus,* muscle; *Nod,* nodule; *Pct,* procuticle; *SenSe,* sensory seta; *Snu,* sensory nerve cell; *Spn,* spine; *SrSe,* secretory seta; *Ta,* taenidia; *Tf,* tonofibrillae; *Tor,* tormagen cell; *Tri,* trichogen cell.

(2) the **basement membrane,** a cellular inner sheet; and (3) the **cuticle,** a series of noncellular layers secreted on the outside by the hypodermal layer.

The cross section of a hypodermal cell is more or less hexagonal, a shape normally resulting from close packing. The cells vary at different places and among different species in height and shape from cuboidal to columnar to irregular. Their general structure most closely resembles that of the cuboidal or columnar epithelium of vertebrates. The hypodermis directly secretes the cuticle and plays the key role in ecdysis by secreting the molting fluid, which loosens the cuticle from the cell layers through enzymatic action; it also absorbs the digested products resulting. Furthermore, the hypodermis serves as a relay for secretions transported by the blood and contributed to or affecting the condition of the cuticle.

The basement membrane is an exceedingly thin, entirely continuous sheet of flattened stellate cells loosely bound together with intracellular material of unknown composition. This membrane most nearly resembles the connective tissue of vertebrates, but no fibers have been demonstrated in its matrix.

The laminated, noncellular cuticle generally has two main layers, the inner **procuticle** (endocuticula, dermis, secondary cuticle) and the outer **epicuticle** (exocuticula, primary cuticle). The former is laminated and often strengthened by vertical or diagonal rods of homogeneous composition; it is penetrated by minute canals (**pore canals**) leading to the outer layers. The epicuticle is from less than one to more than six micra in thickness and commonly has four layers: (1) an innermost **cuticulin layer** composed of lipoproteins, (2) a **polyphenol layer,** (3) a **waxy layer** and (4) an outermost **cement layer** (epicuticula of Snodgrass). Some of these proteins are plasticized (Richards, 1944). Chitin often is present and may make up as much as sixty per cent of the cuticle by dry weight, but it is not the invariable ingredient it once was thought to be.

The epicuticle, quite impermeable to water, protects the animal from desiccation through the loss of body fluids and is resistant to the action of most materials ordinarily found in the environment. Its thickness, hardness and toughness vary greatly. When first secreted it is light, flexible and translucent; the more delicate membranes of the exoskeleton are not much changed from this initial condition. However, the heavier membranes, the leathery surfaces and particularly the hard skeletal sclerites are produced from the initial cuticular condition through a complex series of chemical changes resulting in tanning the outer layers. These changes give toughness and inelasticity to the epicuticle, as well as darkening the color (due to the tanned proteins). Cuticular pigments frequently are also present, particularly the melanins.

The hypodermis, with its basement membrane and cuticle, covers the entire surface of the body. It is infolded to form the **apodemes** and is invaginated at most orifices: at the mouth and anus to form the fore- and hindgut walls, at the spiracular openings to form the tracheae (Fig. 2.2B), at the genital openings and at the ducts of some of the glands.

The apodemal invaginations involve little or no histological change in the hypodermis. The invaginations of the fore- and hindgut, however, lead to some histological alteration unquestionably related to the specialized function of those regions. The hypodermis becomes the **epithelium,** the cells are cuboid or even flattened and sometimes become syncytial. The gut **intima** is continuous with the external cuticle, but is much thinner, even delicate, and forms a tubular lining. Only the basement membrane continues into the gut regions with little alteration.

Hypodermis invaginated at the tracheae also becomes thin, with pavement-like cells having large nuclei, while the basement membrane remains unchanged (Fig. 2.2B). The cuticle secreted as the tracheal lining (**intima**) is greatly modified and specialized. It is much thinner than the external cuticle. Providing support to the thin, tube-like tracheal walls, this intima is characterized by internal ridge-like thickenings. Typically these ridges are arranged in a helical pattern, though they sometimes are annular; near the spiracles the thickenings tend to be longitudinal. The ridges are called **taenidia.** A favorite laboratory exercise is to have the student tease out the larger tracheae; the intima tends to sever along the thinner, weaker lines between the taenidia. It should be emphasized that these spiral taenidia are not really structures, but merely the intimal thickenings.

APODEMES

Apodemes are invaginations of the integumentary layers into the body cavity (Fig. 2.2A). Basically they afford advantageous attachment for somatic muscles. Because of their shape, position and firmness they often provide additional structural support to associated skeletal areas, but this function must be considered as secondary and more or less adventitious. It is not correct to refer to the apodemes as an "endoskeleton." Merely because a skeletal part happens to lie *within* the body does not necessarily make it an endoskeleton. One must remember that the somatic muscles of an endoskeleton lie *ectad* of the skeletal elements and are attached to their *outer* surfaces. The apodemes of arthropods are exclusively exoskeletal; muscles are always attached to their histologically *inner* surfaces. No arthropod has an endoskeleton.

Nor would it be entirely accurate to refer to the "apodemal system." The apodemes are less a system than a method, as it were, a solution to the phylogenetic problem of how to increase the effectiveness of a muscle or a set of muscles. The selective advantage to the animal having more favorable muscle attachments, hence more effective muscular action, seems obvious.

At their origins, strands of somatic muscle appear to be more or less continuous with the basement membrane and to abut against the hypodermal layer. In most cases fibrillar, nonstriated structures (**tonofibrillae**) extend through the hypodermis into the cuticle, apparently providing an anchorage (Fig. 2.2A). The principal somatic muscles, especially those running longitudinally, originate at the anterior end of the primitive, unspecialized somite; from this position some of them have migrated, in a sense, during phylogenetic change. It is no accident that most apodemes, particularly those most consistently present, are found at the anterior margins of somites in those parts of the body where the greatest demands are placed upon muscles. Apodemes may be invaginated, however, at any point where an important muscle group is attached. Those apodemes appearing to lie under the middle of a sclerite probably were formed at the edge of a previously independent skeletal element which later fused with another to form a compound plate.

In shape, an apodeme may be merely an inflection of a scleretic margin (Fig. 2.2A), it may be a finger-like process and the finger may have terminal branchings, or it may be a wide, complexly formed plate (Fig. 2.11). The typical insect tentorium (Fig. 2.9) has a pair of anterior arms, a pair of posterior arms and a pair of dorsal arms connecting the cranial skeleton to a central body (**corporotentorium**), and such a structure is present in the heads of all true insects. A succession of variations present in the order Thysanura suggest its evolution. The more primitive groups such as the Myriapoda and most Collembola all have simple cranial apodemes based on invaginations from a pair of ventral **premandibular sclerites** (lying just above the bases of the mandibles). Protura and Aptera have no apodemal development in the cranium and the muscles of the mouthparts are attached directly to the head sclerites; this situation is also found in some of the Collembola (Snodgrass, 1951).

The thoracic apodemes (Fig. 2.11) are exceedingly variable in winged insects, but they appear to be based always on the three dorsal **phragmata** invaginated at the anterior margins of the **tergites** (dorsal sclerites) of the mesothorax, the metathorax and the first abdominal segment, respectively. Lateral apodemes develop from pleural sclerites, and in the dragonflies there may be as many as five pairs present. The **sternites** (ventral sclerites) of the thoracic region give rise to the **furca** and **spina.**

Because of the importance of the mouthpart muscles in the head and of the muscles of locomotion in the thorax, apodemes are better developed in those regions. Dorsal and ventral apodemes are often present in the abdomen but are rarely large. Commonly they are little more than simple invaginations at the anterior margins of segmental tergites and sternites. However, the apodemes associated with muscles of the copulatory and ovipository structures in some insects may be large.

MUSCLES

Muscles of insects, arachnoids and myriapods always are of the general striated type. The polynucleate muscle fibers contain numerous parallel myofibrils made up of contractile protein chains with alternating light- and dark-staining segments. As in vertebrate striated muscle, the apparent transverse bands are caused by the fact that the dark-staining segments of all the **myofibrils** lie side by side. Mononucleate smooth, unstriated muscle is not present in arthropods.

The simplest type of muscle, found in all immature stages and in the adults of many of the more primitive groups, has a wide layer of nucleated protoplasm enclosing a relatively few, very fine myofibrils with poorly differentiated dark and light segments. The usual type of adult muscle has the myofibrils densely but irregularly arranged throughout the fiber, which is ensheathed in a structureless elastic membrane (**sarcolemma**). The nuclei either lie next to the sarcolemma or are scattered among the myofibrils. In advanced groups such as the wasps, bees and flies the fibers may be columnar, with the nuclei forming a core from which rows of myofibrils radiate. The indirect flight muscles (see Chapter Four) of many insects are composed of unusually large myofibrils enclosed by a loose lacework of tracheal endings; the sarcolemma is often absent.

Muscular contraction is, of course, in response to neural stimulus. Such stimuli are transmitted from the ganglia by motor axons which ramify throughout the bundle of fibers. The neural terminations ordinarily enter the sarcolemma.

A muscle connects a relatively stationary point (the **origin**) with a movable point (the **insertion**). Its action is to pull these two points toward each other by contraction of the myofibrils, specifically of the dark-staining segments. Each end of a muscle is anchored in the integument in some fashion. The anchorage may not be very firm, as when the sarco-lemma of the muscle fiber merely abuts the hypodermis. More often the anchorage is quite firm, with the tonofibrillae extending from the muscle fibers through the hypodermal cells and even into the cuticle. Whether tonofibrillae are really continuations of the myofibrils or are just fastened to their ends has not been settled. The degree to which the muscle fiber is anchored to the integument probably is proportional to the stress involved in the particular muscle's action; muscles exerting greater force are un-doubtedly better anchored. It has been suggested that muscular force, by pulling the hypodermis inward, leads to the formation of tendons and other apodemes, but it should be noticed that many apodemes project in a direction not parallel to the pull of attached muscles.

The musculature falls into two groups: the **somatic muscles,** which act on skeletal elements and appendages, and the **splanchnic muscles,** which act on the internal structures and organs. The former take both origin and insertion at the external integument or its apodemes, the latter rarely have either end associated with the external integument; the former are associated with **peripheral** branches of the central nervous system, the latter with the **visceral** nervous system (Chapter Six).

The arrangement of the somatic musculature is one of the basic distinc-tions between the Annelida and the Arthropoda. In the Annelida the somatic muscles are incorporated with layers of the body wall to form a tubular, muscular dermis. In Arthropoda the somatic muscles are entirely *entad* of the hypodermis and are arranged into separate units of fibers or bundles of fibers.

For each muscular action there must be an available counteraction, so that in general the somatic muscles are found in antagonistic pairs or paired sets. A movable part, such as the segment of a leg, articulates on a fulcrum—frequently formed by a condyle or a pair of condyles—with a muscle unit on each side of the fulcrum. Thus if one serves as a flexor, the other acts as an extensor. In a few instances the necessary counteraction is supplied by means other than an antagonistic muscle unit. At certain articulations the cuticle is springy, the spring action being antagonistic to that of the single muscle unit present. In a few other cases (some of the joints in spider legs) counteraction is provided by hydrostatic blood pressure, but this in turn depends upon the contraction of muscles, though they may be remote from the part moved.

So variable is the musculature of arthropods that it is difficult to estab-lish general homologies in the way that has been done in vertebrate anat-omy. The muscles of many kinds of arthropods have been described in detail, but putting names to muscles is one thing and showing their homologies is a different matter. The best general, basic description of insect musculature is to be found in Snodgrass (1935), and of muscular physiology in Gilmour (1953).

The feats of relative strength and endurance accomplished by arthropods depend primarily upon the more advantageous leverages provided by an exoskeleton and upon the fact that arthropods are small and light. The **absolute power** of a muscle is defined by the maximum load it can lift per area of cross section; in this respect arthropod muscles are not appreciably different from those of vertebrates. The biochemistry of muscular action in arthropods is the same for all invertebrates, insofar as is known; available information is summarized by Gilmour (1953).

One extraordinary phenomenon peculiar to insects is the ability of certain muscles to contract rapidly and repeatedly and to continue to do so for surprisingly prolonged periods, whereas the phenomena of twitch, chronaxis and tetany observed in these and other muscles seem to be entirely normal. The indirect flight muscles, for example, may approach a vibration of 1000 cycles per second. Stridulation in grasshoppers, crickets and cicadas also is produced by vibratory muscle action. No full explanation of how this works has been obtained. Pringle (1949) thought it might depend upon mutual stimulation by antagonistic pairs of muscles, that the stimulation increases with the load on the muscles and that the vibration can be maintained by continuous low frequency impulses from the central nervous system.

The arrangement of splanchnic muscles tends to be even more irregular, so that it is quite impractical to try to identify or name individual muscles; they are better discussed in terms of layers, patterns and directions. The most orderly arrangement is likely to be found around the enteron. In the foregut region the epithelial wall is enclosed by an inner layer of longitudinal muscles and an outer layer of circular muscles. Frequently one or both layers become somewhat skewed and are actually diagonal in direction, or such skewing may occur only in a part of the foregut. The hindgut muscles are similar to those of the foregut, but an additional layer of more or less circular muscles may be present within the longitudinal layer. In the midgut the inner muscular layer is circular, the longitudinals lying ectad, though in many areas the two layers seem to be combined into an irregular reticulated network of anastomosing fibers. The heart, aorta, hemocoelic diaphragms and the accessory pulsating structures all include splanchnic muscular tissue. In more primitive forms and in some immature stages the muscles of the heart and aorta may be arranged into circular and longitudinal layers, but more usually the layers are combined into a network of lightly striated myofibrils running in all directions. Similar myofibril networks frequently enclose the ovaries and other mesodermal parts of the reproductive system.

CUTICULAR STRUCTURES

The surface of the cuticle is rarely smooth. Sculpturing is almost always present, though sometimes visible only microscopically, and there are a variety of projections and structures called **apophyses.** These fall into two categories, the **fixed apophyses** and the **articulating apophyses,** depending upon whether or not the projection or structure moves in relation to the cuticle.

Fixed apophyses are integral parts of the cuticle itself (Fig. 2.2A). A **nodule** is a mound-like projection formed by a thickening of the cuticle. A **fixed hair** (**microtrichia**) is merely a thin, pointed nodule. A **spine** is larger than a microtrichia and involves not just thickened cuticle, but evagination of the hypodermal layer itself.

Articulating apophyses have been called "cuticular appendages," but to avoid confusion the term *appendage* should be reserved for the paired metameric appendages. The two main types are the **spurs** (Fig. 2.2C), which are multicellular, and the **setae** (Fig 2.2B), which are monocellular. Spurs are most commonly encountered on the legs; when examining a leg one must be careful to distinguish between spurs and spines; they often appear similar but are quite different in structure and function.

Unlike other cuticular apophyses, the setae arise from modified hypodermal cells rather than from the cuticle itself. The inner, basal part of a setal cell lies against the basement membrane among or below the other hypodermal cells and contains the nucleus. A cytoplasmic extension protrudes through a cup-like cavity in the cuticule; the cell wall of the protruding part is invested with a stiffened protective layer of epicuticle which is not continuous with the surrounding cuticle. The setal cell (**trichogen**) is associated with another specialized hypodermal cell (**tormogen**), which provides on its ectal surface in the setal pocket (**alveolus**) a ring of light, flexible cuticle, the **setal membrane.**

There are a great many modifications of setae in the Arthropoda. A frequently encountered function is that of body clothing: the hairs of the bee and of the diving beetle are setae, as are also the flattened scales on the wings of butterflies, moths and mosquitoes. In the case of the diving beetle, dense setae serve to retain a thin layer of air beneath the animal's body, thus enabling direct respiration during submersion in the water. Setae may be penetrated by neural dendrites, thus making possible additional function as tangoreceptors.

The trichogen cell may be secretory, serving as a one-celled gland. In some lepidopterous larvae, for example, the trichogen cells secrete an urticant or other kind of poison which exudes when the needle-like tip is broken by contact. In other cases the external projections of the trichogen cells may be short, extending but little or not at all beyond the alveolar pocket, and small quantities of viscous or oily material are secreted. Such cells generally are chemoreceptors and enter into taste-smell sensations, but sometimes the secretion has only a protective function. On the **post-tarsus** (terminal leg segment) of certain flies, trichogen cells secrete the sticky substance that helps the animal perform such tricks as walking on the ceiling. In many butterflies and moths, groups of wing scales (**androconial patches**) are also secretory, the secretions being believed to be attractive to the opposite sex; the odor is sometimes easily detectable by man.

METAMERISM

Metamerism is the construction of an animal's body from a longitudinal series of essentially similar units (Fig. 2.3) called **metameres** (**somites, segments**).[1] Four major phyla of animals have metamerism. In the Annelida it is found in its simplest form and, lacking articulated appendages, they remain worm-like animals. Probably the Mollusca originally had metameric bodies, but serial segmentation is now so obscured that it is not recognizable in adults. Nor is metamerism in the Chordata particularly obvious externally, but both ontogeny and internal organization clearly indicate its presence. The Arthropoda, while preserving typical metamerism, also have paired articulated appendages: this combination of structures enables almost infinite variation and adjustment—which helps explain why the phylum is the largest and most diverse inhabiting the world today.

As a frame of reference for understanding and relating the complex of existing structural modifications, it is helpful to consider a single generalized arthropod metamere. This basic unit of the arthropod body has certain standard structures (Fig 2.4). The integument, with its layer of hypodermis and its cuticle, forms an enclosing skeletal cylinder with a dorsal sclerite (**tergite**) and a ventral sclerite (**sternite**). The two lateral (**pleural**) surfaces have thinner, more flexible cuticle. Above the outer edges of the sternites the integument evaginates to form appendages, one on each side. The appendages are made up of a series of sclerotized cylinders

[1] Efforts to limit "metamere" and "somite" to structures of the embryo have been unsuccessful and these three terms generally are used interchangeably in entomology. "Segment" also is used for a section of an appendage, interchangeably with "joint," a word preferred in the latter application by purists.

(**segments, joints**) connected by articulations, where the cuticle is flexible and unsclerotized.

Within the metamere are numerous muscles. Some lie parallel to the long axis of the body and connect with adjacent metameres or with muscles there. Other muscles connect the tergite and sternite, enabling dorsoventral compression. The proximal segment (joint) of each appendage is moved by muscles originating on the skeleton of the segment proper.

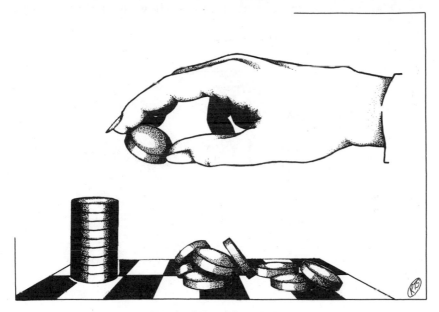

Figure 2.3.   Metamerism.

The longitudinal center of the metamere is occupied by a length of enteron held in position by the dilator muscles originating in the body wall. The enteron walls are composed of the epithelial cell layer and the cuticular intima secreted within it, the whole being enclosed by a network of splanchnic muscle fibers, both longitudinal and circular. Along the midventral floor of the body cavity lie the paired cords of the central nervous system, thickened near the middle of the metamere and there forming a pair of ganglia from which axons lead throughout the segment to the muscles and which receive axons from sensory sites. Oxygen is supplied directly to muscles and other internal tissues by **tracheoles**, a system of tiny tubes ramified from the **tracheae**. The tracheae are larger, main trunks leading into the body from the lateral apertures (**spiracles**), one on each side of the metamere diagonally above the appendage. The residual space within the metamere and its appendage is called the **hemocoel** and is filled with blood.

The simplest possible arthropod would be constructed by joining together a series of such metameres. At the junctures of the metameres the lengths of enteron would be connected, forming a tube running from one end of the body to the other, and the ventral nerve cords would be similarly connected. The longitudinal bundles of muscles would have their free ends attached to skeletal material in adjoining metameres. At each

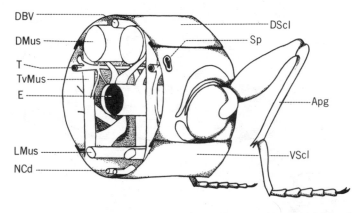

Figure 2.4.   A metamere. *Apg*, appendage; *DBV*, dorsal blood vessel; *DMus*, dorsal muscle; *DScl*, dorsal sclerite; *E*, enteron; *LMus*, longitudinal muscle; *NCd*, nerve cord; *Sp*, spiracle; *T*, trachea; *TvMus*, transverse muscle; *VScl*, ventral sclerite.

end the body would be "capped," the **acron** at the front and the **telson** at the rear; the enteron would penetrate through both.

The result would resemble a worm with legs, but it would have no head and hence no anterior-posterior orientation. It would have little general co-ordination and no way to find food, to protect itself from certain dangers or to reproduce its kind. Although this theoretical construction represents the basic arthropod plan of organization, it cannot be considered complete. Much of the rest of this book is devoted to discussing some of the modifications of the basic arthropod body plan, modifications which are wonderfully adapted for survival under a great variety of conditions.

BODY REGIONS

One of the most ancient developments in arthropods was the formation of a head, which established anterior-posterior orientation. The anterior opening of the enteron is the mouth, the posterior opening the anus, with one-way traffic between them. The head logically develops sensory sites receiving impressions of the situation out in front and sending the stimuli to the ganglia of the head metameres. These ganglia, becoming more and more important, develop into a complex co-ordinating center for the whole body, an elementary "brain." The skeletal elements of the metameres contributing to the head generally ankylose into a heavy-walled protective capsule, and their appendages become specialized either as sensory structures or as mouthparts.

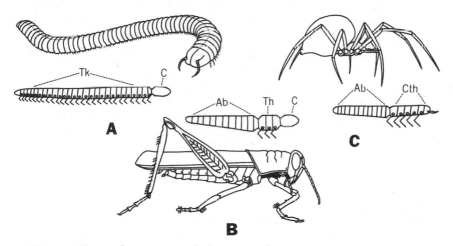

Figure 2.5. Body regions in (A) myriapods, (B) insects, and (C) arachnoids. *Ab,* abdomen; *C,* head; *Cth,* cephalothorax; *Th,* Thorax; *Tk,* trunk.

All arthropods have such a head, in which are concentrated the functions of primary perception, food selection, ingestion and basic co-ordination; the metameric elements are highly modified, specialized to contribute to these functions.

The division of the body into regions does not stop with a head. Among the arthropods within the purview of this book there are three principal types of arrangement (Fig. 2.5 and Table 2.1): (1) the myriapod type, in which the body is divided into a **head** and a long abdomen (**trunk**) bearing functional locomotory appendages on all or nearly all metameres; (2) the insect type, in which the body is divided into the **head,** the **thorax** with its locomotory structures and an **abdomen** having no locomotory appendages; (3) the arachnoid type, in which the locomotory thorax is combined with the head as a **cephalothorax** and the **abdomen** has no locomotory appendages.

THE HEAD CAPSULE

Insects and myriapods have a head capsule essentially similar in structure. No separate head capsule is present in arachnoids.

The head region of insects and myriapods consists of two parts (Fig. 2.6), an anterior **procephalon** and the **gnathocephalon.** The adult procephalon bears the eyes and antennae. The three procephalic ganglia are dorsal of the enteron and are functionally associated with the eyes, antennae and integumental receptors. The gnathocephalon bears the mouthparts and contains the three pairs of segmental ganglia which innervate them. The gnathocephalic ganglia frequently are fused into a single mass, the **subesophageal ganglion.** The subesophageal ganglion is connected to the procephalic ganglia ("brain") by two **circumesophageal connectives** between which the enteron passes ventrally to the mouth.

The procephalon apparently was an ancient development since it is found, though in a very different form, in annelids as well as arthropods. In crustaceans it bears an additional pair of antennae innervated by the posteriormost of the procephalic ganglia (**tritocerebrum**). Three coelomic sacs have been accounted for in embryos (Wiesman, 1926; Roonwal, 1936), and three pairs of limb primordea. These facts led to the classical explanation of the procephalon: that it is formed from the three anteriormost metameres plus, of course, the nonmetameric acron or anterior skeletal closure. Goodrich (1897) summarized the evidence available at that time and this theory was adopted in the monumental *Gli Insetti* (1909) by Berlese. Recent reviews supporting the classical theory are to be found in Imms (1937), Tiegs (1940), Manton (1949), Weber (1952) and Imms, Richards and Davies (1957).

According to the available evidence, the procephalon is made up of the following metameres (Fig. 2.6A): (1) the **preantennal segment** containing the **protocerebrum**—embryonic coelomic sacs and limb primordea have been found by the few observers in certain insects but seem to be absent in the majority of embryos; (2) the **antennal segment** containing the **deutocerebrum**—a coelomic sac is frequently present in embryos and has often been observed; the segmental appendages become the antennae; (3) the **intercalary segment** containing the **tritocerebrum**—embryonic coelomic sacs have been observed; the appendages are the second antennae of crustacea but do not develop in insects or myriapods.

This generally accepted explanation of the procephalic composition is a position difficult to defend because no single arthropod embryo has ever been found with all three coelomic sacs or all three limb primordea. The evidence is comparative and deductive.

Among alternative theories to explain the composition of the procephalon, one proposed by Holmgren (1896–1916) and elaborated by Hanström (1925–1930) has been widely discussed in recent years. Based primarily on studies of adults, especially of the nervous systems, of many arthropods and annelids, this theory assumes that the optic and antennal parts of the head are derived from the acron rather than from metameres (Fig. 2.6B). The protocerebrum and deutocerebrum are explained as sec-

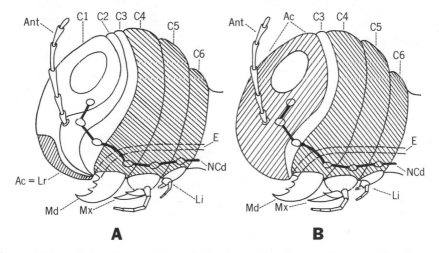

A   **B**

Figure 2.6. Composition of the insect head according to (A) the classic interpretation and (B) the Holmgren-Hanström theory. *Ac,* acron; *Ant,* antenna; *C1,* preantennal segment; *C2,* antennal segment; *C3,* intercalary segment; *C4,* mandibular segment; *C5,* maxillary segment; *C6,* labial segment; *E,* enteron; *Li,* labium; *Lr,* labrum; *Md,* mandible; *Mx,* maxilla; *NCd,* nerve cord.

ondary subdivisions of the ganglion of the acron. The antennae are thought to belong to the acron and thus not to be true segmental appendages. This reasoning is predicated on several assumptions: that the mouth, marking the anterior pole of the body, is and has always been located between the intercalary and antennary segments; that close homology exists between the the arthropod procephalon and the annelid **prostomium** (the part of the annelid head lying anterior of its mouth). Accordingly, everything anterior of the arthropod mouth is said to be "preoral" in origin— that is, acronic—and the intercalary segment is counted as the first true metamere. Embryonic evidence on coelomic sacs and limb primordea is discounted or ignored. Snodgrass (1936, 1951) and Du Porte (1958) adopted this theory and ably reviewed their evidence. Their arguments are unconvincing. The notion that the acron bears appendages and has a ganglion seems particularly weak. The acron as visualized by the Holmgren-Hanström theory appears to be suspiciously like metameric material. Both the casual dismissal of evidence from embryogenesis (see Chapter Seven) and the great weight given to comparison between *living* arthropods and *living* annelids (see Chapter Ten) are scientifically unsound. The theory is historically interesting but is no longer espoused by most morphologists and entomologists.

There is, in fact, a much better case to be made for a third theory, brought forward by Henry (1947–1948) and Ferris (1947), that *four* procephalic metameres are respectively represented by the labrum, clypeus, hypopharynx and oculo-antennary structures. In any event, the classical theory is the one best supported by all the evidence from all sources.

Morphologists agree that the gnathocephalon consists of three metameres (Fig. 2.6). The three pairs of appendages are modified to assist in feeding, and the three pairs of ganglia are often coalesced into a single mass (subesophageal ganglion). The appendages are the **mandibles,** the **maxillae** and the **labium** (second maxillae).

Most arthropods with a distinct head, as in insects and myriapods, have the cephalic sclerites fused into a strong compact head capsule in the adult. It is difficult or impossible to observe the metameric relationships of these skeletal elements, particularly those of the procephalic region.

THE MYRIAPOD PLAN

The myriapods have their bodies divided into two regions, a head and an abdomen (trunk), but each group has its own characteristic variation of the plan.

The chilopods (Fig. 2.7A, B) are flattened dorsoventrally. The head capsule is firmly ankylosed, with little or no evidence of the segmental contributions. When present, the eyes approach those of insects in structure. The antennae have many sections and are placed well forward on the head capsule. The **labrum** is a narrow, often dentate plate at the margin of the **clypeus** and commonly is reflexed so that it seems to be inside the mouth. The mouthparts are a pair of mandibles and two pairs of leg-like maxillae (see Fig. 3.11). No true tentorium is present within the head capsule; a pair of apodemes arising from premandibular sclerites at the ventral margin of the cranium may be homologous with the **anterior tentorial arms** (Fig. 2.9) of insects (Snodgrass, 1951).

The trunk consists of from 15 to 175 segments, according to species, each with a pair of legs, and followed by a highly modified segment and the telson, neither of which bears legs. The first three trunk segments

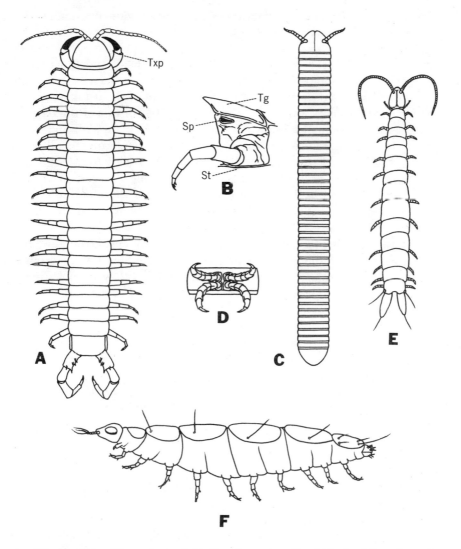

Figure 2.7. The principal kinds of myriapods. (A) A chilopod, with (B) a lateral view of a trunk segment; (C) a diplopod, with (D) a ventral view of a diplosegment; (E) a symphylid; (F) a pauropod. *Sp*, spiracle; *St*, sternum; *Tg*, tergum; *Txp*, poison claw. (A–D drawn from specimens in Carnegie Museum; E from Verhoeff, 1934, after Latzel, 1884; F after Remy, 1931)

differ somewhat from the others and form a subregion not unlike the insect thorax, but less specialized and not so distinct. The first (anterior-most) trunk segment bears a pair of large leg-like appendages, the **poison claws** (see Fig. 3.11D), which are held under the head and function in feeding and, incidentally, in protection. The legs of the next two segments are slighter and shorter than those on the rest of the trunk.

The skeleton of a leg-bearing segment (Fig. 2.7B) consists of the **tergum** (tergite) and **sternum** (sternite), both strong and plate-like, and relatively narrow pleural areas (**pleuron**) of leathery membrane. Small crescentate or annular sclerites are usually present at the leg bases. Originally each trunk segment probably bore a' pair of spiracles placed in an annular sclerite located in the dorsoposterior corner of the pleuron, but in living species some of the segments lack spiracles, the exact number present being characteristic of genera and species.

The telson is present as a small ring on the last segment surrounding the anus. Appendages of the last segment are either absent or, in some groups, present as nonlocomotory structures termed **cerci,** but they are not strictly homologous with the cerci of insects. The genital opening lies ventrad between the last segment and the telson.

The diplopods (Fig. 2.7C, D) have few-faceted eyes or (many species) no eyes at all. The antennae are short. The head capsule is very firmly fused into a strong cranium with few **sutures** (grooves). The labrum is a narrow plate above the mouth and almost never articulates. Hypopharyngeal apodemes, similar to those of Chilopoda, are present. The mouthparts are the mandibles and the **gnathochilarium,** the latter having been variously interpreted as the maxillae only, the labium only or as both combined. Uncertainty on the point has led to various interpretations of the composition of the diplopod gnathocephalon, and some authorities (Silvestri, Snodgrass) have adopted the view that the labial segment does not even contribute to the head but rather to the neck (**collum**). Pflugfelder (1932) found rudiments of both maxillae and labium in the embryo and showed that the gnathochilarium forms from both pairs of appendages.

The trunk segments are enclosed by a subcylindric, almost continuous sclerite formed by the fusion of tergal, pleural and sternal elements. Each of the first four trunk segments ordinarily bears a small pair of legs, but in certain species one or another of these leg pairs may be atrophied. The paired genital openings lie ventrad between the second and third of these segments. Behind this somewhat specialized region, the trunk segments are fused in pairs (**diplosegments**), with conjunctival membrane only between alternate true segments. Usually the boundary between two fused segments is marked by a suture. Each diplosegment bears a pair of legs (Fig. 2.7D) placed close together on the ventral side, suggesting that the sternal skeleton has been greatly reduced. Spiracles are present near the leg·bases on nearly every segment. The trunk may consist of from twenty-five to more than a hundred segments, according to species.

Pauropods have no eyes, and their antennae have the terminal segments branched. The mouthparts are a pair of mandibles and a pair of maxillae, but the labium is not present in adults; it has been claimed that the labial segment does not enter into the gnathocephalic organization. Hypopharyngeal apodemes essentially similar to those of diplopods and chilopods are present in the head. Like the diplopods, the trunk segments are fused in pairs; twelve segments form six diplosegments bearing nine pairs of legs. The paired openings of the reproductive system lie ventrad between the second and third trunk segments.

The head capsule of the Symphyla has a Y-shaped epicranial suture, a feature shared with the insects and one of the principal bases for speculation that the two groups are closely related. The mouthparts consist of the mandibles, similar in structure to those of diplopods, the maxillae and the labium, both of which are closely similar to the homologous appendages of insects. Hypopharyngeal apodemes are present as in other myriapods.

The trunk consists of fifteen segments plus the telson, and eleven or twelve pairs of legs are present. The base of each leg lies close to the base of the other member of the pair, with the sternite strongly reduced in width, as in diplopods, but unlike them, diplosegments are not formed. The coxal part of the symphylid leg bears a **stylus** (a process of the leg base), sometimes viewed as evidence of close relationship with insects. Snodgrass (1935) pointed out that in these myriapods the stylus lies on the inner side of the leg and therefore is an **endite,** whereas the stylus of certain primitive insects (some Thysanura and Aptera) lies on the outer side of the leg and is an **exite.** The anus opens through the telson, and the appendages of the last segment are strongly modified in a way resembling those of chilopods and also termed *cerci.* The genital opening is ventral between the second and third trunk segments, an anterior position similar to the position in diplopods and pauropods.

In creatures which otherwise give the impression of being a somewhat random combination of various myriapod and insect structures, it is interesting to note that the position of the spiracles is unique. They are located on the head in a membranous area just above the mandibles and none are present on the trunk.

THE INSECT PLAN

Something like a million different species of insects are known to exist. With few exceptions, easily recognized external morphologic characteristics serve to distinguish each of the twenty-nine orders. Another way of saying the same thing is that there are at least twenty-nine *major* variations of the basic insect body plan. Accordingly, the description of a "generalized insect" which follows is necessarily diagrammatic and is intended only to serve as a basis for understanding the external morphology of insects in general. Almost none of the statements made in this description applies to *all* insects; nor, for that matter, do they adequately describe any *one* insect.

As in myriapods, the external skeleton of the insect head is a strong, sclerotized capsule bearing the eyes, ocelli, antennae and three pairs of metameric appendages modified for feeding. The capsule is marked off by certain grooves (**sutures**) into areas. The sutures, eyes and antennae serve as landmarks for recognizing the named areas of the head. These areas are suggestive of the basic skeletal sclerites of the cephalic segments, but it is not possible to associate all of them satisfactorily, especially those of the procephalon.

From a frontal view of a generalized head (Fig. 2.8A), the **labrum** is seen to be the upper lip and overhangs the mouth. It is attached to the lower margin of the **clypeus** by a membranous hinge and is moved by two pairs of muscles that take their origins on the inner side of the capsule beneath the **frons**; while serving as a mouthpart, it is really a skeletal sclerite rather than a modified appendage. The clypeus is joined solidly to the frons at the **frontoclypeal suture.** On either side of the midline on this suture are the **anterior tentorial pits,** which mark the point of invagination of a pair of apodemes, the **anterior tentorial arms** (Fig. 2.9). On the top and front of the capsule is the **epicranial suture,** formed as an inverted **Y**, a recognizable characteristic of nearly all insect orders. The area between and below the arms of the epicranial suture is the **frons,** which bears the **median ocellus** when it is present. On either side of the frons are the antennal sockets (**foramina**), each containing the annular **antennal sclerite.** The proximal segment of the antennae fits within the antennal sclerite and articulates on a condyle, the **antennifer.** In all insects the antennifer is placed at the ventro-lateral margin of the **antennal foramen.**

From a lateral view (Fig. 2.8B), the **parietal area** is seen to be defined dorsally by the epicranial suture, by the frons anteriorly and by the **occipital suture** posteriorly. On the parietal area are found the compound eye, the antenna and one of the **lateral ocelli.** The area on the top of the head is called the **vertex.** Like the antennae, the compound eyes have narrow annular sclerites (**ocular sclerites**) set off by the **ocular sutures.** The ventral part of the parietal area is the **gena** and often is separated from the frons by the **genal suture.** That part of the gena immediately behind the eyes often is termed the **postgena.**

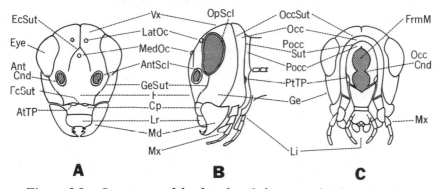

A   **B**   **C**

Figure 2.8. Structure and landmarks of the insect head in (A) frontal view, (B) lateral view and (C) posterior view. *AntCnd*, antennifer; *AntScl*, antennal sclerite; *AtTP*, anterior tentorial pit; *Cp*, clypeus; *EcSut*, epicranial suture; *Eye*, compound eye; *F*, frons; *FcSut*, fronto-clypeal suture; *FrmM*, foramen magnum; *Ge*, gena; *GeSut*, genal suture; *LatOc*, lateral ocellus; *Li*, labium; *Lr*, labrum; *Md*, mandible; *MedOc*, median ocellus; *Mx*, maxilla; *Occ*, occiput; *OccCnd*, occipital condyle; *OccSut*, occipital suture; *OpScl*, optic sclerite; *Pocc*, postocciput; *PoccSut*, postoccipital suture; *PtTP*, posterior tentorial pit; *Vx*, vertex. (A and C modified from Ross, 1948, by permission of John Wiley & Sons)

From the rear (Fig. 2.8C) it is seen that the **occipital suture** is followed by a horseshoe-shaped sclerite called the **occiput** and bounded posteriorly by the **postoccipital suture,** in which lie the **posterior tentorial pits.** The last cranial sclerite is the **postocciput,** which frames the dorsal and lateral aspects of the **foramen magnum.** Its lateral edges bear the **occipital condyles** on which the head nods.

Within the head is a framework of apodemes, the **tentorium,** which serves both to strengthen the head capsule and to afford attachment for muscles. As fully developed, the tentorium (Fig. 2.9) consists of a central bridge (**corporotentorium**) from which three pairs of arms extend to the cranial wall. The **anterior arms** are invaginated from the anterior tentorial pits on the postoccipital suture. The **dorsal arms** extend to the capsule between the antennae and the lateral ocelli, but their position is not marked externally by pits. They are thought to be continuations of the other arms rather than primary apodemes. The **posterior arms** connect the corporotentorium with the rear of the capsule and are apodemes invaginated at the posterior tentorial pits. The primitive insect orders (Collembola, Protura, Thysanura, Aptera) have simpler, less developed tentoria—Snodgrass (1951) has found interesting similarities between them and the cranial apodemes of myriapods.

Because of the attachment of the mouthparts to the various cephalic sclerites it is believed that the postocciput, the occiput and at least a part of the parietal area belong to the three metameres of the gnathocephalon.

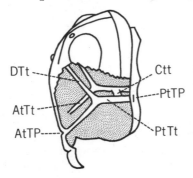

Figure 2.9. Lateral view of insect head, cut away to show the tentorial apodemes. *AtTP*, anterior tentorial pit; *AtTt*, anterior tentorial arms; *Ctt*, corporotentorium; *DTt*, dorsal tentorial arms; *PtTP*, posterior tentorial pits; *PtTt*, posterior tentorial arms.

By implication the sclerites of the face and near the antennae and eyes belong to the procephalon.

Heads of insects may be classified as belonging in general to either of two types, distinguished by general shape, the apparent position of the mouth and its posture relative to the rest of the body. In the **hypognathous head** the mouth is *ventral* and the foramen magnum is *behind* the long axis of the head. A line drawn from the occipal condyles to the eyes and thence to the base of the mandibles would be almost a right angle. The posture of the head relative to the body is somewhat like that of a man's head when he is walking on all fours. The **prognathous head** has the mouth *anterior* and the foramen magnum *on* the long axis of the head. The posture of the head resembles that of a dog. A line drawn from the occipital condyles through the eyes of the base of the mandibles would be almost straight. Certain insects with hypognathous heads may acquire a prognathous appearance through elongation of the ventral elements without any real change in the position of the foramen. Among Hemiptera the mouthparts are reflected posteriorad and lie between the legs, with the ventral parts of the head greatly reduced. This variation of the hypognathous head is sometimes treated as a third type, the **opisthognathous head.**

The neck (**cervix, collum**) contains the true intersegmental line between the head and the first thoracic segment and is not a separate
metamere as some (e.g., Verhoeff) have thought. On each side of the
neck there are one or two small sclerites which connect the head with
the thorax, articulating with the occipital condyles anteriorly and with
the prothorax posteriorly. The anterior articulation permits the head to
nod, and the posterior articulation allows the head to turn sideways. In
some insects there is also a dorsal and a ventral cervical sclerite, but
muscles are associated only with lateral cervical sclerites. Probably all
these skeletal elements of the neck are derived from the first thoracic
segment.

Specialized for locomotion, the insect thorax consists of three segments,
the **pro-**, the **meso-** and the **metathorax**, each bearing a pair of legs. When
they are present, wings are found only on the last two of these segments.

The simplest thoracic skeleton is found in those primitive insect orders
which do not have wings and had no winged ancestors (**primarily** or
primitively wingless). The three segments are much alike (Fig. 2.10A),
each with a dorsal **notum** (tergite) and ventral **sternum** present as single,
separate skeletal plates. The lateral (pleural) aspects of these segments
are largely membranous and unsclerotized. Spiracles are located on the
meso- and metathorax near the lateral margins of the nota as simple
openings in the body wall leading into the tracheae. The prothorax develops spiracles only in the embryo. In those rare cases where an adult
insect seems to have prothoracic spiracles (certain Aptera), it has been
shown that they are in fact the mesothoracic spiracles displaced forward
to the prothorax during development.

On all three segments the legs are inserted in the pleural area, with
three small sclerites associated with them: the **sternopleurite** lies just
below the base of the leg and the **coxopleurite** just above it; each bears a
condyle (**coxal process**) and the leg articulates between them. The third
sclerite is the **anapleurite,** which lies above the coxopleurite. These three
sclerites were derived, according to Snodgrass, from the proximal part
of the coxa and serve to strengthen the pleural membrane around the
leg base.

In Figure 2.10 it may be noted that the lines of division between the
successive nota or the successive sterna, marked by flexible tissue, do not
coincide exactly with the true divisions between the segments. This
illustrates in one of its simplest forms the fact that apparent segmentation
of the adult body, interpreted from the sclerites, does not necessarily
coincide with the true metameres. Segmentation as found in the embryo
is **primary**; the apparent segmentation found in adult sclerotization gen-

erally is **secondary** and is brought about by displacement of skeletal elements during development.

The presence of wings places a severe strain on the thorax and requires that the thoracic skeleton be firm enough not to buckle during flight, while the development of an elaborate flight musculature is associated with the presence of better developed apodemes. Accordingly, the thoracic skeleton

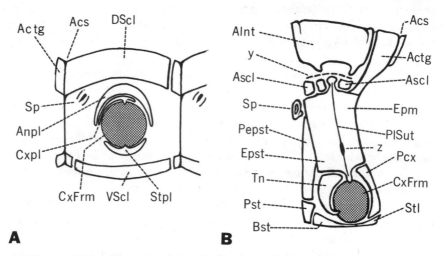

A   **B**

Figure 2.10. Thoracic skeletal elements of (A) an apterygote insect and (B) a pterygote insect. *Acs,* antecostal suture; *Actg,* acrotergite or post-notum; *Alnt,* alinotum; *Anpl,* anapleurite; *Ascl,* alar sclerite; *Bst,* basister-num; *CxFrm,* coxal foramen; *Cxpl,* coxopleurite; *DScl,* notum or tergite; *Epm,* epimeron; *Epst,* episternum; *Pcx,* postcoxale; *Pepst,* pre-episternum; *PlSut,* pleural suture; *Pst,* presternum; *Sp,* spiracle; *Stl,* sternellum; *Stpl,* sternopleurite; *Tn,* trochantin; *VScl,* sternum; *y,* position of wing base; *z,* position of pleurodemal apodeme.

of winged insects is somewhat more complex than that of primitively wingless groups.

A wing-bearing segment (Fig. 2.10B) has its notum displaced forward, a condition foreshadowed in wingless insects, so that only the anterior three-quarters of the segment is covered by its own notum, now called the **alinotum,** which articulates with the dorsal side of the wing base. The true intersegmental line is approximately marked by a transverse groove, the **anterior notal suture.** The notum continues forward to cover the posterior part of the next segment where it is termed the **postnotum,** and is firmly joined to pleural sclerites that form the support between the notum and sternum. Primitively there is a line of flexibility between the anterior edge of the postnotum and the posterior edge of the alinotum. The winged insects generally have the nota ankylosed, particularly between the meso- and metathorax, eliminating the intersegmental articulation and adding strength and power to flight action.

The principal pleural sclerites of each segment are the **episternum**, lying anterior to the legs, and the **epimeron**, above and behind the leg bases. These two sclerites are separated by a nonarticulate **pleural suture**, on either side of which they project upward and approach the alinotum, forming the supports for the ventral side of the wing base. Also con-

Figure 2.11. A diagrammatic thoracic segment drawn as if the nearer pleural area were transparent, showing the thoracic apodemes. *CxFrm*, coxal foramen; *Fu*, furca; *Ph*, phragma; *Pld*, pleurodema; *Sn*, spina.

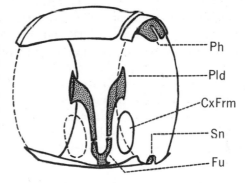

tributing to the support and articulation of the wing are the small **alar sclerites**, discussed further in Chapter Four. One coxal process is borne at the ventral end of the pleural suture. In winged insects the second condyle is placed anterior of the leg base on the tip of the **trochantin**, a small crescentate sclerite probably derived by subdivision of one of the other coxal sclerites.

The sternum, too, is displaced so that its anterior part is associated with the next segment. The larger ventral plate (**eusternum**) is crossed by the **sternacostal suture** on a line between the legs, dividing the eusternum into an anterior **basisternum** and a posterior **sternellum**. Behind the sternellum lies the narrow **spinasternum** covering the true segmental boundary and derived from the segment next posterior.

Thoracic apodemes are particularly well developed in winged insects (Fig. 2.11). The **phragmata** (singular, **phragma**) are three transverse plates invaginated from dorsal elements, placed under the antecostal sutures at the anterior ends of the mesothorax, the metathorax and the first abdominal segment, respectively. The **pleurodemata** (singular, **pleurodema**) are invaginated at the pleural sutures of the two wing-bearing segments, positioned beneath the wings and above the middle and hind legs. Directly ventral of these arm-like pleurodemata are the **furcae** (singular, **furca**), U- or Y-shaped apodemes invaginated from the sterna-costal suture of the eusternum. The tips of the arms of the furca reach and sometimes fuse with the tips of the right and left pleurodemata in a segment. Consequently, these apodemes collectively form within a segment a strong bridge which connects and supports the ventral and two pleural skeletal walls. Most of the muscles attached to this bridge, as well as those attached to the phragmata, function in flight or ambulation. At the posterior end of each thoracic segment a small finger-like apodeme, the **spina** (plural, **spinae**), is invaginated from the spinasternum. The prothorax of winged insects ordinarily is less complex than the two wing-bearing segments. The pronotum does not bear a phragma, the postnotum is small or vestigial and the pleurites associated with the wings on the meso- and metathorax are not present.

A few of the major developments deviating from the foregoing simpli-fied account are worth noting in a general discussion.

In certain of the primitive winged insects such as the Plecoptera, the three thoracic segments remain distinct, and, except for the presence of wings with their necessary associated structures on the meso- and meta-thorax, they differ but little from each other. The greater number of orders of winged insects tend to combine the two wing-bearing segments into a functional unit, the **pterothorax.** In some of the advanced orders fusion is carried so far that the pterothoracic skeletal elements often cannot be assigned to one or the other segment. The formation of a pterothorax is correlated in most instances with the use of wings and efficiency in flight. The Coleoptera do not use the forewings for propulsion during flight and the metathorax is much larger than the mesothorax. In contrast, the Hymenoptera and Diptera rely upon the forewings and the mesothorax is the larger. In the Hymenoptera, furthermore, the dorsal elements of the first abdominal segment, which bears the posterior phragma, are fused with the metathorax while the ventral skeletal elements are largely atrophied. In these insects the first abdominal segment becomes a part of the thorax, and such a condition is the final refinement of the pterothoracic trend.

The development of a pterothorax involves some displacement of the primitive pleural sclerites. New sutures appear, subdividing the sclerites into new units, each of which requires its own name for descriptive designation. Some of the previously existing sutures may become ob-literated. As a result it is frequently difficult to homologize the skeletal elements among the more highly modified insects. A bewildering nomen-clature has arisen, with homologous parts being given different names in different orders while the same term may be used in different contexts in different insects. Fortunately, this is a situation which need not trouble the beginning student, though it has long been a vexation to professional entomologists.

To the insect abdomen are reserved all functions, with their specialized structures, not particularly performed by the head or thorax. Included among these functions are alimentation, excretion, elimination, reproduction and much of respiration. The abdomen is not merely a container for the principal viscera, however; it is the vital *sine qua non* supporting the functions of the head and thorax. Its very catchall nature makes it indispensable.

The prototypic abdomen consists of eleven metameres plus the postsegmental telson—sometimes incorrectly counted as a twelfth. The telson is the posterior closure of the body, the analogue of the acron. Eleven complete segments and a telson are evident only in Protura and in the embryos of many other orders. A major trend in the Insecta is the reduction of the number of abdominal segments in the adult. This reduction is accomplished through the loss of some of the terminal metameres or through the coalescence of either terminal or anterior metameres or both. Only by comparing the adult with its embryo can the fact and nature of reduction, when it occurs, be understood.

An exception to the typical metameric constitution of the insect abdomen is found in the order Collembola; never at any point in their existence do they have more than five abdominal metameres and a telson. This fact, along with numerous other peculiarities, sets the Collembola off from all other insects and strongly suggests a closer affinity with the myriapods.

The anus is situated in the telson, whether it be preceded by eleven, ten or nine abdominal metameres, or as in Collembola by five. The telson is infrequently a recognizable entity in most adult insects and is rarely mentioned in descriptive insect morphology. If it is represented at all in an adult insect, it generally is reduced to a tiny annular sclerite at the anus, or to an annular membrane easily overlooked. The genital aperture of female insects opens ventrad behind the ninth, eighth or seventh segments. The male genital system opens ventrad at the posterior end of the ninth segment. In Collembola the genital opening of both sexes is between the fifth segment and the telson.

Since the abdomen of the adult insect is not concerned with locomotion, the metameric appendages of that region either atrophy after forming in the embryo or become specialized for functions other than locomotion. Some of the members of the orders Thysanura and Aptera preserve vestigial appendages on many of the abdominal segments in the adult as **styli.** Other than these vestiges, the adult abdomen may retain the appendages of the eleventh segment, the **cerci,** generally developed either as sensory structures or as protective pincers; and the appendages of the segments behind the genital opening may be modified to assist in copulation or, in females, to contribute to the **ovipositor** (egg-laying apparatus). An exception is presented by the Collembola, which have two pairs of highly modified appendages used in jumping. The abdominal legs found in immature insects are not regarded as constituting an exception because leg-bearing larvae are, as will be shown in Chapters Seven and Eight, morphologically embryonic stages in which the abdominal legs have not yet regressed.

The basic skeleton of the mature insect abdomen consists of a generally simple, plate-like tergum and sternum on each segment and on some of them there are small pleural sclerites. Secondary segmentation is shown in the abdomen as in the thorax. The posterior margin of each tergum and sternum forms a flange overlapping the segment behind it. Small apodemes are often invaginated at the true intersegmental lines beneath the antecostal sutures, affording attachment for longitudinal muscles. Terga or sterna may be united with those of adjacent segments. Snodgrass (1935) thought that the pleural sclerites of the abdomen are derived either from the bases of the regressed appendages or as secondary subdivisions of the sterna or terga.

The abdomen may be divided into two subregions, the anterior **visceral abdomen** and the **genital abdomen.** The skeleton of the visceral abdomen is less complicated, except where the first segment is added to the thorax, as in Hymenoptera, or atrophied, as in Lepidoptera and other orders. The first eight abdominal segments each primarily bears a pair of spiracles located on the pleural region, with or without a protective annular sclerite. Eight pairs of abdominal spiracles is the maximum number known in adult insects and very frequently the number is reduced.

The posterior part of the abdomen usually is strongly modified in connection with copulation and egg laying, but it must not be supposed that the genital abdomen is clearly or consistently distinct from the visceral part. Modifications of the genital abdomen are more conveniently detailed in Chapter Three.

THE ARACHNOID PLAN

In a functional sense the arachnoid cephalothorax is comparable to the insect head and thorax combined, but the comparison is not strictly true in the sense of morphologic homologies. Six pairs of segmental appendages are present (Figs. 2.12 and 2.13), the anteriormost being the **chelicerae.** The other five pairs are generally ambulatory, but one of the first three pairs may be specialized for sensation in certain orders. The pair next behind the chelicerae are called **pedipalps** in spiders, mites and ticks, but are true legs in other arachnoids. With the cheliceral segment counted as number one, the adult cephalothorax includes six segments. The mouth is situated between the chelicerae; antennae are never present. The eyes are arranged in three groups, the median eye or eyes and two lateral clusters. The adult nervous system has a small **supraesophageal ganglionic mass** and a larger **subesophageal ganglion.** By tracing the nerves, it can be shown that the supraesophageal mass includes ganglia concerned with the eyes and chelicerae and that the ganglia of the other five leg segments contribute to the subesophageal mass. The general arrangement is thus similar to that found in insects and myriapods in that there is a "brain" above the esophagus as well as a secondary "brain" below it; the extent of possible homology between the nervous systems of these three classes is explored in Chapter Six.

Even in more primitive arachnoids such as scorpions, the adult cephalo-thoracic segments are fused and covered by the large plate-like **prosomal tergite** (carapace). In only a few species is it even crossed by transverse sutures suggesting the divisions between the original segments. On the ventral side (Fig. 2.12) the bases of all the appendages lie close together on either side of the midline and are separated only by a variously shaped **sternite.** This cephalothoracic sternite is thought by some to be derived from sternal elements of all the leg-bearing segments and by others only from the elements of the sixth segment.

The abdomen of scorpions is divided into the wider anterior **mesosoma** and the tail-like **metasoma** tipped by the **sting,** the modified telson. Twelve segments can be counted in adults. A thirteenth is present at the anterior end of the embryonic abdomen and though it atrophies in the course of development, the scorpion abdomen consists of thirteen *basic* segments, the maximum number found in the class. In most arachnoids the abdomen is not divided into meso- and metasoma, but is a round to ovoid unit. The **genital pore** is always on the second true segment. The telson is wanting or reduced to a vestigial ring around the anus in most orders. The last two or three segments are fused or missing alto-gether. In such highly evolved groups as the spiders (Fig. 2.13), ticks and mites (see Fig. 8.8D), metamerism is completely obscured and even the distinction between cephalothorax and abdomen is frequently diffi-cult or impossible to make. Limb rudiments typically appear on all

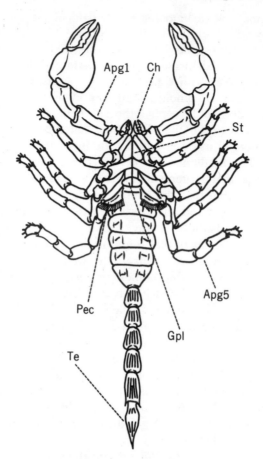

Figure 2.12. Ventral view of scorpion.
Apg1, Apg5, first and fifth legs; *Ch*, chelicera; *Gpl*, genital plate; *Pec*, pectine; *St*,
sternum; *Te*, telson, bearing the sting on its
tip. (Drawn from a *Pandanus* from Liberia,
Africa, in Carnegie Museum)

segments of the embryo, but the adult abdomen bears no locomotory
appendages. In scorpions there is a pair of highly modified appendages,
the **pectines**, beneath the third abdominal segment. Spiders retain on the
fourth and fifth abdominal segments the rudiments of paired appendages
as the **spinnerets**. The anus is always on the last true segment present:
the nineteenth body segment in scorpions, the eighteenth in spiders and
harvestmen, the seventeenth in other arachnoids.

The question of homologies between the arachnoids and the mandibulate arthropods is a difficult problem on which authorities through
the years have disagreed. For a long time the arachnoid chelicerae were
believed, with minor prophets dissenting, to be homologous with the
antennae of insects and the first antennae of crustaceans. The implications
of this explanation are: (1) the cheliceral segment of arachnoids is the

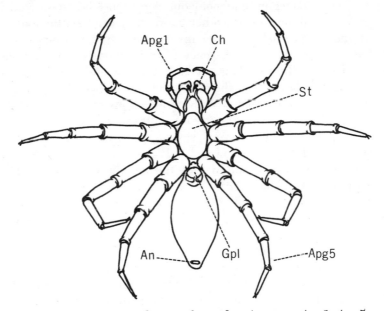

Figure 2.13. Ventral view of a spider. *An,* anus; *Apg1, Apg5,*
first and fifth legs; *Ch,* chelicera; *Gpl,* genital plate; *St,* sternum.
(Drawn from specimen in Carnegie Museum)

anteriormost; (2) the intercalary segment of insects is missing in arachnoids; (3) the spider pedipalps are homologous with the insect mandibles.
Evidence adduced from study of adult arachnoids supports this theory
as well as almost any other.

The crux of the difficulty lies in the fact that arachnoids are a very
ancient branch of the Arthropoda. Already differentiated from mandibulate arthropods as long ago as the Cambrian period, the chelicerate
arthropods have followed their separate evolutional destiny for a very
long time. It should come as no surprise that prototypic structures have
become obscured and altered and that chelicerates have diverged from
the structural specializations evolved by the mandibulate lines. The only
recourse is to study the embryo.

According to Dawydoff (1949) two observers—Jaworovsky in 1894 and Pokrovsky in 1899—reported finding in spider embryos limb buds anterior of the cheliceral buds. If these observations were verified, it would be conclusive evidence that the cheliceral segment is not the primitively anteriormost in the spiders. Since no one else has recorded such limb buds, there may have been a mistake in the original interpretations. Precheliceral appendages in arachnoid ontogeny must be considered to be an unproved possibility. On the other hand, there can be little doubt about the existence of precheliceral coeloms in many spider embryos (Dawydoff, 1949), establishing the existence of at least one embryonic segment anterior of the chelicerae. This precheliceral coelom (see Fig. 7.10) is, for a time, rather larger than the coelom of the cheliceral segment. It has several constrictions correlated with convolutions of the overlying ectoderm, suggesting that it may be in fact a fusion of several basic coeloms. The development of the nervous system presents even more startling evidence. L. and W. Schimkewitsch (1911) demonstrated that no less than *five* ganglia develop anterior of the ganglia corresponding to the cheliceral segment. The anteriormost is a median, unpaired ganglion; perhaps it represents merely the connection at the acron of the two central nerve cords. The outer four are paired and seem to correspond to two metameres. Dawydoff believes that *at least* three pairs of segmental ganglia contribute to the composition of the supraesophageal ganglion, of which the cheliceral ganglia are the posteriormost. In the development of the coeloms, nervous system and limb rudiments, there is no indication that a segment, even a vestigial one, exists between the cheliceral and pedipalpal metameres.

It now appears that the chelicerae of arachnida are homologous with the *second* antennae of Crustacea, that the cheliceral segment is the intercalary segment of insects and that the cheliceral ganglion is the tritocerebrum. The ocular part of the arachnoid supraesophageal mass is probably the deutocerebrum, while the protocerebrum is represented only by transient ganglia in the embryo, those designated x and y by the Schimkewitsches.

Table 2.1 summarizes the three systems of body regions and the apparent segmental homologies.

Table 2.1 Body regions and segmental homologies of insects, chilopods, diplopods and arachnoids, showing the segmental appendages

Segment	Insecta (region)	Insecta	Chilopoda	Diplopoda	Arachnida	Arachnida (region)
1	Head — Pro-cephalon	No appendage	No appendage	No appendage	—	Cephalothorax
2		Antennae	Antennae	Antennae	—	
3		No appendage	No appendage	No appendage	Chelicerae	
4	Head — Gnatho-cephalon	Mandibles	Mandibles	Mandibles	1st legs	Cephalothorax
5		Maxillae	Maxillae	Gnathochilarium	2nd legs	
6		Labium	Labium	Gnathochilarium	3rd legs	
7	Thorax	Forelegs	Poison claws	1st legs	4th legs	Cephalothorax
8		Midlegs	1st legs	2nd legs genital	5th legs	
9		Hindlegs	2nd legs	3rd legs	Genital plate	Abdomen — Metasoma
10	Abdomen	No appendage	3rd legs	4th legs	Pectines [c]	
11		No appendage	4th legs	5th legs [b]	Spinnerets [d]	
12		No appendage	5th legs	6th legs [b]	Spinnerets [d]	
13		No appendage	Variable number of segments, most bearing legs; not fused in pairs; genital pore on last segment	Variable number of segments, most bearing legs; fused in pairs as diplosegments	No appendage	
14		No appendage			No appendage	
15		No appendage			No appendage	
16		♀ genital			No appendage	
17		No appendage			No appendage	Mesosoma
18		♂ genital			No appendage	
19		No appendage (Cerci) [a]			(No appendage) [a]	
20		(Telson) [a]	Telson	Telson	(Telson) [a]	

[a] Not always distinct, sometimes absent. [b] Diplosegment. [c] In scorpions only. [d] In spiders only.

CHAPTER THREE

The Appendages

Many shall run to and fro, and
knowledge shall be increased.

DANIEL 7:4

The organization of the body into metameres each bearing a pair of appendages presents the arthropods with a remarkable opportunity to take advantage of almost any available ecologic situation. At first, all appendages probably were used for walking, but with legs to spare, some could be assigned other functions without interfering with the animal's locomotion. Contemporary insects, myriapods and arachnoids—the results of a good many millions of years of evolution—have quite a variety of appendages which resemble legs only remotely, not to mention the many special modifications of entirely recognizable legs. To understand these adaptive variations it is first necessary to examine the point of departure.

Arthropod appendages are hollow evaginations from the ventral part of the lateral body wall. They are divided into sclerotized segments separated by flexible joints. The prototypic appendage has two main parts, the **coxopodite,** articulated with the body, and the **telopodite,** joined to the distal end of the coxopodite. The telopodite consists of six segments named, in sequence away from the coxopodite, the **first trochanter, second trochanter, femur, tibia, tarsus** and **post-tarsus** [1] (Fig. 3.1).

Each of the seven leg segments is provided with muscles which originate in a proximal segment. The muscles inserted in the coxopodite originate in the body wall. Each segment articulates with the one pre-

[1] Following German usage, Snodgrass (1935) and others adopt "pretarsus" for this segment. While frequently used, the term is inappropriate because the segment in question is *beyond,* not *before,* the tarsus. The more exact "post-tarsus" (Millot, 1949) has much to commend it.

ceding it by a hinge joint. The coxopodite is placed between the dorsal and ventral skeletal sclerites, articulating with them so that the movement is forward and backward parallel to the long axis of the body. Of the telopodite segments, this same forward and backward direction of movement is possible also for the second trochanter, femur, tarsus and post-tarsus. Moving in a direction perpendicular to that of the others, the first trochanter and the tibia have an up and down angle of motion which makes the articulation of each a "knee" joint.

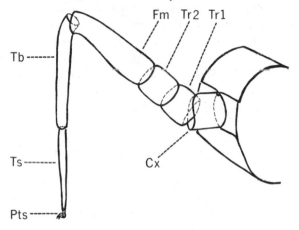

Figure 3.1. Diagram of a generalized leg showing segments. *Cx,* coxopodite; *Fm,* femur; *Pts,* post-tarsus; *Tb,* tibia; *Tr1, Tr2,* first and second trochanters; *Ts,* tarsus.

These prototypic segments may develop movable lobes on their inner or outer margins or both. Those on the inner margin are **endites,** those on the outer margin are **exites.** Such lobes frequently occur and are of great interest in the study of certain extinct groups and of the marine arthropods. The terrestrial arthropods of concern here sometimes preserve such lobes, but only those of the coxopodite.

The primitive condition where the coxopodite is inserted directly in the pleural membrane and articulates between the tergum and sternum is found in the arachnoids. Insects have the coxopodite divided into two sections, the **subcoxa** and the **coxa.** The subcoxa is fixed in the pleural body wall and provides improved support for the leg as a whole. It is believed that the lateral aspects of the metameres do not inherently possess skeletal plates and that pleurites are derived by the "capture" of the subcoxa from the leg. These pleurites may be preserved even after the leg regresses during ontogeny, as on the insect abdomen. When the subcoxa becomes part of the pleural wall, the muscles originally inserted at its proximal end migrate outward to the proximal end of the coxa, thus maintaining function while altering position.

The apparent number of telopodite segments may be increased by division of a segment into subsegments or may be reduced by fusion of two adjacent segments or by suppression of one of them. It is not easy to establish the true nature of such an altered leg, though analysis of musculature and articulations often sheds light on the situation. Subsegments, for example, are never provided with separate muscles, although the joints between them may be flexible; the components of the basic segment are moved collectively rather than individually. Where fusion or suppression has taken place it is also important to study the angles of articulation, keeping in mind that "knee" joints occur only at the base of the first trochanter and at the base of the tibia.

LOCOMOTORY APPENDAGES

Appendages retaining the original locomotory function are more likely to approximate prototypic organization than are those modified for such special uses as feeding, sensation or reproduction. Locomotory appendages are present on the cephalothorax of arachnoids, the trunk of myriapods and the thorax of insects. Legs with eight segments, the maximum number, are sometimes found in arachnoids; seven are typically present in chilopods, diplopods and symphylids; six are characteristic of insects and pauropods.

ARACHNOIDS

The cephalothorax of arachnoids bears six pairs of appendages, of which the first are the **chelicerae**, highly modified and exclusively used in feeding. The other five pairs are for the most part generalized in segmentation, but only the last three are *always* used in locomotion (Table 3.1). The second pair of appendages, the so-called **pedipalpi**, are walking legs in two orders, the Solpugida and the Palpigradida; in the other seven orders they are variously specialized for mastication, for grasping prey or for sensation. Only in the Araneida and Acarida are they mainly sensory. The third pair is locomotory in four orders, exclusively sensory in four, and combines mastication with locomotion in one. In two orders (Thelyphonida and Phryneida) the only walking legs are the last three pairs. An examination of Table 3.1 at once dispels the notion that arachnoids

Table 3.1 Functions of the appendages in arachnoid orders

| Order | Chelicerae | 1st Legs | | | | 2nd Legs | | | 3rd, 4th, 5th Legs |
	Grasping	Masti-cation	Sensa-tion	Grasp-ing	Loco-motion	Masti-cation	Sensa-tion	Loco-motion	Locomotion
Scorpionida	x	x	x	x		x		x	x x x
Pseudoscorpionida	x	x	x					x	x x x
Solpugida	x		x		x		x		x x x
Palpigrada	x				x		x		x x x
Thelyphonida	x	x		x			x		x x x
Phryneida	x	x		x			x		x x x
Phalangiida	x		x	x				x	x x x
Araneida	x		x		x			x	x x x
Acarida	x [a]		x					x	x x x

[a] Or piercing.

always have four pairs of legs and thereby are distinguished from insects with three pairs. (Larval mites and ticks have only three pairs of legs.)

The telopodite segments (Fig. 3.2) basically present are the two trochanters, the femur, patella, tibia, tarsus and post-tarsus. The **patella** is present in all arachnoids except the pseudoscorpions, but is not found in myriapods or insects. Students of arachnoids often count the patella as a true segment, but it has no independent musculature and has been shown to be a subdivision of the tibia, though sometimes larger and stouter than both the tibia and the femur. Two trochanters are distinctly present and fully functional in only a few cases: on all five legs of most genera of pseudoscorpions, on the first legs of scorpions and on the two posterior pairs of Solpugida (Fig. 3.2A). Where there is only one trochanter to be found, one of two things has happened. The second trochanter may be fused with the femur, as in the Phalangiida (Fig. 3.2B, D), the Acarida (Fig. 3.2C) and those pseudoscorpions with only one apparent trochanter. This condition is revealed by the presence in some cases of an annular suture near the proximal end of the femur and is supported by study of muscles and articulations. An alternative situation is where the two trochanters have fused with each other, as in the first three pairs of legs in Solpugida (Fig. 3.2E). This second state probably is the more usual and better explains the presence of a single trochanter in many arachnoids.

The femur is always present as a distinct, undivided segment. The tibia is undivided only in pseudoscorpions; in all other orders the patella and tibia both are typically present on walking legs. In some orders, only the first pair of legs has the tibiae undivided; the pedipalpi of Scorpionida,

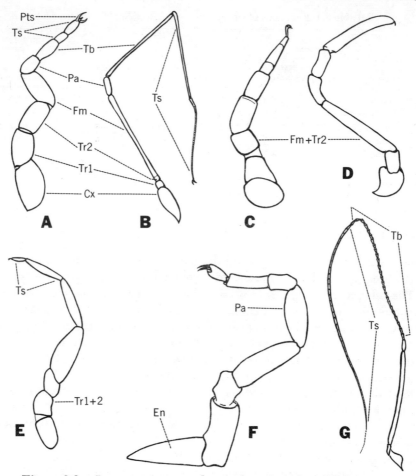

Figure 3.2. Locomotory appendages of arachnoids. Fifth legs of (A) a solpugid, (B) a phalangid and (C) a mite; (D) first leg or pedipalpus of a phalangid; (E) second leg of a solpugid; (F) third leg of a scorpion; (G) second leg of a pharynid. *Cx*, coxa; *En*, masticatory endite lobe of coxa; *Fm*, femur; *Pa*, patella; *Pts*, post-tarsus; *Tb*, tibia; *Tr1, Tr2*, first and second trochanters; *Ts*, tarsus. (A–F drawn from specimens in Carnegie Museum; G redrawn from Gray, 1961)

Araneida, Phalangiida and Acarida have the patella. The tarsus commonly has two subsegments (Fig. 3.2A, C, F), and these in turn may be divided (Fig. 3.2B). Extreme subsegmentation of the tibia and tarsus occurs in the antenna-like second legs of Phryneida, where forty or more sections can be counted (Fig. 3.2G).

The post-tarsus is hinged to the tip of the tarsus and has an elaborate musculature for both levation and depression. In the scorpion (Fig. 3.9C) the levator and accessory depressor arise in the tibia; the inferior and superior depressors in the patella. These four muscles can be of help in correctly identifying segmental homologies. For example, the first pair of legs (so-called pedipalps) of scorpions (Fig. 3.9B) has been a point of confusion, with many authorities naming the segments differently. The movable "thumb" has a levator muscle [2] arising in the "hand" and two depressors, one filling most of the "hand" and the other originating in the next proximad segment. The "thumb" is therefore the post-tarsus, as stated by Millot and Vachon (1949a). The "hand" must be the tibia, with the tarsus contributing the fixed "finger" and at least the articulation with the post-tarsus. The next proximal segment is the patella. Counting back toward the body it is clear that only one trochanter is present.

The post-tarsus is ordinarily quite small, with a pair of lateral articulate claws and a median sclerite. One or both claws may be missing. The median sclerite may be prolonged to form an extra fixed claw, or it may bear on its tip an eversible vesicle having the action of a suction cup. Many spiders have a comb of setae on the post-tarsus, used to guide the silken threads during construction of the web.

Legs near the mouth may have on the coxopodites endite expansions or lobes with sharp or serrated medial margins that meet under the mouth and thus function as auxiliary masticators. Such structures of the coxopodites are found in scorpions on both the second (Fig. 3.2F) and third legs but not on the first pair of legs (pedipalps). The arrangement is reversed in the order Pseudoscorpionida, masticating lobes being present only on the first legs. Among the Phalangiida there are masticating lobes on all three anterior pairs of legs.

A remarkable copulatory procedure usual among arachnoids involves the transference of sperm to the female genital orifice "by hand," as it were, by use of various of the male legs, but no special modification for the purpose is needed where the sperms are encased. Most male spiders use the pedipalpi for the purpose and have a syringe-like structure on the post-tarsus which has previously been filled from the genital pore. Actual copulation consists of the male placing his pedipalpus over or in the female genital pore and ejecting the sperms from the syringe by hydrostatic blood pressure.

2 This description is based on a *Pandinus* species we collected in Liberia, in which the levator tendon and muscle are small but very clearly present. It seems unlikely that the "thumb" of other species is the tarsus rather than the post-tarsus.

MYRIAPODS

Like the insects but unlike the arachnoids, myriapods lack the levator muscle of the post-tarsus. The segments of each walking leg of chilopods and diplopods are normally the coxa, two trochanters, femur, tibia, tarsus and post-tarsus. A single trochanter is present in the pauropod leg.

The leg-bearing segments of the diplopod (see Fig. 2.7D) are strongly sclerotized. The tergal plates are U-shaped and cover not only the dorsal surface but most of the lateral surface of the segment, displacing the true lateral elements so that much of the ventral surface is covered by them, while the sternites are compressed, narrow or even vestigial. Thus the leg comes to be inserted into the ventral aspect of the body, though it must be emphasized that there is no change in the relationships between the legs and the elements of the skeleton, that the apparent change of leg position is the result of proportional change in size and thus of position of the skeletal parts. The leg itself is, however, rather generalized. The coxa is inserted in the true ventro-lateral part of the body segment—now shifted so that the two coxae are separated only by a very narrow sternite. Analysis of the articulations and musculature confirms the identification of the leg segments, despite which various specialists in this class have invented some rather original names for the parts.

The coxa of the chilopod leg (see Fig. 2.7B) is immovably imbedded on the body wall, the telopodite articulating with it. The first trochanter is small, or in some species vestigial, but it is always sufficiently present to provide the "knee joint" articulation with the coxa. The second trochanter is well developed and prominent; specialists in chilopods often apply the name "prefemur" to it. The tarsus of the long-legged centipedes is divided into numerous annular subsegments, but in other chilopods it normally consists of only two subsegments.

The segmentation of the symphylid leg (Fig. 3.3B) is not clear. Arrangement of muscles confirms the identity of the five terminal parts as trochanter, femur, tibia, tarsus and post-tarsus. Proximal of the trochanter is a segment with a single condyle located in the ventral position. The leg is borne on a mound placed on the latero-ventral wall of the segment. The true nature of this mound is problematic. It is not marked off in any way except that it projects. In addition to the leg, it bears a stylus and an eversible vesicle. This combination of structures recalls the thysanuran insects (Fig. 3.19D), but the relative position of the parts is different. The stylus lies between the leg base and the vesicle in Symphyla, while in the Thysanura it lies on the other side of the leg as an

exite lobe of the coxa. A careful study of both adult structure and embryogenesis led Tiegs (1940) to conclude that the mound is not derived
from the coxopodite and that the first movable segment of the leg is
therefore the coxa. This interpretation fails to explain satisfactorily the
stylus and vesicle, both leg parts which have been shown (Snodgrass,
1935) to be borne on the coxae of primitive insects. It would seem doubt-

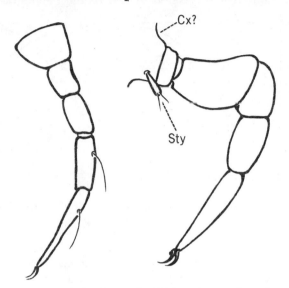

Figure 3.3. Leg of (A) a pauropod and
(B) a symphylid. *Cx*, coxa; *Sty*, stylus. (A re-
drawn from Kenyon, 1895; B redrawn from
Latzel, 1884)

ful that any other relationship exists in the Symphyla or that they, alone
of all arthropods, develop styli and vesicles on the body wall itself. If
the mound is the coxopodite fused with the body wall, the stylus is a coxal
endite and the vesicle is homologous with the similar structure found in
primitive insects. The first movable leg segment then is either the coxa
separated from the subcoxa, or it is the first trochanter: the ventral position of the condyle suggests that a dorsal one may have been lost, which
favors the identification as the separated coxa.

Except for proportionate length and development of the segments, the
pauropod leg (Fig. 3.3A) is essentially similar to that of the insect. There
is only one trochanter and the tarsus is sometimes divided into several
subsegments.

INSECTS

Two trochanters are found only in the Odonata, and they are immovably fixed on each other. In all other insects the two trochanters may be completely fused, but in any event only one can be identified. The "trochantellus" of certain Hymenoptera (Braconidae, Ichneumonidae) is not a trochanter, but is a subsection of the femur (Snodgrass, 1935). The

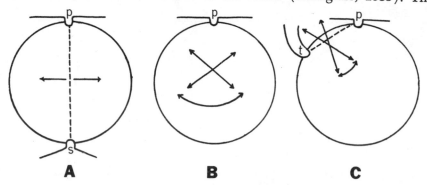

A   **B**   **C**

Figure 3.4. Diagrams to show three types of articulation between the coxa and elements of the thorax. In the primitive type (A) the coxa is hinged between a pleural condyle (*p*) and a sternal condyle (*s*), with a forward-backward motion as indicated by the arrows. An advanced type (B) has only a pleural condyle (*p*), allowing the coxa a limited rotation as well as the backward-forward motion. In many insects (C) the pleural condyle (*p*) is supplemented by an anterio-lateral condyle (*t*) on the trochantin, establishing a hinge axis indicated by the broken line but allowing some rotation in addition to the forward-upward and backward-downward movements.

characteristic insect leg segments (Fig. 3.6A) are the coxa, trochanter, femur, tibia, tarsus and post-tarsus.

The condyles that articulated the coxopodite with the tergal and sternal plates were lost when that segment divided and the subcoxal part was incorporated into the pleuron. Dorsal and ventral condyles are supplied for the coxa by the subcoxal pleurites, and the resulting hinge allows the coxa to swing in a simple forward and backward direction (Fig. 3.4A). Most insects have modified this primitive arrangement. The ventral condyle is usually lost, so that the leg moves freely on the remaining condyle, placed at the lower end of the pleural suture (Fig. 3.4B). In some insects a new second condyle is present on the tip of the trochantin, a pleurite derived from part of the subcoxa, but its position is anterio-lateral (Fig. 3.4C). Either of these arrangements frees the leg from the restriction in movement imposed by the original hinge. The coxa may be able to move not only on the backward-forward plane, but in the up and down direction as well and, where the musculature has suitably developed, even may be capable of limited rotation.

A longitudinal suture sometimes divides the coxa into two evident lobes, the anterior of which is called the **meron**. Especially in Mecoptera, Neuroptera, Trichoptera, Lepidoptera and Diptera the meron is enlarged and prominent (Fig. 3.6A). In the more advanced Diptera the meron is actually separated from the coxa and incorporated into the body wall as a new pleurite.

Styli, as definite exite lobes of the coxa of walking legs, are found only in the family Machalidae of the order Thysanura (Fig. 3.19D). This situation provides an interesting clue to the nature of structures found on insect abdomens and will be discussed in that connection.

The trochanter, generally small in insects, always retains its knee action relative to the coxa, but its motion relative to the femur is frequently limited or obliterated. Because it houses the tibial muscles so important to most forms of ambulation, the femur is characteristically the largest and strongest segment. Noteworthy is the very large hind femur of leaping Orthoptera (Fig. 3.6B). In parasitic Hymenoptera the femur is divided. The resultant small proximal subsegment is termed the **trochantellus**. Arrangement of the muscles demonstrates that the trochantellus is *not* the second trochanter, as some have thought. The tibia generally is long and slender. It is jointed with the femur in a way permitting the two segments to be drawn close together into a nearly parallel position.

The tarsus of functional walking legs of Pterygota is primarily subdivided into five sections. When fewer are present, as frequently is the case, a study of phylogeny suggests that reduction has taken place. An example of this rather usual evolutionary trend is the lepidopterous family Ithomiidae. The Lepidoptera have basically five tarsal subsegments (Fig. 3.6A). The Ithomiidae are one of a group of families in which only the mid- and hindlegs are used in ambulation. Although forelegs are present, they have not acquired any other function and are, in effect, "vestigial organs" (see Dodson, 1960: 42 ff.). In *Roswellia*, the most primitive living genus of the family Ithomiidae, the male fore tarsus has already been reduced to two subsegments (Fig. 3.5A) which have lost their mutual articulation and may be recognized only by the presence of an annular suture dividing them. The total length of the tarsus is drastically reduced, and the posttarsus is missing. In related genera the suture between the two tarsal subsegments has been obliterated (Fig. 3.5B). Reduction progresses in the proximal direction. The tibia is next shortened while the tarsus shrinks to an inarticulate knob on its tip (Fig. 3.5C); the femur is then shortened (Fig. 3.5D). Meanwhile, the entire leg becomes quite tiny in proportion to the useful mid- and hindlegs. A parallel but much less drastic reduction occurs in females of the family.

Such an evolutional trend should not be interpreted as a case of "use and disuse." The reduction of the foreleg of Ithomiidae does not occur just because the leg is not used, but rather because mutations leading to reduction are selectively acceptable in that they do not interfere with function—since there is none—having survival value (Fox, 1956). Through-

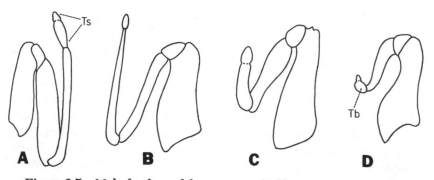

Figure 3.5   Male forelegs of four genera of Ithomiidae (Lepidoptera) illustrating successive stages in reduction of the terminal segments. (A) *Roswellia,* (B) *Eutresis,* (C) *Melinaea,* (D) *Ithomia.* (From Fox, 1956, 1960)

out the Insecta numerous similar examples may be found. When correctly interpreted they not only support the view that the presence of five tarsal subsegments is the primitive condition in Pterygota, but also demonstrate that study of the process of reduction is a useful tool for analysis of phylogeny.

The post-tarsus is present in insects as a variable group of tiny structures on the tip of the tarsus. Not all entomologists have realized that the post-tarsus is a real segment; hence the structures have frequently been misinterpreted as belonging to the tarsus and have been called "tarsal claws." Essentially the insect post-tarsus consists of a short segment inserted into the tip of the terminal tarsal subsegment and bearing a pair of lateral claws. The only muscle, a depressor, originates in the tibia and femur. It is inserted on a long apodeme, the "tendon," from the median part of the post-tarsus. Though movable, the claws have no muscles. Generally they articulate between the median pretarsal sclerite and the tip of the tarsus. The median structure, as well as the claws, is subject to a wide range of modification related to the needs of the insect concerned. No attempt need be made here to unravel the confusing, often conflicting terms that have been devised to designate these variations. The median structure sometimes is subdivided; the resultant proximal sclerite is then the **unguitracotor,** the distal sclerite is the **planta,** the lateral plates under the claws are the **auxiliae.** The tip of the median sclerite may be produced into a claw, it may be bristle-like (**empodium**), it may form a membranous lobe (**arolium**), or a pair of lateral membranous lobes (**pulvilli**) may be formed. The articulate claws (**ungues**) likewise undergo variation: one may be much the larger, or one or both may be absent. All these modifications characterize species, genera or families and include the extraordinary eversible vesicles on the post-tarsi of Thysanoptera, the sticky pads that enable a fly to walk on the ceiling and the various devices that enable fleas and lice to cling firmly to the hairs or feathers of their hosts.

Some of the adaptations of locomotory legs in insects are shown in Figure 3.6. The generalized midleg of the butterfly (Fig. 3.6A) is included for comparison. The hindleg of the grasshopper (Fig. 3.6B) produces the leap when suddenly extended. The hindleg of the hydrophilid beetle (Fig. 3.6C) is provided with a fringe of hairs (setae) which collectively serve as an oar for swimming, as do the flattened hindlegs of the belostomatid water bug (Fig. 3.6D). An unusual adaptation is found in the Gerridae, water striders belonging to the order Hemiptera. The lightness of these insects, combined with the complex plumose setae on the middle tarsi (Fig. 3.6F), enables them to skim along on the water without breaking through the surface film. For grasping prey the foreleg of the mantis (Fig. 3.6G) is equipped with a formidable array of spines along the opposing edges of the femur and tibia. A different device for grasping prey is found on the foreleg of the predaceous water bug *Naucoria* (Hemiptera), in which the tarsus is formed (Fig. 3.6E) as a single sharply pointed segment. The bird louse (Mallophaga) (Fig. 3.6I) closes the post-tarsal spur around a feather of its host and clings there. The crab louse (Anoplura) achieves the same end with the claw-like modifications of its tibia and tarsus (Fig. 3.6J). The digging foreleg of the mole cricket (Orthoptera) is one of the most striking adaptations of all (Fig. 3.6H). Short and sturdy, it is tipped by a hand-like arrangement of tibia and tarsus. Phasmids of the tropical family Phyllidae are dramatically adapted in shape and coloring to simulate foliage; femora and tibia have leaf-like expansions to contribute to the illusion (Fig. 3.6K).

Certain functions in addition to locomotion sometimes are performed by legs, functions that require special structures or special adaptations of existing structures.

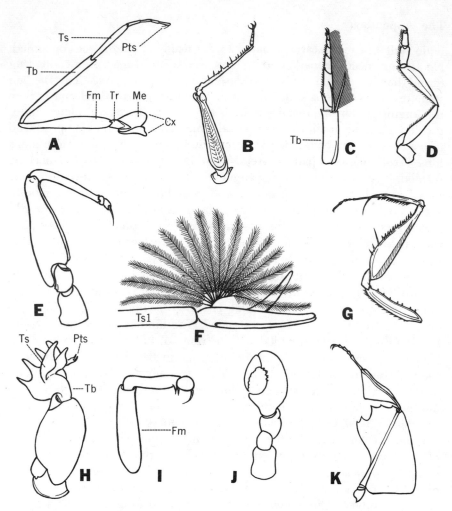

Figure 3.6. Modification of insect legs. (A) Hindleg of *Cymothoe,* a butter-fly; (B) hindleg of an African lubber grasshopper; (C) hind tibia and tarsus of *Hydrous triangularis* (Hydrophilidae), a swimming beetle; (D) hindleg of *Lethocerus grandis,* a Brazilian water bug (Belostomatidae: Hemiptera); (E) foreleg of *Naucoris* (Naucoridae: Hemiptera), a predaceous water bug; (F) tip of midleg of *Rhagovella obesa* (Gerridae: Hemiptera), a water strider, greatly magnified; (G) foreleg of a mantis (Dictyoptera) from Cameroons; (H) foreleg of a mole cricket, *Neocurtilla borealis* (Gryllotalpidae: Orthoptera), from western Pennsylvania; (I) foreleg of a bird louse (Mallophaga) from Colorado; (J) foreleg of the crab louse *Phthirus pubis* (Anoplura); (K) foreleg of a phyllid walking stick (Phasmida) from Sumatra. *Cx,* coxa; *Fm,* femur; *Me,* meron; *Pts,* post-tarsus; *Tb,* tibia; *Tr,* trochanter; *Ts,* tarsus. (A–E, G–K drawn from specimens in Carnegie Museum; F redrawn from Torre-Bueno, 1907)

One such extra function is stridulation, although stridulation does not always involve the legs. When a leg is used for this purpose it has a roughened area which, when drawn across a ridge or projection on some conveniently located part of the body, produces sound. In the Acrididae (Orthoptera) the males of most and the females of a few species produce

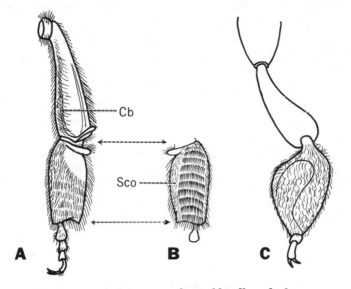

Figure 3.7. (A) Inner surface of hindleg of a honeybee worker and (right) outer surface of tibia; (B) foreleg of *Oligotoma* species (Embioptera) with enlarged first tarsal segment containing silk glands. *Cb*, corbicula or pollen basket; *Sco*, scopa or pollen comb. (A redrawn from Comstock, 1940, by permission of Cornell University Press; B redrawn from Ross *in* Essig, 1948, by permission of The Macmillan Company)

a buzzing sound when the hind femur is drawn across an enlarged vein of the forewing. In this family the inner surface of the hind femur usually has a row of tiny peg-like projections, but in some species the row of pegs is on the wing and the femur has a longitudinal ridge. Somewhat similar adaptations for stridulation have been noted in many other insects, particularly among Hemiptera and Coleoptera.

An "ear" may be present on the fore tibia of many Orthoptera. The flat tympanum is sometimes uncovered and easily seen, or it may be sunk into a cavity with slit-like external openings (Fig. 3.6H). The internal organization of this auditory apparatus is complicated and involves modifications of both the nervous and tracheal systems; it will be discussed with the nervous system (Chapter Six).

Except for the more primitive groups, most Hymenoptera have a large terminal spur (**calcar**) on the fore tibia which fits into a cavity on the proximal end of the tarsus. The antennae are drawn through this structure so that the fine hairs in the cavity remove pollen and other things clinging to them.

Bees transport pollen to their hives by means of special equipment on the hindlegs (Fig. 3.7A). The pollen basket (**corbicula**) is formed on the dilated hind tibia by a smooth area ringed by high, curved setae. The enlarged first tarsal subsegment of each hindleg has a row of stiff setae serving as the pollen comb (**scopa**). Pollen adheres to the hairy bodies and legs of bees. It is transferred to the pollen basket on one side by use of the comb of the other side.

Silk glands are located in the fore tarsi of two completely unrelated groups of insects, the order Embioptera and males of some genera of the family Empididae (Diptera). The Embioptera live in silken tunnels which they spin ahead of themselves wherever they have occasion to go, working by rapidly crossing and recrossing the front legs. The first subsegment of the foretarsus is swollen and contains chambers serving as reservoirs for viscous material secreted by silk glands (Fig. 3.7B). These chambers are connected by ducts to hollow bristles on the under surface of the tarsus, each bristle emitting a silken thread. The silk produced by similar modification of the foretarsi of males of *Hilara* (Empididae) apparently is used to enclose some choice food morsel to offer the female as part of the mating ritual, a sort of bribe to secure her cooperation.

ANTENNAE

The first question in connection with the antennae is whether or not they are true serial metameric appendages. Entomologists always thought they were, but some years ago Snodgrass (1935), espousing the Holmgren-Hangström interpretation of head segmentation, decided they were not. Since this theory holds that the procephalon consists of an intercalary metamere preceded by nonmetameric material derived from the acron, the antennae accordingly would arise from the acron and therefore could not be true segmental appendages; they would have to be analogous, perhaps, with the prostomal tentacles of living Annelida. Störmer (1959) completes the circle by arguing that the Holmgren-Hangström theory must be correct because Snodgrass showed that the antennae are not segmental appendages!

If, however, the antennae are indeed true appendages, they necessarily arise from a segment, not from the acron, and the Holmgren-Hangström interpretation falls.

Snodgrass claimed that the antennae differ both in segmentation and in musculature from "true segmental limbs," but the evidence he produces can as well or better be used to support the opposite conclusion. His argument that because the first antennae of Crustacea are not biramous, they are not serially homologous with the second antennae and the other limbs, appears to be inconsistent with discussions of limb evolution he presents in other contexts; its use as an argument in this context seems to be based on the doubtful assumption that Crustacea are ancestral to insects and myriapods. It might be observed that the antennae agree *even less* with annelid tentacles in segmentation and musculature.

As a matter of fact, antennae of insects and myriapods give every indication of being true segmental appendages which assumed an exclusively sensory function with appropriate morphologic adjustments at a very early stage in the evolution of the phylum. The gene "aristopedia" discovered in *Drosophila* is most provocative. One of the many "throwback" mutations observed in the fruit fly, it causes the antennae to become leg-like. Similar leg-like antennae have been produced in regeneration.

The problem is of historical interest only, since the Holmgren-Hangström theory is no longer widely supported, though it still has proponents.

The proximal segment, the **scape** (Fig. 3.8A), is inserted in an annular membrane. In most cases it articulates on a condyle, though it sometimes is free in the membrane. In chilopods and symphylids the condyle is mid-dorsal, in diplopods it is rotated a little in the anterior direction, and in insects it usually is anterio-ventral. The position of the condyle (**antennifer**) is difficult to use in interpreting homologies in the head, but the fact that it exists is entirely concordant with the view that the antennae are segmental appendages. Muscles inserted on the proximal margin of the scape arise, as they should, from the cranial walls or from apodemes invaginated from them (tentorium). The second antennal segment, the **pedicel**, articulates at an angle to the movement of the scape, with which it forms something like the "knee joint," and its muscles arise in the scape. The scape may be coxa, the pedicel a trochanter. The rest of the antenna is called the **flagellum** and probably represents one or more of the other telopodite segments. In myriapods and in certain primitive insects with myriapod-like structures (Collembola and Aptera) the segments of the flagellum are each provided with muscles (Imms, 1939, 1940). The loss of the flagellular muscles doubtless is correlated with the development of the much more useful Johnston's organ, present in all

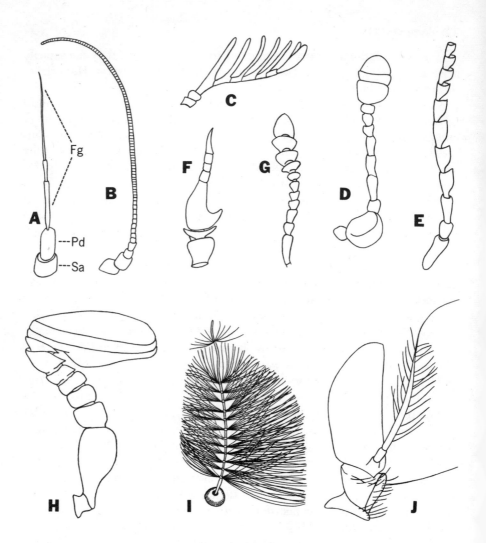

Figure 3.8. Some variations of insect antenna and the terminology applied. (A) *Setiform,* Odonata (*Rhodopygia* sp.); (B) *filiform,* Orthoptera (mole cricket); (C) *flabellate,* Coleoptera (Rhipiphoridae); (D) *capitate,* Coleoptera (Nitidulidae); (E) *serrate,* Coleoptera (Buprestidae); (F) *aristate,* with terminal arista, Diptera (Tabanidae); (G) *clavate,* Coleoptera (Silphidae); (H) *lamellate,* Coleoptera (Scarabaeidae); (I) *plumose,* Diptera (*Anopheles* male); (J) *aristate,* with subterminal arista, Diptera (Muscoidea). *Fg,* flagellum; *Pd,* pedicel; *Sa,* scape.

higher insects. If, as has been suggested, Johnston's organ is a statireceptor reacting to the position of the antennae or to its movements in response to environmental stimuli, then muscles in the flagellum would be useless or even detrimental.

The wide diversity of modifications of antennae is extensively used in taxonomy to distinguish orders, families, genera or even species. Figure 3.8 illustrates some of the more important variants and the terms applied to them.

MOUTHPARTS

The mouthparts of arthropods are segmental appendages specialized for feeding. Generalized mouthparts, those the least modified and in which the elements of locomotory appendages are the most recognizable, are the biting and chewing type. The anteriormost of the mouthparts is a pair of jaw-like appendages.

The jaws of arachnoids, called chelicera, are the appendages of the third head segment, homologous with the second antennae of crustaceans. To assist the chelicerae, the next or the next two pairs of appendages may be partly modified for mastication, and either pair may bear specialized sensory structures used in food selection.

The basic biting and chewing structures of insects and myriapods are the mandibles, the appendages of the fourth cephalic segment. Appendages of the next two segments in insects have become the paired maxillae and the fused labium, generally contributing both to mastication and sensation. Certain skeletal elements also may function with the mouthparts and will be discussed in this connection.

The mouthparts of myriapods are essentially similar to those of insects. In chilopods the first pair of trunk appendages, the poison claws, also function as mouthparts. In diplopods the mandibles are followed by a gnathochilarium probably derived from both the maxillae and the labium.

Certain insect and arachnoid groups feed on the juices of plants or of animals; their mouthparts are modified into a piercing and sucking apparatus. The homologies of such modified mouthparts are not obvious and may be understood only inferentially by observing intermediate stages of specialization and by study of ontogeny.

ARACHNOIDS

The chelicerae of scorpions (Fig. 3.9A) are placed above and a little ahead of the mouth, the "fixed finger" of the hand-like pincers toward the middle, and a proximal segment is hidden under the cephalothoracic tergite (carapace). The movable "thumb" has a shearing action against the "fixed finger." All articulations are on the horizontal plane, including the comparatively limited motion of the proximal segment. Though problematic, the homologies of the scorpion chelicerae are suggested by comparison with the "pedipalps" (Fig. 3.9B). Here too the "thumb" must be the post-tarsus. The levator and one depressor muscle of the post-tarsus originate in the "hand"; the other depressor originates in the basal seg-

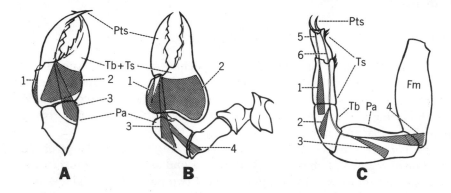

Figure 3.9. (A) Chelicera, (B) first leg or pedipalpus and (C) part of fourth leg of *Pandinus* species, a scorpion. *Fm,* femur; *Pa,* patella; *Pts,* post-tarsus; *Tb,* tibia; *Ts,* tarsus; *1,* levator muscle of post-tarsus; *2,* accessory depressor of post-tarsus; *3,* inferior depressor of post-tarsus; *4,* superior depressor of post-tarsus; *5,* post-tarsal levator tendon; *6,* post-tarsal depressor tendon. (Drawn from dissections of specimens collected by the authors in Liberia, West Africa)

ment. Thus, as in the pedipalpi, the "hand" apparently represents the tibia with the tarsus fused to it as the "fixed finger." The patella, in which the longer depressor muscle must originate (Fig. 3.9C), apparently is at least a part of the basal segment. Examination of the basal segment shows that a suture on its mesial aspect sets off a distal triangular area of the wall and that the post-tarsal depressor originates there. This triangular area probably is the vestigial patella, an interpretation supported by the fact that the points on which the tibio-tarsus articulates lie at the ends of the suture but are formed from the triangular piece. The rest of the basal segment may be derived from the femur. The trochanters and coxopodite are either entirely lost or incorporated into the body wall to form the pocket in which the chelicerae lie.

Similar chelicerae are found in the order Palpigradida and Phalangiida, but in neither case is the basal segment divided by a suture. In Pseudoscorpionida and Solpugida the basal segment is lost entirely and the hand-like pincers articulate directly on the body wall.

In Thelyphonida, Phryneida and Araneida (Fig. 3.10A) the "fixed finger" is lacking so that the tarsus is reduced to a vestige, little more than the condyles on which the post-tarsus articulates. In these orders the post-tarsus has a scissors-like action against the tip of the proximal segment.

Both the second and third appendages of scorpions are modified to assist in mastication. Coxal endites of the second appendages (first pair of legs) oppose molar faces to each other at the mouth; below them are the wide, shearing coxal endites of the third appendages (Fig. 3.2F). In Pseudoscorpionida the coxal endites of the second appendages are blade-like and help in mastication, but the third appendages are entirely loco-motory. In Thelyphonida and Phryneida masticating lobes are present on the second appendages on either the coxopodite or trochanters or both. In all other arachnoids mastication is exclusively the function of the chelicerae or only fluids are ingested.

Food selection as a sensory function is normally associated with the mouthparts. The grasping pedipalpi of scorpions are provided with areas of sensory hairs which probably serve in this respect, and no anterior appendage of the scorpion is devoted solely to sensation. The exclusively sensory pedipalpi of pseudoscorpions, spiders and acarines apparently combine food selection with other sensory functions which, in myriapods and insects, are associated with the antennae. The same is true of the sensory third appendages (second legs) of Solpugida, Palpigradida, Thelyphonida and Phryneida (Fig. 3.2G).

The large, complex order Acarida is characterized by the presence of a **gnathosome** (**capitulum**) (Fig. 3.10B) formed from anterior segments and having the appearance of a little head bearing the mouthparts. The mouth itself opens at the anterior end of the conical gnathosome, with the chelicerae placed immediately above it and the pedipalpi immediately below it. The most primitive acarines have the "hand-finger-thumb" chelicerae with a basal segment—an arrangement closely resembling the chelicerae of scorpions and doubtless the homologies are the same. Some of the many variations include reduction of the tarsal contribution with loss of the "fixed finger," so that the chelicerae resemble those of spiders, and the development of the chelicerae into long needle-like stylets with tiny saw teeth on their tips (Fig. 3.10B). The chelicerae of certain immature acarines are said to have six segments.

The coxopodites of the second appendages, along with some contribution from sternites, form the latero-ventral area of the gnathosome under the mouth. The pedipalpi (often termed **maxillary palpi** by acarologists) apparently are the telopodites. Where maximum segmentation is present the femur, patella, tibia, tarsus and post-tarsus can be found, the whole borne on a lobe representing the trochanters, but generally there are fewer segments. Endite coxal lobes (**galeae**) are present. When the telopodite is hand-like, it may become a grasping organ or it may be developed as an

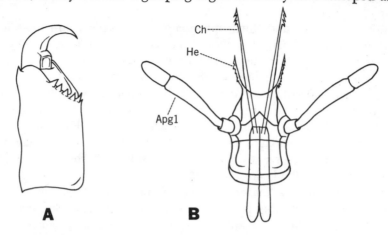

A   **B**

Figure 3.10. (A) Chelicera of a spider (Araneida); (B) gnathosome or capitulum of a mite (Acarida). *Apg1*, first leg modified as "maxillary palpus"; *Ch*, chelicera modified as a stylet; *He*, epistome or tectum, the produced dorsal sclerite. (Drawn from specimens in Carnegie Museum)

accessory biting and chewing structure. In a few instances the pedipalpi are reduced to tiny sensory lobes.

Three skeletal elements become accessory mouthparts in some acarines. The dorsal plate of the gnathosome (**epistome** or **tectum**) may be a slender, spear-like projection. The ventral plates, which are the fused coxopodites of the second appendages plus sternal material, may similarly be drawn out, assisting in piercing or lacerating or functioning as hooks. In a few mites the labrum may become a rasping structure.

MYRIAPODS

The mandible of myriapods (Figs. 3.11 and 3.12) is composed of the coxopodite and the endite coxal lobe, the telopodite having been lost. It was seen that in certain arachnoids the appendages near the mouth sometimes bear endite lobes used in mastication, and furthermore that the telopodite sometimes loses its locomotory function, becoming entirely sensory. Indeed, the pedipalpi of pseudoscorpions combine sensory perception and mastication in just this manner. In some of the primitive Crustacea the mandible-like endite lobes are present, with the telopodite reduced to a little sensory palpus. There is no thought that either crustaceans or arachnoids are in any way ancestral to myriapods or insects, but the comparison helps to clarify the true composition of the mandibles

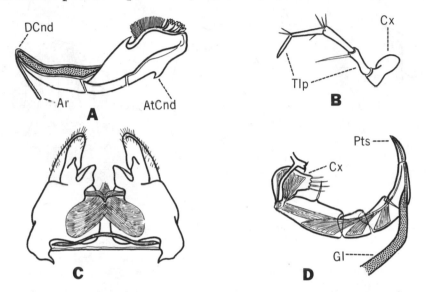

Figure 3.11. Mouthparts of *Scutigera* species, a chilopod. (A) Mandible, dorsal view; (B) labium, lateral view; (C) maxilla, dorsal view; (D) poison claw, dorsal view, with the gland displaced. *Ar*, articulating rod of mandible; *AtCnd*, anterior condyle; *Cx*, coxa; *DCnd*, dorsal condyle; *Gl*, poison gland; *Pts*, post-tarsus; *Tlp*, telopodite. (After Snodgrass, 1951, by permission of Cornell University Press)

and something of the events which must have led to their structure as now found in myriapods and insects.

The diplopod mandible (Fig. 3.12A) has a basal coxopodite, articulated on a single condyle at its base with the head capsule, and a distal toothed endite segment articulating with the basal segment. A transverse suture divides the basal segment into two immovable sections. The proximal of these sections is the homologue of the **cardo**, the distal corresponds to the **stipes** of insect maxillae, and the articulate terminal segment corresponds to the **lacinia** (cf. Fig. 3.13).

The chilopods have a similar mandible (Fig. 3.11A), but the coxopodite is not divided into two sections and the lacinia is less movable—that is, its articulation is springy rather than flexible. The proximal part of the mandible is enclosed in a pouch of the head and is not externally visible. In addition to the apical condyle, a second point of articulation with the head is present in a dorso-posterior position.

The mandibles of pauropods are like those of the chilopods, but the

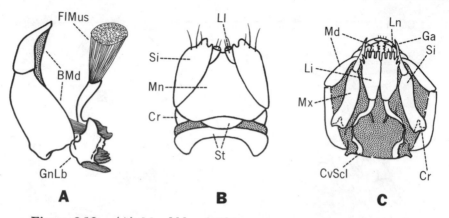

Figure 3.12. (A) Mandible of *Thyropygus* species, a diplopod, dorsal view; (B) gnathochilarium of *Narceus annularis*, a diplopod, ventral view; (C) mouthparts of *Scutigerella immaculata*, Symphyla, ventral view. *BMd,* base of mandible; *Cr,* cardo; *CvScl,* cervical plate; *FlMus,* flexor muscle; *Ga,* galea; *GnLb,* gnathal lobe; *Li,* labium; *Ll,* lingual lamina; *Ln,* lacinia; *Md,* mandible; *Mn,* mentum; *Mx,* maxilla; *Si,* stipes; *St,* sternal plates of labial segment (hypostoma and prebasilare). (A and C after Snodgrass, 1951, by permission of Cornell University Press; B after Keeton, 1960, by permission of the American Entomological Society)

laciniae lack muscles. The mandibles of the symphylas (Fig. 3.12C) are like those of the diplopods.

Skeletal structures involved in mastication are the labrum and hypopharynx. The labrum, it will be recalled, is a sclerite placed at the dorso-anterior margin of the mouth. Its oral edge may be sharp or dentate, presenting a surface that works efficiently in conjunction with the action of the mandibles. It generally is articulated on the **epistomal sclerite** (partly homologous with the insect clypeus) and provided with muscles, but in some chilopods and most diplopods it is fused with the **epistome** and cannot move.

The hypopharynx is formed from ventral skeletal elements. It projects forward toward the mouth from a point behind the maxillae and ahead of the labium. In most myriapods it is a comparatively simple lobe which serves as a sort of fixed molar surface just behind and above the mandibles. Some recent students have incorrectly interpreted this structure in diplopods as rudimentary first maxillae.

The appendages next behind the mandibles have become the maxillae (Fig. 3.11C). Ordinarily quite small, they tend to retain a formation in which it is easy to recognize their origin from a generalized appendage. In chilopods the endite lobes are essentially sensory, though their inner margins sometimes are provided with cutting edges, and the telopodite is reduced to a two- or three-segmented palpus. In some chilopods the coxopodites of the two pairs of maxillae are separated from each other, but in many members of the class they are fused along the ventral midline.

The next pair of appendages of chilopods forms the leg-like second maxillae (Fig. 3.11B) or labium, homologous with the labium of insects (Fig. 3.13D). When endite lobes are present, they are not articulate. The entirely sensory telopodite may have up to five segments and is carried beside the mouth or, in some species, erect like an extra pair of antennae.

The poison claws of the chilopods, the first pair of trunk appendages, function as mouthparts (Fig. 3.11D). They are carried under the head so that the poison can be injected into the prey through gland ducts at the tips of the pointed post-tarsi. The coxae of these appendages are united with the sternum of the first trunk segment, as is shown by the presence of longitudinal sutures in some species.

Diplopods have an accessory feeding structure located behind and between the mandibles, a highly modified affair called the **gnathochilarium.** In what probably is its most generalized form (Fig. 3.12B), it consists of a triangular basal plate crossing the width of the head ventrad, to which two pairs of more or less elongate lobes are fixed. The inner pair are the **laminae linguales,** the outer pair the **stipites.** Each stipes sometimes bears two articulate papillae on its tip, and each lamina may have an articulate terminal segment. In some species there is a median lobe at the tip of the suture dividing the laminae, probably representing a fusion of a pair of separate lobes. It has been debated whether the gnathochilarium is the fused maxillae and labium, or the maxillae alone. Silvestri (1903) thought it develops only from the maxillary limb rudiment of the embryo, that the labial rudiment regresses and its segment becomes the first trunk segment. Pflugfelder (1932) made a much better case for his position that the maxillary and labial limb rudiments fuse during ontogeny to form the adult gnathochilarium; this is now the accepted view.

In the pauropods the gnathochilarium is a lip-like structure representing the full fusion of the right and left elements.

The symphylans (Fig. 3.12C) combine a diplopod type of mandible with maxillae and labrum of the insect type. The parts of the accessory organs are easily identified with those of insects. The maxilla consists of an elongated coxal part divided into **cardo** and **stipes,** tipped by the **galea** and **lacinia;** the telopodite is vestigial or absent. The labium lies between the maxillae and is a pair of narrow proximal pieces, sometimes fused along the midline but definitely dichotomous at the extreme base, bearing three terminal lobes and some lateral dentations. The two basal elements probably are the **submentum** and **prementum** (cf. Fig. 3.13). The terminal lobes apparently represent the **glossae** and **paraglossae,** though they are not movable, and the third lobe may be either the **palpus** (telepodite) or the divided paraglossa (a condition found in some insects). In more advanced symphylans, the labial elements are fused in various ways.

INSECTS

No group of arthropods presents a greater diversity of mouthparts than the insects. The primitive type is organized for biting and chewing (Fig. 3.13). The appendages involved are the mandibles, the maxillae and the labium (second maxillae), with which must be considered the labrum and the hypopharynx. Several phylogenetic lines have devised adaptations of these structures to enable puncturing the tissues of plants or animals and sucking the juices. Others have developed modifications for drinking nectar from flowers and still others have evolved industrial or defensive adaptations not directly connected with feeding. Between the basic biting-chewing type and these various specializations are many intermediate stages of modification, each signalizing progression from one sort of food to another.

The insect mandible (Fig. 3.13A) differs fundamentally in its articulation from the myriapod mandible. The latter is elongated and has a single condyle at its apex at the posterior corner. The second articulation acquired by some chilopods is also posterior. The action of the mandibles in myriapods thus is on the horizontal plane. The insect mandible is shortened. The posterior condyle is present, but the second articulation, the **ginglymus,** is placed at the anterior end of its dorsal margin at the corner of the clypeus and just below the fronto-cranial suture. These two condyles give the insect mandible a hinged action with motion on the vertical plane, an arrangement basic to all adult Pterygota. Among the Apterygota, the Collembola, Protura and about half the Thysanura have mandibles of the myriapod type. The mandibles of Aptera have lost all direct condylic connection with the head capsule. Only the family Lepismatidae (Thysanura) have the dicondylic insect-like mandible.

Biting and chewing mouthparts are present in many insect orders. The labrum almost always is articulate at its base, the muscles originating in the head capsule. Its inner side and its lower margin sometimes are roughened to enhance its jaw-like' action, which is perpendicular to that of the mandibles. The opposed faces of the mandibles have molar surfaces for grinding or dentate projections for rending, as best suits mastication of

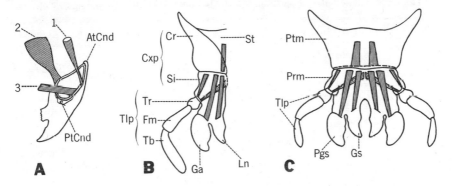

Figure 3.13. Diagrams of generalized mouthparts of insects. (A) Left mandible; (B) right maxilla; (C) labium, the right and left members fused at the base. *AtCnd,* anterior condyle (ginglymus); *Cr,* cardo; *Cxp,* coxopodite; *Fm,* femur; *Ga,* galea; *Gs,* glossa; *Ln,* lacinia; *Pgs,* paraglossa; *Prm,* prementum; *PtCnd,* posterior condyle; *Ptm,* postmentum; *Si,* stipes; *St,* sternal plate; *Tb,* tibia; *Tlp,* telopodite; *Tr,* trochanter; *1,* dorsal abductor muscle; *2,* dorsal adductor muscle; *3,* ventral adductor muscle. (After Snodgrass, 1932, by permission of Smithsonian Institution)

the normal food of the insect involved. Often both kinds of masticating surfaces are present.

The hypopharynx of insects, as in myriapods, is a projection from the sternal skeleton between the maxillae and labium and generally reaches forward between the mandibles. Its median lobe is the **lingua** (glossa). Sometimes there is a pair of lateral lobes, the **superlinguae** (also termed paraglossae or paragnatha). The salivary duct opens just ventral of the base of the hypopharynx, but in Hemiptera and Diptera it traverses the length of the hypopharynx and opens at the tip.

The maxillae (Fig. 3.13B) are more generalized than the mandibles or the labium and the parts a little easier to homologize (Table 3.2). The coxal part is divided by a flexible suture into the proximal **cardo** (plural, **cardines**) and the distal **stipes** (plural, **stipites**). The cardo articulates on a basal condyle with the head capsule. Each of these parts is provided with muscles originating within the cranium or on the tentorium. Two endite lobes lie on the tip of the stipes, the medial lacinia, which may have a mandible-like action with its homologue on the opposite side, and the lateral **galea**. The telopodite is represented by the maxillary palpus, a sensory structure having as many as six segments, though in most cases there are fewer.

Table 3.2 Homologies of undifferentiated leg with cephalic appendages of insects

Undifferentiated Leg		Labium	Maxilla	Mandible	Antenna
Coxopodite	⎧ Subcoxa	Postmentum	Cardo	⎫	⎫
	⎨ Coxa	Prementum	Stipes	⎬ Mandible	⎬ Scape
	⎪ Medial endite	Glossa	Lacinia		—
	⎩ Lateral endite	Paraglossa	Galea	⎭ —	—
	⎧ Trochanter 1	⎫		—	Pedicel
	⎪ Trochanter 2	⎪		—	⎫
Telopodite	⎨ Femur	⎬ Palpus	Palpus	—	⎬ Flagellum
	⎪ Tibia	⎪		—	⎭
	⎪ Tarsus	⎪		—	
	⎩ Post-tarsus	⎭		—	

Less generalized insects often have the stipes divided into subsections by sutures. The more frequently encountered subdivisions are a proximal area to which the term stipes is then limited, a medial **subgalea** bearing the lacinia and galea and a lateral **palpifer** from which the palpus arises. The galea also may be subdivided into a proximal and a distal section.

The labium is essentially similar to the maxillae, but because the right and left appendages are fused to some extent along the ventral midline, it gives the impression of being a single structure rather than a pair (Fig. 3.13C). A generalized labium such as is found in Thysanura has the two coxae fused with the sternum, but the basic parts are still separated by sutures. Each coxa bears an irregularly shaped lobe, in this case clearly endite, and a three-segmented palpus representing the telopodite. In pterygote insects the labial palpus has four segments in a few cases, but three or fewer are more usual. In orthopteroids—the cockroach, for example—the labium assumes the basic form typical of most insects. The **postmentum** swings on a pair of condyles placed at its corners and its right and left members are fully fused, though a median suture is sometimes present. The postmentum is homologous with the maxillary cardo (Table 3.2). The **prementum** is comparable with the stipes of the maxillae. It bears the palpus on its lateral margin and two endite lobes on its tip. The medial lobes, termed the **glossae**, are equivalent to the maxillary laciniae; the lateral lobes or **paraglossae** (notice the conflicting use of this term by some writers to designate the superlinguae) are homologous with the maxillary galeae. The prementum may be subdivided so that there is a separate palpus-bearing section, the **palpiger**. The labium serves as the posterior lip under the mouth and its lobes are essentially sensory. In chewing mouthparts the labium sometimes enters into mastication with an action opposed to the labrum or by working with the mandibles and maxillary laciniae.

It may be seen from this brief review of chewing mouthparts in insects that even in their most generalized form they are already greatly modified from the locomotory legs from which they originated. Two-thirds of the insect orders, including almost all of the primitive Pterygota, retain biting and chewing structures for feeding. In sixteen of these orders the mouthparts are essentially the same, though some variation is found in the relative size of this or that structure and in details of subdivision or fusion of basic parts. Four other orders—the Plecoptera, Ephemerida, Trichoptera and Strepsiptera—have the basic chewing structures, but the mouthparts are weakened, reduced or partly atrophied and adults feed but little or not at all, depending upon the nutrition stored from immature instars; in main, these insects enjoy only a brief adult life. In two orders (Neuroptera and Coleoptera) counted as having biting and chewing mouthparts, a few species have modifications which enable sucking. In the primitive order Collembola, either of two types of mouthparts occur: some species have the biting and chewing type, with all structures elongated and narrow; others have developed sucking mouthparts.

The other nine orders all have sucking mouthparts of various kinds. The bees (Hymenoptera) and Lepidoptera feed on flower nectar and similar liquids and accordingly have developed a flexible, coiled (Lepidoptera) or an extrusible (bees) proboscis. Adult Protura, Thysanoptera, Hemiptera, Anoplura, Diptera and Siphonaptera feed on the juices of either plants or animals. Their mouthparts are modified not only for sucking but also to inflict a wound either by rasping (Thysanoptera) or by puncturing (the others) to gain access to the juices.

Functional sucking mouthparts not only require modification of the mouthparts themselves but also the development of special mechanisms in the foregut. A sucking pump is present in the head of every sucking insect. It always represents an elaboration of the muscles and other structures already present near the mouth, especially in the pharyngeal region, of the chewing insect (Snodgrass, 1935). The generalized insect with chewing mouthparts pushes chewed particles toward the mouth proper, collecting them in a cavity (**cibarium**) between the base of the hypopharynx and the clypeus. Action of muscles on each side of this cavity—

those of the clypeus and those of the hypopharynx—forces the particles through the mouth and into the anterior gut. In sucking insects the cibarium becomes becomes a definite closed cavity with flexible walls, the musculature becomes elaborated and the true mouth is moved from its proximal to its distal end.

Ingestion by sucking is more rapid than ingestion by chewing. The salivary secretions must therefore be issued more rapidly for sucking ingestion in order to ensure the correct mixture with the food. The salivary duct opens just below the hypopharynx and just above the labium in chewing insects, and contractions of the labial muscles keep the secretions flowing. In sucking insects the flow is increased by greater development of the musculature and in some cases a muscular **syringe** is developed, a structure capable of ejecting secretions forcibly.

A review of the mouthparts of a representative series of Hymenoptera beginning with the more generalized phytophagous sawflies and proceeding to the specialized social bees would demonstrate many degrees of modification within that order, ranging from more or less typical chewing mouthparts to a sucking apparatus, the parts of which bear but little obvious similarity to those of the grasshopper. Two examples will serve to illustrate the point.

The sawfly, a relatively primitive hymenopteran, has biting mandibles (Fig. 3.14A) with no special modification. While the maxillae and labrum are combined into a single composite structure, the elements of the separate appendages are recognizable. This maxillolabium lies under the head and articulates with a basal segment, hanging from the capsule in such a way that when the maxillolabium swings back- and forward, it may be withdrawn behind the mouth or thrust ahead of it. The vertical basal segment consists of the maxillary cardines, each articulated to the capsule by a condyle, with a flat sclerite derived from the base of the labium lying between them and serving as a supporting strut. The elongated stipites with the membranous postmentum and the sclerotized prementum fastened between them collectively make up the horizontal part of the maxillolabium. Maxillary palpi are found on the lateral aspects of the stipites, which terminate with the broad, flat galeae and the tiny laciniae. On the premental part the right and left glossae are fused to form a medioterminal tongue-like structure flanked by the much smaller paraglossae. The labial palpi are reduced.

Skipping the many, many intermediate levels of modification and proceeding directly to the bee (Fig. 3.14B), the mouthparts are seen to be greatly elongated. The basal sclerite (**lorum**) of the labrum is V-shaped and bridges the lower ends of the long, narrow cardines. The triangular mentum and long prementum articulate with the midpoint of the lorum. The fused glossae form a slender flexible tongue and, with the small paraglossae, can be partly retracted into the prementum. The labial palpi are nearly as long as the tongue and are flattened. The stipites articulate on the lateral ends of the lorum and are attached to the prementum only by membrane at the base. The galeae are elongated and flat, the maxillary

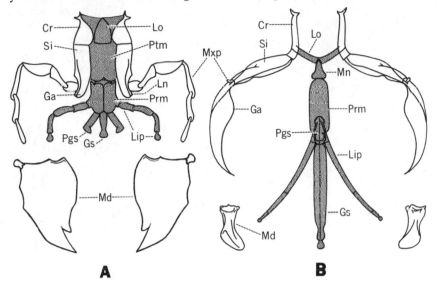

Figure 3.14. Mouthparts of Hymenoptera. (A) *Tremex columba,* a sawfly; (B) *Apis mellifera,* the honeybee; labium stippled in both figures. *Cr,* cardo; *Ga,* galea; *Gs,* glossa; *Lip,* labial palpus; *Ln,* lacinia; *Lo,* submental sclerite or lorum; *Md,* mandible; *Mn,* mentum; *Mxp,* maxillary palpus; *Pgs,* paraglossa; *Prm,* prementum; *Ptm,* postmentum; *Si,* stipites. (Drawn from original dissections)

palpi are vestigial pegs and the laciniae are entirely absent (vestigial laciniae are present in some related species).

When feeding on flower nectar, the bee forms a proboscis by bringing the flat galeae and labial palpi together beside and over the tongue. Movements of the tongue, now forming the floor of the proboscis, bring the liquid to the mouth, and it is sucked in by the pumping action of the muscles around the buccal cavity and pharynx.

The mandibles of social bees are not used for feeding. Generally they are spatulate or spoon shaped and are chiefly employed in nest (hive) construction. In the honeybee, for example, they are used to work the wax and fashion the hexagonal cells.

The nectar-sipping mouthparts of Lepidoptera are entirely different from those of the bees. The proboscis (Fig. 3.15A) is formed from the two maxillary galeae, enormously elongated and with a medial groove which forms a tube between them when they are pressed together. The galeae are annulated externally, are quite flexible and contain many tiny

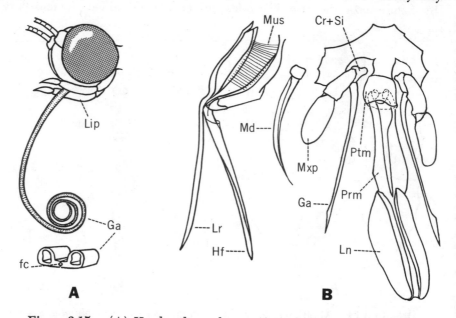

Figure 3.15. (A) Head and mouthparts of *Mechanitis lycidice*, a butterfly (Lepidoptera), with a transverse section of the proboscis below; (B) dissected mouthparts of a horsefly, *Tabanus atratus* (Diptera). *Cr+Si*, fused cardo and stipes; *fc*, food channel; *Ga*, galea (in A the galeae combined as the proboscis); *Hf*, hypopharynx; *Lip*, labial palpus; *Ln*, lacinia; *Lr*, labrum; *Md*, mandible; *Mus*, muscles of cibarium; *Mxp*, maxillary palpus; *Prm*, prementum; *Ptm*, postmentum. (Drawn from specimens in Carnegie Museum)

diagonal muscles which coil the structure when not in use. The two elements (galeae) of the proboscis are held together by interlocking hooks and spines. The maxillary palpi are vestigial or absent; the cardo and stipes are reduced. The labium is represented only by a small plate or a membrane bearing the prominent labial palpi. In the adult the mandibles are completely atrophied. A pharyngeal pump is present, but the salivary duct is not equipped with a syringe.

The above description applies to the mouthparts of butterflies and most moths. In some families of moths the adults do not feed at all and mouthparts are nonfunctional or atrophied, but several very primitive families of this order retain mandibles. In the Micropterygidae the mandibles are used for grinding the pollen on which the adults feed and no proboscis has been developed. In the Eriocranidae the mandibles are present but not functional; these insects feed with an abbreviated but typically lepidopterous proboscis. In a few other families of moths, tiny vestiges of the mandibles may be found.

All living adult Diptera have sucking mouthparts. Even in the most primitive families the homologies and origins of the feeding structures are not entirely obvious, but the extraordinary modifications of the mouthparts in the more advanced families can be analyzed only by comparison with the primitive forms.

Among the more generalized and recognizable sets of mouthparts in this order are those of the family Tabanidae. Six tiny "stilettos" project downward from the front of the head (Fig. 3.15B). These are the elongated, flattened and double-edged labrum, the narrow, sharp mandibles, the two sharp maxillary galeae and an elongated, spear-like hypopharynx. This formidable equipment is used by the horsefly to inflict its "bite" by placing the six "stilettos" against the skin and driving them in, like a composite hypodermic needle, with a downward thrust of head and body, sometimes coupled with a slashing motion.

The inner face of the labrum has a longitudinal groove which becomes the food channel when pressed against the mandibles. The mandibles are articulated on condyles and are able to move in much the same way as the mandibles of biting insects. The maxillae consist of a basal piece representing the fused cardo and stipes, bearing the palpi on its distal (stipital) part, and the attenuated galeae. The salivary duct traverses the length of the hypopharynx, opening at its tip. Just proximad of the base of the hypopharynx the duct forms a small chamber encircled by powerful muscles, the salivary syringe. In addition to digestive enzymes the salivary secretion contains anticoagulant to facilitate feeding on animal blood. The labial prementum is represented by a membrane connecting the maxillary stipites. The rest of the labium projects under the other mouthparts and consists of the prementum and the fleshy labella. It has a medial groove in which the other mouthparts lie. Each **labella** (paraglossa?) has numerous tiny grooves on its under side leading to a basomedial cleft. During feeding, blood runs along these grooves from the wound to the food channel formed between the labrum and mandibles.

The mouthparts of the female mosquito (Fig. 3.16A, B) consist of the

labrum, the two mandibles, two maxillae and the hypopharynx, all developed into long, hair-like **stylets** enclosed within a groove of the
labium. The labium here serves only to ensheathe and support the stylets.
The food channel is formed by the tubular labrum. The tips of the maxillae are serrate and they are the primary puncturing structures. The

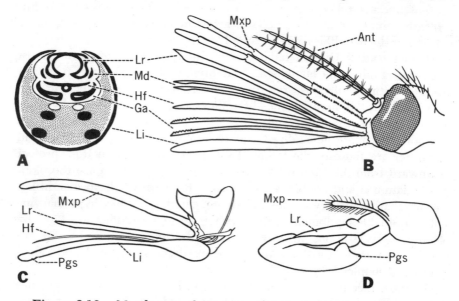

Figure 3.16. Mouthparts of Diptera. (A) Proboscis (in section) and
(B) head and mouthparts of a female *Anopheles* mosquito; (C) mouth-
parts of the tsetse fly, *Glossina*; (D) proboscis of a late pupal blowfly,
Calliphora. *Ant*, antenna; *Ga*, galea; *Hf*, hypopharynx; *Li*, labium; *Lr*,
labrum; *Md*, mandible; *Mxp*, maxillary palpi; *Pgs*, paraglossa or labella.
(A and B from Russell, West and Manwell, 1946, by permisison of W. B.
Saunders Co.; C after Hansen *in* Austen, 1903; D after Lowne, 1890–1892)

salivary duct opens at the tip of the hypopharynx. To feed, the mosquito
makes a puncture, then pumps salivary juice into the wound, partly in-
hibiting coagulation and consequent blockage of the food channel. This
practical mechanism is the basis for the transmission of many kinds of
pathogenic organisms by blood-feeding Diptera and other insects with
piercing and sucking habits. Pathogens lodged in the salivary glands are
injected with the secretion during feeding.

The mouthparts of the tsetse fly (*Glossina*) are reduced to essentials
(Fig. 3.16C). The U-shaped labium is tightly closed above by the elongated labrum, thus forming a food channel through which blood is sucked.

The needle-like hypopharynx serves both as the piercing structure and as a route for the salivary secretions. Mandibles are absent and only the well-developed palpi remain of the maxillary structures.

An entirely different line of mouthpart development found in Diptera is exemplified by the blowfly (Fig. 3.16D). Here there is no puncturing. Liquid food is lapped or sponged, then sucked up. Beneath the head there projects a cone-shaped, largely membranous **rostrum** bearing maxillary palpi on its anterior aspect. While its components are far from clear, there is reason to believe that the rostrum is derived from the clypeus, the maxillae and the basal elements of the labium. Attached to the lower end of the rostrum is the **haustellum,** a fleshy structure which can be swung down for feeding or, at rest, up against the anterior face of the rostrum. On its upper surface is a deep longitudinal groove, the food channel, in which the hypopharynx rests and which is covered by the flat, widened labrum. On the tip of the haustellum is a pair of ovoid, fleshy lobes, the **labella.** The under sides of the labella are crossed diagonally by innumerable microscopic grooves leading to a larger longitudinal central groove. Liquid lapped by the labella passes up these tiny grooves (**pseudotracheae**) by capillary action, reaches the medial groove and passes by way of the food channel to the mouth, where the pharyngeal pump sucks it in. The musculature of the haustellum and labella, which collectively form an efficient tongue, is quite complicated. Solid particles of food are not ingested directly. The fly first "vomits" on them, bathing them in secretions from the foregut, ingesting them only after they have been dissolved by the enzymes. This habit of feeding augments the medical importance of the housefly, since the "vomit spots" include many pathogenic organisms. In many species of Muscidae and related families the inner walls of the cleft between the labella are armed with minute teeth used as rasps.

The mouthparts of Siphonaptera (Fig. 3.17) are not unlike those of the male mosquito—that is, similar to the female mosquito but *without* the mandibles. The three stylets present are the labrum and the two maxillae, all three carried in the grooved labium. Four-segmented maxillary palpi are the primary sensory structures. They are borne on a short triangular plate, perhaps representing the coxal part of the maxillae, which helps support and guide the stylets. The maxillary laciniae are stiletto-like, equipped with serrate edges, and articulated to the stipital part of the maxillary plate by a short rod-like sclerite. The dorsal stylet is a sclerotized prolongation of the inner side (epipharynx) of the labrum. The labial prementum is a triangular plate with its margins folded upward. The labial palpi on its tip have one, three or five segments and lie on either side of the stylets, functioning to hold them in the groove of the prementum. Blood is sucked through the food channel formed between the U-shaped maxillary laciniae and the overlying labral epipharynx. When pressed together they form a channel which leads from the opening of the salivary duct on the hypopharynx and serves as the salivary channel.

The peculiar feeding beak of the Hemiptera (in the broad sense) is best understood by comparison with the related order Thysanoptera.

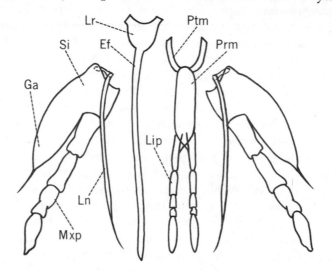

Figure 3.17. Separated mouthparts of the dog flea, *Ctenocephalides canis*. *Ef,* epipharynx; *Ga,* galea; *Lip,* labial palpus; *Ln,* lacinia; *Lr,* labrum; *Mxp,* maxillary palpus; *Prm,* prementum; *Ptm,* postmentum. (Drawn from original dissections)

Thrips (Fig. 3.18A) have three stylets enclosed in a short cone projecting from the posterio-ventral angle of the oddly asymmetric head. The cone consists of four more or less triangular pieces fitted together. The anterior piece is the labrum, the labium is posterior and the maxillae are lateral. The stylets are the left mandible (the right mandible is atrophied) and two maxillae. The maxillary plates enclosing the sides of the proboscis cone probably are the asymmetric stipites. On the outer side of each is a short palpus. On the inner side is a short bar articulating at its lateral end near the base and bearing a fine stylet at its medial end. This bar is provided with protractor and retractor muscles, enabling the puncturing action of the stylets. A tiny lobe on the tip of the stipes is probably the fused lacinia and galea. The stylet and its articulating bar arise during ontogeny from the basal part of the stipes, thus having no homology with structures in chewing mouthparts. The wide triangular body of the labium consists of the prementum, which articulates on a membranous hinge with the postmentum. Tiny labial palpi are placed laterad near the tip of the prementum; two flap-like medial lobes are the fused glossae and paraglossae of each side. The hypopharynx is a lobe that seems to project from inside the base of the labium. The salivary duct opens at its base into a muscular pocket which is an elementary salivary syringe. On the anterior side of the base of the hypopharynx is the **cibarium**, a well-developed chamber with muscular walls.

Despite the great diversity of shape and size among members of the large order Hemiptera, their feeding habits are much the same throughout. The mouthparts, while they vary in detail from family to family, are essentially alike in all. Most Hemiptera feed on sap from plants, but a few groups have transferred to animal blood. Both the cibarial food pump and the salivary syringe are well developed.

The Hemiptera have a beak (**rostrum; proboscis**) (Fig. 3.18B) which is carried under the body between the legs when not in use and swung forward for feeding. It may be joined to the anterior or the posterior angle of the head or somewhere between, so varied is head development in the order. The beak is composed of the long, grooved labium enclosing four stylets—two mandibles and two maxillae. At their bases the stylets lie in a pair of pouches invaginated from the ventral integument of the maxillary segment on either side of the hypopharynx. Muscles on the pouch walls are able to protrude the stylets. In some Hemiptera there are sclerite levers in the pouches to enhance the swinging out of the stylets. The mandibles, puncturing structures, are serrated at their tips. The maxillae are flattened laterally and bear along their opposing surfaces two longitudinal grooves. When pressed together the grooves on the maxillary stylets form two tubes, the upper (anterior) of which is the food channel, and the lower the salivary channel. In some Hemiptera the maxillae are merely appressed, but in most they are interlocked with tongue and groove devices. Both maxillary and labial palpi are wanting, their function being taken over by a sensory area on the tip of the labium. The labium is divided into sections, believed to be formed from the prementum, connected to each other by membranous hinges. There are four sections in most families, but in some there are fewer. The comparatively short labrum supports the bases of the stylets, where the labial groove is not present. During feeding, the labial sections fold backward at the hinges, effectively shortening the distance between the puncture point and the head and allowing the stylets to puncture the host tissues.

In some advanced Hemiptera the stylets are far longer than the body. When not in use they are coiled and retracted into a pouch, which may extend into the thorax and which probably is a development from the paired stylet pouches of other Hemiptera. In such cases the labium has a modified muscular region which serves as a clamp to prevent the withdrawal of the stylets while being uncoiled during feeding.

The mouthparts of Anoplura (Fig. 3.18C) are truly cryptic in both senses: they are carried hidden within the head and their homologies are doubtful. The short rostrum is formed from the labrum, its inner side armed with teeth which grip the host when it is everted during feeding. The cibarial pump is very well developed. Below the mouth in the ventral part of the head is a deep sac in which are three stylets. The ventral stylet is broad, its tip armed with three short points used for puncturing. A groove runs its length and accommodates the other stylets. Probably this ventral stylet is the labium. The median stylet is a slender rod enclosing the salivary duct. It has been interpreted as a modification of the salivary duct or as the hypopharynx; the latter seems more likely. The dorsal stylet forms the food channel and probably is composed of the two flattened maxillae partly fused along their ventral edges, the dorsal edges curled over each other to form the tube. The base of the dorsal stylet divides to the right and left; when mouthparts are everted for feeding, the food channel lies under the functional mouth. To extend the mouthparts, the entire enclosing sac is pulled forward. Though most puzzling, the mouthparts of the louse seem to resemble those of the Hemiptera more than those of any other insects.

The mouthparts of insects often are classified as **ectognathous** when they are visible and external, or **endognathous** if they are enclosed within the head. The biting mouthparts of the grasshopper, the sipping proboscis of the butterfly, the lapping structures of the fly, the puncturing and sucking mouthparts of the flea all are ectognathous because they are easily seen externally. The biting mouthparts of Collembola and the sucking mouthparts of the louse both have been called endognathous because they are enclosed and not easily seen externally. Endognathous mouthparts, however, may come to be enclosed within the head as the result of either of two totally different processes. The endognathous structures of Collembola, for example, are enclosed by skeletal flaps which grow down around them; the mouthparts themselves are not particularly modified, and they probably would function just as well without the enclosing flaps. For this kind of enclosing, we retain the term endognathous. In contrast, we use the term **cryptognathous** to designate mouthparts which come to be enclosed as the result of *invagination*. Such mouthparts, like

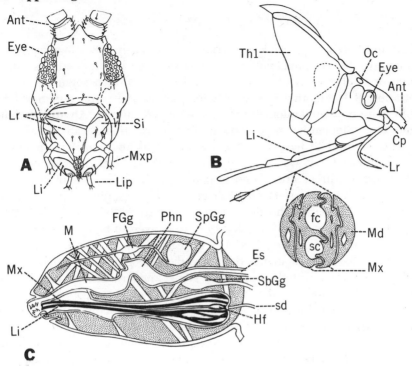

Figure 3.18. Mouthparts of hemipteroid insects. (A) Frontal view of head of *Chirothrips hamatus* (Thysanoptera); (B) the squash bug *Anasa tristis* (Hemiptera), side view of prothorax and head, with (below) a diagrammatic section through the stylet showing the relationships of the mandibles and maxillae; (C) a diagrammatic median vertical section of the head of a louse (Anoplura). *Ant*, antenna; *Cp*, clypeus; *Es*, esophagus; *Eye*, compound eye; *fc*, food channel; *FGg*, frontal ganglion; *Hf*, hypopharynx, the median stylet; *Li*, labium; *Lip*, labial palpus; *Lr*, labrum; *M*, position of true mouth; *Md*, mandible; *Mx*, maxilla; *Mxp*, maxillary palpus; *Oc*, ocellus; *Phn*, pharynx; *SbGg*, subesophageal ganglionic mass; *sc*, salivary channel; *sd*, salivary duct; *Si*, stipes; *SpGg*, supraesophageal ganglionic mass or "brain"; *Thl*, prothorax. (A after Jones, 1954; B after Tower, 1914; C redrawn from Snodgrass, 1944, by permission of Smithsonian Institution)

those of Anoplura, are strongly modified, and were they not placed in membranous invaginated pockets with walls supplied with muscles, they could not function. These three words, in conjunction with words descriptive of function, serve to describe and designate the mouthparts of insects.

ABDOMINAL APPENDAGES

The undifferentiated trunk of myriapods ordinarily bears legs on every segment. In the Symphyla not every trunk segment has appendages, since eleven or twelve pairs of legs are found on the fifteen segments. Concentration of locomotion in the anterior part of the trunk region led to the formation of the abdomen in arachnoids and insects. Almost by definition, the abdomen has no functional legs. What, then, has happened to the legs believed to have been on the ancestral abdominal metameres?

In Chapter Two it was postulated that each arthropod metamere initially bears a pair of articulated appendages. The absence of such appendages on a metamere of an adult arthropod can only be explained in one of two ways: either the appendages fail to develop after appearing in the embryo, or they indeed develop but are converted to some specialized use and are not easily recognized as legs. Either explanation may be true. On some abdominal metameres the appendages begin development in the embryo, but are arrested at an early stage and are not present in the adult. On other abdominal metameres the appendages continue to develop, not into legs but into modified, specialized structures. Such events have already been observed in the formation of the mouthparts.

If all this is true, it might be expected that somewhere in the phylogenetic history of typical winged insects there must have been ancestral forms that had not yet perfected the scheme of conversion or elimination of the abdominal·appendages. Do we know any such? No, not directly. Ancestors are never alive. If they survive at all it is as fossils. Unfortunately the sketchy fossil record of insects sheds but little light upon this particular question. An indication of the possible ancestral condition of the abdominal legs (we are considering only adults, for the present) seems to have been preserved in certain primitive insect-like groups, notably the orders Protura, Aptera and Thysanura. Not by any stretch of the imagination can any of these orders be considered ancestral to pterygote insects. But they do seem to be arthropods that have progressed just so far and no further in the insect direction, then managed somehow to survive while other arthropods continued to evolve and became true insects.

VESTIGIAL LEGS

In the Protura the first three abdominal segments bear paired appendages which seem to be serially homologous with the thoracic legs, since they are similarly placed in the membranous pleural area just above the sterna. A pair of pleurites probably derived from the subcoxa lie above and anterior of the coxa. Coxal muscles provide for movement on the anterio-posterior axis of the body. The second segment is annular, quite short and terminates in a vesicle. The vesicle apparently is everted by blood pressure and retracted by a muscle inserted in its membrane and originating on the body wall. The second segment is moved by muscles originating in the coxa and was regarded by Berlese (1909b) as representing the telopodite. Intriguingly reminiscent of the prolegs found on caterpillars, these legs evidently aid in locomotion.

A more complicated situation is observed in the order Aptera. Appendages are found on the first seven abdominal segments, but here each is typically double. The coxopodite (Fig. 3.19A, B, C) is completely incorporated into the body wall and fused with the sternum. On the outer side of the coxal area projects a stylus, a narrow articulating lobe provided with muscles. Mesad of the stylus is the other part of the appendage, which may take one of three different forms. It may be a stylus (*Anajapyx*) (Fig. 3.26A), it may be a retractile vesicle (*Japyx*) (Fig. 3.19B) very like the vesicle terminating the abdominal appendages of Protura, or it may be represented only by a raised lobe covered by sensory setae (Fig. 3.19C). If Berlese was correct in calling the second segment of abdominal appendages in Protura the telopodite, and if the vesicles of Aptera are homologous with the vesicles of Protura, then the stylus can only be an exite coxal lobe. But there are too many "if's" and not enough concrete evidence presented by the Aptera and those who have studied them.

The Thysanura may hold the key to the problem. On the coxae of the second and third legs in the family Machilidae are slender styli. Although they are not provided with muscles, they seem to be endite lobes (Fig. 3.19D). Similar, serially homologous styli are also present on the second to ninth abdominal segments, and retractile vesicles are found on the first seven abdominal segments. This might appear to decide the matter, as the vesicles always are mesad of the styli. But the issue is beclouded by the presence in most Machilidae of a second vesicle beside the first. Snodgrass (1935) thought that the presence of two vesicles precludes interpreting them as representing the telopodite, and no one seems to have investigated the possibility that one of them represents still another coxal lobe or that the two vesicles are formed by secondary separation of the telopodite vestige.

The Collembola have three abdominal appendages on the five abdominal segments (Fig. 3.19E, F, G). Though medial and unpaired in the adult, apparently they are developed from segmental appendages that fuse in the course of ontogeny. On the first abdominal segment is a hold-

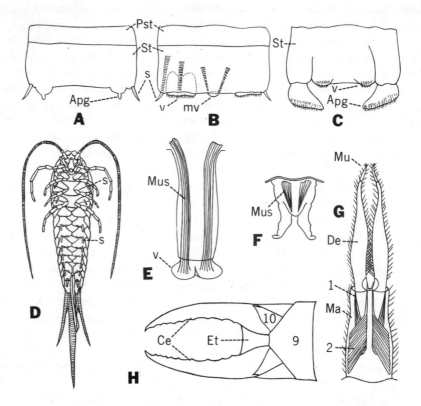

Figure 3.19. Abdominal appendages of insects. (A–C) Ventral surface of first abdominal segment of Aptera; (A) *Anajapyx,* (B) *Japyx,* (C) *Campodea;* (D) ventral view of *Machilis* species (Thysanura); (E–G) abdominal appendages of a Collembola, *Tomocerus vulgaris;* (E) collophore, (F) tenaculum, (G) furcula; (H) tip of abdomen of an earwig (Dermaptera). *Apg,* appendage; *Ce,* cercus; *De,* dens; *Et,* epiproct, eleventh abdominal tergum; *Ma,* manubrium; *Mu,* mucro; *Mus,* retractor muscle of collophore, adductor muscle of tenaculum; *mv,* median vesicle; *Pst,* presternite or apotome; *s,* stylus; *St,* sternite; *v,* vesicle; *1,* abductor muscle of furcula; *2,* adductor muscle of furcula; *9,* ninth abdominal segment; *10,* tenth abdominal segment. (A–C from Denis, 1949a, by arrangement with Masson et Cie; D from Comstock, 1940, by permission of Cornell University Press; E–G from Snodgrass, 1931, by permission of Smithsonian Institution; H drawn from specimen in Carnegie Museum)

fast structure, the **collophore** (Fig. 3.19E), consisting of a thick membranous cylinder terminating in a vesicle. It is everted by blood pressure and retracted by a muscle originating in the body wall. In some species this structure has a pair of vesicles lying side by side on its tip. The presence of a groove along the sterna of the thorax, connecting the collophore with the labium has led to speculation that the labial glands secrete the sticky material that flows to the vesicles of the collophore by way of this channel. On the fourth abdominal segment is a more or less elongated structure, the spring (**furcula**) (Fig. 3.19G), which functions in conjunction with the clasp (**tenaculum**) (Fig. 3.19F) on the third segment. When the furcula is brought forward under the body, its distal arms grip the tenaculum. Sudden release of the grip allows the furcula to spring downward and throw the animal up and away. The action is something like that of a mousetrap which, after being set, is placed upside down on the floor.

The furcula (Fig. 3.19G) consists of an elongated basal segment, the **manubrium,** on which are borne a pair of two-segmented arms, each consisting of a longer proximal segment (**dens**) and a short terminal part (**mucro**). The paired extensor and flexor muscles of the manubrium originate on the walls of the fourth segment; the muscles of the arms arise in the manubrium. Apparently the manubrium is formed from the fused coxae, while the arms are the respective telopodites. The tenaculum (Fig. 3.19F) is a tiny structure consisting of a conical basal segment bearing a pair of prongs. Its general shape is like a Y and the outer margins of the prongs are dentate. The tenaculum thus is essentially similar to the furcula. The basal segment is formed by fusion of the coxae, the prongs being the right and left telopodites.

Many immature insects bear appendages on the abdomen. Often they are locomotory, as in the larvae of Lepidoptera. In other cases the abdominal appendages in aquatic immatures bear gills—in some of the larvae of Neuroptera, for example. The immature stages of insects and their structures are discussed in Chapter Seven. The state of the appendages on immature forms reflects the level of development toward the adult and is of interest primarily in that connection. In adult Pterygota locomotory appendages are never found on the abdomen and locomotion is exclusively the function of the thorax.

It may well be asked, if such is the case, how does one explain locomotory appendages on the abdomens of Apterygota? In brief, the Apterygota are not truly insects, but are sufficiently insect-like that for purposes of taxonomy they are associated with Insecta rather than with the myriapods. In some respects, adult Apterygota are better compared with immature than with adult Pterygota. The abdominal appendages of Protura, Aptera and Thysanura are suggestive of appendages present on immature Pterygota. The resemblance is not only to the abdominal appendages of some of these immatures, but also to their thoracic appendages. In progressing toward maturity, Pterygota pass through stages, in many cases, resembling the adult stages of these three apterygote orders. Conversely, Protura, Aptera and Thysanura as adults arrive at a condition of almost-insect-ness. It would be an error to suppose that the Apterygota are ancestors of the Pterygota. It cannot be too often emphasized that all ancestors are dead. Unquestionably the Pterygota developed from wingless arthropods; whether any of those ancestral groups had half-formed appendages on their abdomens and used them for locomotion, nobody knows and nobody will ever know—except in the unlikely event that a fossilized ancestor is found and recognized. Thus the four most primitive orders are understood as being side branches from the trunk of the family tree of insects, distant cousins rather than ancestors.

CERCI

The cerci are the appendages of the eleventh and last abdominal segment of insects (Collembola have but five). The eleventh segment is recognizably present in primitive orders, often being annular and with distinct tergal and sternal regions between which the cerci arise. The three caudal "bristles" of Thysanura are the two cerci and the appendage-like eleventh tergite. Reduction of the eleventh segment in some insects results in the tergum becoming a small separated plate, the **epiproct,** between the cerci, and the sternum becoming a bilobed affair called the **paraproct** (Snodgrass, 1935). Further reduction leads to association of the cerci directly with the posterior margin of the tenth segment, but in Mecoptera and Trichoptera cerci are retained without any trace of the skeletal elements of the eleventh segment. To attribute ten segments to these two orders, as is generally done, is not strictly correct, therefore, since the cerci constitute clear evidence of the eleventh segment and certainly must be regarded as its vestige. In adults of most highly evolved orders, the cerci and all other traces of the eleventh segment are absent.

Maximal development of the cerci is found in Aptera, Thysanura and Ephemerida. The filiform cerci of these orders consist of a distinct coxa and a telopodite subdivided into numerous annuli. These subsegments have no direct homology with the segments of an unmodified leg. While the coxal segment has muscles arising in the body wall, the telopodite never does, a situation analogous with the condition of the antennae of higher insects; it is difficult to understand why the (supposed) lack of muscles in the antennae has been thought to disqualify them, but not the cerci, as appendages (Snodgrass, 1935).

In primitive insects the muscles of the cercal coxae originate in the eleventh tergum (epiproct). With the reduction of the eleventh segment and association of the cerci with the margin of the tenth, the muscles shift to the tenth segment. Filiform cerci often have a sensory function, but in some insects they probably may be regarded as vestigial structures of little importance. In certain Aptera (Japygidae) and in the Dermaptera they are forceps-like and are used to catch prey as well as in defense (Fig. 3.19H).

EXTERNAL GENITALIA

Special structures for oviposition in females or for copulation in males are present in most insects. These structures, the external genitalia, may in either sex include modified appendages, as well as parts not originating from appendages. The very diversification of the external genitalia makes them of great value in taxonomy for separating many species from otherwise similar relatives. So various and variously developed are the genitalia that direct comparison between orders is quite difficult. Through the years specialists have been forced to devise names to apply to the structures they found in an order or a part of an order under investigation so that they could get on with their work. Consequently certain morphologic terms have come to be used in different groups for entirely different, nonhomologous structures in the genitalia, while homologous parts sometimes get different names in different orders. The net result is a confused terminology most discouraging to the student of comparative morphology. The situation is something like the streets of Paris where a perfectly straight boulevard may change its name with every cross street, but another avenue will keep its name through all sorts of twists and turns. In recent years many excellent investigators have turned their attention to problems of homology in insect genitalia. That no satisfactory solution has been reached is itself the measure of the problem's difficulty. Useful presentations have been made by Snodgrass (1935), who compares these structures, as found in various orders, in general terms and with some degree of consistency.

Female insects deposit their eggs in one of three ways: (1) directly from the external opening of the reproductive system, (2) by use of a tubular eversible abdomen or (3) by use of an ovipositor mostly derived from modified appendages of the eighth and ninth segments. Snodgrass believed the last of these was the prototypic method in insects and that the other two conditions have been therefore derived. In essence, this

view probably is correct, but one notes that the first of the methods mentioned above may be reached by either of two routes. It seems likely that
the Collembola deposit eggs directly from the genital opening because
at no point in their phylogeny has an ovipositor been developed, whereas
the Lepidoptera perform the operation in the same way because the ovipositor has been lost.

Again the Thysanura present an example of a generalized structure.
The coxae of the eighth and ninth abdominal segments of that order bear
two styli and two lobes (Fig. 3.20A, B): the **gonopophyses,** coxal endites
developed as four elongated processes serving collectively to place the
egg. The styli probably are only vestigial structures and contribute little
to oviposition.

The ovipositor of Orthoptera (Fig. 3.20C) represents a basic pattern
found in the more advanced pterygote orders. It consists of the coxae of
the eighth and ninth segments (**valvifers**) developed as skeletal plates
and bearing three elongated processes (**first, second** and **third valvulae**).
The anterior (first) valvulae are the endite lobes (**gonopophyses**) of the
eighth abdominal appendages, the second valvulae are the gonophyses of
the ninth appendages and the third valvulae are posterior extensions
(styli?) of the coxae of the ninth appendages. In certain Orthoptera with
only two pairs of valvulae it is the second pair that is missing; in other
orders with only two pairs, the third pair has disappeared.

The ovipositor is present in its fully developed form, with three pairs of
valvulae, in Phasmida, Grylloblatodea, Dictyoptera, Odonata and Corrodentia, though some members of each of these orders may have the
ovipositor reduced, vestigial or absent entirely. The Dermaptera have only
four valvulae, when they are present at all, with the third pair missing.
A similar situation is present in the Thysanoptera, while the Hemiptera
fuse the second valvulae to form a sheath for the functional first pair. In
the few Mallophaga with an ovipositor, only the first pair is present. The
Neuroptera have two pairs of valvulae, the third being absent. In the
Coleoptera the ovipositor is vestigial, with only the coxae of the ninth
segmental appendages present as an egg guide, though these residual
structures are sometimes used (*Dytiscus* and others) even to penetrate
hard plant tissue.

The Hymenoptera have the full set of six valvulae, but a great deal of
variation is found because these parts fuse in various ways. In stinging
Hymenoptera (Fig. 3.20D) the ovipositor entirely loses its egg-depositing
function and becomes a formidable weapon, with which are associated
glands producing toxic secretions. In these insects the eggs are dropped
directly from the oviduct, located at the base of the sting.

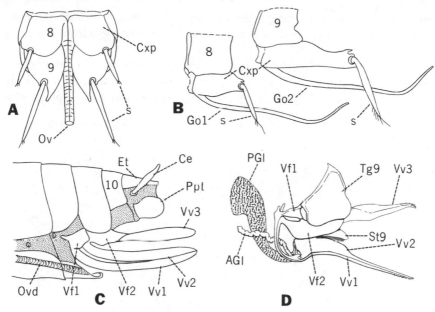

Figure 3.20. Structure of the ovipositor in insects. (A) Ventral view of eighth and ninth abdominal segments of *Thermobia* (Thysanura); (B) lateral view of right gonopods and supporting tergal plates of *Machilis* (Thysanura); (C) diagrammatic lateral view of a hypothetical insect to illustrate the relationship of the parts of the ovipositor in pterygote insects; (D) sting of a worker honeybee, *Apis mellifera* (Hymenoptera). *AGl,* alkaline gland; *Ce,* cercus; *Cxp,* coxopodite; *Et,* epiproct, eleventh abdominal tergum; *Gol, Go2,* first and second gonopods; *Ov,* ovipositor; *Ovd,* oviduct; *PGl,* reservoir of poison gland; *Ppt,* paraproct, ventro-lateral elements of the eleventh abdominal segment; *s,* stylus; *St9,* ninth abdominal sternite; *Tg9,* ninth abdominal tergite; *Vf1, Vf2,* first and second valvifers; *Vv1, Vv2, Vv3,* first, second and third valvulae; *8, 9, 10,* eighth, ninth and tenth abdominal segments. (A–C from Snodgrass, 1933, and D from Snodgrass, 1910, by permission of Smithsonian Institution)

The second method of depositing eggs, by means of an elongated, eversible abdomen, is found in the suborder Tubulifera of the order Thysanoptera, in most Mecoptera, in some Trichoptera and some Lepidoptera, in many Diptera and in a few Coleoptera.

In general the presence and form of the ovipositor are correlated with the protection needed for the immature insect which will emerge from the egg and the food it will need. Certain Orthoptera deposit eggs underground using ovipositors especially constructed for digging, and thus

provide overwinter protection to the eggs. The ovipositors of parasitic
Hymenoptera are modified to facilitate deposing the egg within the body
of the host.

It is possible that the insects without an ovipositor have lost that structure for reasons in some way related to a lack of need. Mayflies (Ephemerida) generally drop their eggs on the water, and Lepidoptera glue

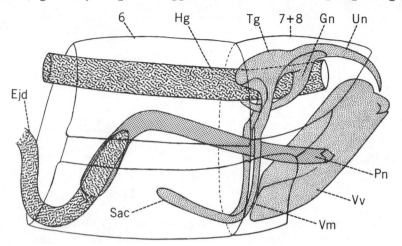

Figure 3.21. Male genitalia of *Mechanitis lycidice,* a butterfly
(Lepidoptera), drawn in relation to abdominal skeleton. *Ejd,* ejaculatory duct; *Gn,* gnathos; *Hg,* hindgut; *Pn,* penis; *Sac,* saccus;
Tg, tegumen (tergum of ninth segment); *Un,* uncus; *Vm,* vinculum
(coxosternal element of ninth segment); *Vv,* valve (stylus of ninth
segment); *6,* sixth abdominal segment; *7+8,* seventh and eight abdominal segments combined. (Drawn from specimens in Carnegie
Museum)

them to plants. In some orders, both primitive and advanced, gravid
females just drop eggs haphazardly behind them.

The external genitalia of male insects include two groups of structures,
the **phallus** and the **periphallic** organs. The phallus is the intromittent
organ and is the functional opening of the reproductive system. Segmental appendages do not contribute to its structure. A phallus is lacking
in Collembola and Plecoptera but is present in all other insects, though it
may be rudimentary.

The periphallic organs, used for grasping the female abdomen or genitalic structures during copulation, are not present in Collembola, Protura,
Aptera, Plecoptera, Embioptera, Orthoptera, Dermaptera, Phasmida,

Dictyoptera, Isoptera, Mallophaga, Anoplura, Strepsiptera and most Coleoptera. They are present in Thysanura, Ephemerida, Odonata, Grylloblattodea, Hemiptera, Thysanoptera, Neuroptera, Mecoptera, Trichoptera, Lepidoptera, Diptera, Siphonaptera and Hymenoptera. From this it is evident that the presence or absence of periphallic structures has little to do with ordinal phylogenetic lines.

In the Thysanura the periphallic structures are sufficiently generalized that their origins as appendages are easy to establish. They consist of the coxae of the appendages of the eighth and ninth abdominal segments, each with an exite lobe (stylus) and an endite lobe (**gonopophysis**). The phallus is on the ninth segment.

Other orders with periphallic claspers (**harpes, harpagones, valves,** etc.) form them from the coxae and exite styli of the appendages of at least the ninth segment. In some Hemiptera the appendages of both the eighth and tenth segments also contribute to the periphallic organs. In Trichoptera and Lepidoptera the rudiments of the appendages of the tenth segment contribute the **socii** to the complex of external genitalia formed mainly from the appendages of the ninth segment. Typical male genitalia as found in Lepidoptera are illustrated in Figure 3.21.

A noteworthy exception to the general pattern is found in Odonata, in which the intromittent organ and periphallic structures occur secondarily on the third abdominal segment and the periphallic structure, at least, is of appendicular origin. The genital duct opens on the ninth segment.

ARACHNOID ABDOMINAL APPENDAGES

Abdominal appendages are represented on scorpions by the **genital operculum** on the second abdominal segment, by the **pectines** on the third, while the ventral plates of at least the next four abdominal segments include the coxopodites of appendages otherwise regressed during ontogeny. The spinnerets of spiders are also developed from abdominal appendages.

The genital operculum (Fig. 3.22A) is the lid covering the opening of the reproductive system and consists of two plates thought to be the right and left coxopodites. These plates may touch on the ventral midline and swing open on lateral hinges, or they may be fused along the midline and swing open as a unit on an anterior hinge. In either case, the arrangement of the muscles opening and shutting the operculum suggests that its origin is appendicular rather than skeletal. The genital opening frequently is covered by an operculum in other arachnoid groups and while its homology with coxopodites may be more obscure, it doubtless is the same structure of the same origin in all the orders.

Organs typical of the scorpions and not found in any other arachnoid, the pectines (Fig. 3.22A), are a pair of highly modified appendages located on the segment next behind the genital opening. They articulate with a ventral plate probably representing the fused coxopodites, while the free parts of the organ are the telopodite (Millot and Vachon, 1949a).

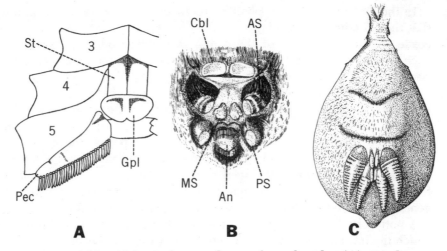

A   **B**   **C**

Figure 3.22. Abdominal appendages of arachnoids. (A) *Pandinus* species (Scorpionida), ventral surface of anterior abdomen and posterior cephalothorax; (B) *Stegodyphus lineatus* (Araneida), ventral surface of the posterior extremity of abdomen; (C) *Liphistius malayanus,* a primitive spider (Araneida), ventral surface of abdomen showing the generalized arrangement of the four pairs of spinnerets. *An,* anus; *AS,* anterior spinneret; *Cbl,* cibellum (genital plates); *Gpl,* genital plate; *MS,* median spinneret; *Pec,* pectine; *PS,* posterior spinneret; *St,* sternite; *3, 4, 5,* coxae of third, fourth and fifth legs. (A drawn from specimen in Carnegie Museum; B and C from Millot, 1949e, by arrangement with Masson et Cie)

Each telopodite consists of three segments, frequently rod-like, each bearing on their posterio-ventral aspects a series of rounded medial elements—fused into a single piece in some species—from which project the "teeth" of the comb. The pectines are moved by muscles inserted on the proximal margin of the first segment of the telopodite and originating in the ventral body wall. A system of longitudinal muscles within the telopodite enables each free section to move while transverse muscles move the articulated "teeth."

The pectines are richly innervated. The tip of each "tooth" has on its ventral aspect a flattened oval plate densely strewn with receptors and sensory cells. Monocellular sensory organs lying in cuticular pits have been described. The pectines have been interpreted—"without much evidence," as Millot and Vachon put it—as being organs of equilibrium, tactile or chemoreceptive organs, fans to direct air currents to the spiracles, and as "organes de volupté." In brief, the function of these odd structures is entirely unknown despite the application of both scholarly investigation and poetic imagination.

Nothing is more characteristic of spiders than their webs; nothing is more necessary to their web spinning than the spinnerets (Fig. 3.22B, C). The spinnerets are modified appendages of the fourth and fifth abdominal segments and present some interesting problems in homology. They are borne on ventral sclerites probably derived from the fused coxopodites in conformity with the trend previously observed in connection with the operculum and pectines.' The maximum number of spinnerets (Fig. 3.22C) is found in the primitive Far Eastern suborder Liphistiomorpha, in which four pairs, an inner and an outer on each segment, are present. The outer pairs in primitive spiders may be three-segmented, but the inner pairs are never segmented. The membranous tips of the spinnerets bear numerous tiny, more or less conical projections through which ducts from the silk glands open. The inner pairs of spinnerets are thought to be endite lobes, the outer pairs modified telopodites. There may be homology here with the abdominal vesicles of primitive insects.

Reduction from the primitive number occurs and characterizes various spider groups. Most living spiders have only three pairs (Fig. 3.20C), the median spinnerets of the fourth abdominal segment being missing. Some spiders retain only the two pairs of the fifth segment, while in a few others only the outer pair of either the fourth or fifth segment is preserved. The considerable variation in form and size of the spinnerets is of value in spider taxonomy.

The Wings

From Icarus to present day
  Man has wanted wings;
Yet the dragonfly can say
  "I've always had the things."
  J. W. F.

All winged arthropods are insects, though not all insects have wings. Flight—an obvious advantage to its possessor—is another of the many adaptations which help explain why insects are today a dominant class of animals in both numbers and variety. Unlike birds and bats, the only other animals that have developed sustained flight, insects do not utilize modified appendages for the purpose. The insect wing is a greatly expanded, evaginated and flattened area of the body wall. It consists of two closely united but distinct layers of integument strengthened by a system of more heavily sclerotized tubes, the **veins**.

Insect flight probably evolved as an improvement on gliding. The gliding apparatus of the ancient insects is thought to have been formed by lateral expansions of the thoracic terga (**paranota**). Although no insect, living or fossil, is known to have paranota that can be clearly interpreted as precursory to wings, paranota are present in certain living insects— some Thysanura, some Hemiptera, some mantids. In other insects there sometimes are structures—for example, the **patagia** (lateral expansions of the prothoracic nota) of Lepidoptera—which suggest the way that paranota might have become wings.

The fossil record provides no example of the insect wing in the making. Where wings are present at all, there are already two fully developed pairs, respectively on the metathorax and mesothorax. It may be significant, however, that several fossil orders had well-developed paranota on the prothoracic segment in addition to the wings on the other two thoracic segment. It is even possible that three pairs of wings were present to

112

begin with, each of the thoracic segments developing in the same way. *Lemmatophora typica* from the lower Permian of Kansas (Fig. 4.1A) had prothoracic structures which apparently were paranota and which certainly look like little wings complete with a venational system. But if the first thoracic segment ever had wings, it was only a passing experiment. Functional wings on the mesothorax and metathorax, along with some reduction of the prothorax, was already an established plan by the Devo-

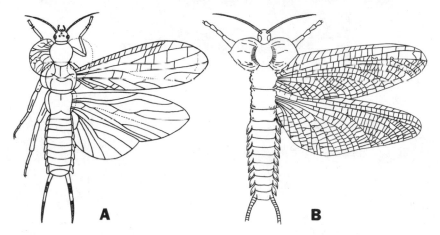

Figure 4.1. Fossil insects. (A) *Lemmatophora typica* Sellards (Plecoptera), Lower Permian of Kansas; (B) *Lithomantis carbonaria* Woodward (Eupaleodictyoptera), Upper Carboniferous of Scotland. (From Jeannel, 1949, by arrangement with Masson et Cie: A after Martynov, B after Handlirsch)

nian, the geologic period in which have been found the earliest undoubted insect fossils.

Just how a rigid expansion of the tergum came to be an articulated wing remains a mystery. Snodgrass (1935) speculated that the first step might have been development of enough flexibility of the notum so that the simple thoracic musculature could cause the paranota to flap sufficiently to enhance or to direct a glide.

STRUCTURE

Whatever the evolutional steps involved in reaching that state, the wings are now attached to the body wall by flexible membranes continuous with the integument. An extension of the body wall, the wing

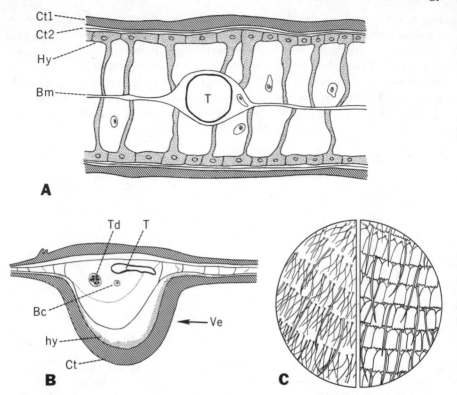

Figure 4.2. (A) Cross section through part of a pupal wing; (B) cross section through part of the wing of an adult moth; (C) two areas on the wing of a butterfly, *Hyalyris norella,* as seen with 80× magnification: the right half shows normally developed scales and hairs, the left half is from a transparent area and shows the scales reduced to forked hairs. *Bc,* blood cell; *Bm,* basement membrane; *Ct,* cuticle; *Ct1,* pupal cuticle; *Ct2,* developing adult cuticle; *Hy,* functional hypodermis; *hy,* degenerate, nonfunctional hypodermis; *T,* trachea; *Td,* degenerate pupal trachea (Semper's rib); *Ve,* wing vein. (A and B from Imms, 1957, by arrangement with Methuen & Co.; C drawn from specimen in Carnegie Museum)

consists (Fig. 4.2A, B) of two layers of integument with their basement membranes pressed together. The external surfaces are cuticular layers secreted by hypodermis. At the end of the last immature instar the wings are fully developed but quite small. After ecdysis the adult insect expands these miniature wings to full size by blood pressure; then the cuticle hardens. During and immediately after the expanding and hardening process, the hypodermal layer is disrupted and the cells soon atrophy. Few hypodermal cells are present in the functional wing (Fig. 4.2B) except those specialized in connection with sensation or secretion.

MICROMORPHOLOGY

The cuticular surfaces bear numerous fixed hairs (microtrichia) and setae, most of which are clothing in function, though some may be associated with neural receptors or with secretory cells. Fixed hairs are scattered over the entire surface of most membranous wings, with the setae confined to rows placed over principal veins. In such wings a row of setae present on the membrane, rather than over a vein, marks the position of a vein lost in phylogeny. In contrast, the entire wing surface in Trichoptera and Lepidoptera is covered by a dense pattern of setae, many of which may be flattened (**scales**) and arranged in overlapping rows like shingles (Fig. 4.2C). Similar scales are found also in mosquitoes, but are mainly restricted to the veins. In many insects elongated clothing setae are placed along the wing margins forming a dense fringe.

Sensory receptors on wings have not been extensively studied, but it has been found that some setae, both hair-like and scales, on the wings of Lepidoptera are tactile. Alar tangoreceptors may be present in other orders, and the possibility that still other sensory functions may be associated with alar setae has not been eliminated. The often extensive nerve supply in the wing needs further investigation.

Secretory cells, present on the wings of many male butterflies, produce detectable odors thought to be attractive to the female. These cells of the hypodermal layer are overlaid with setae (**androconial scales**) differing in size and shape from adjacent clothing scales. They may be arranged in dense raised patches ("brand") or in clusters of elongated hairs ("pencils"), or they may be scattered sparsely over a portion of the wing.

The wing membrane generally has only a thin translucent cuticle, and the basement membranes are more or less fused into a single sheet (Fig. 4.2B). Along the veins the basement membranes separate from each other, leaving a tubular lumen around which the cuticle is heavier. The lumina of the principal longitudinal veins and their branches contain a functional tracheole bathed in circulating blood; sensory nerve branches traverse many veins. The veins are effectively diverticula of the hemocoel; thus the term *vein* is more appropriate than the once-fashionable *nerve*, since nerves are not present in all of these tubes. Blood circulating in them follows a directional plan which may be periodically reversible. Commonly the blood flows out into the wing along the anterior veins and returns to the thorax through the posterior veins. Muscular pulsating organs, in effect auxiliary hearts, have been observed in the wings of certain

Hemiptera and Diptera and may be of much wider occurrence. Sphingidae (Lepidoptera) have a highly developed mechanism in the thorax which ensures effective blood circulation in the wings. Frequently the blood leaving the wing is channeled directly to the head. The considerable length of the tracheoles bathed directly by blood in the veins probably enables an extensive gas exchange and adds internal respiration to the functions of the wings.

VENATION

Because the arrangement of veins is so diverse, yet is characteristically patterned in any given insect group, venation has been of the greatest use to systematic entomology and has been very widely studied. During the nineteenth century many different schemes were devised to designate the veins. Until the extensive studies of Comstock and Needham (1898–1899) all attempts to work out the homologies of the wing veins throughout all orders of insects, and thus to bring order to the chaos of natural diversity, had failed. By analysis of wing ontogeny and particularly of the tracheal contributions in the veins, Comstock and Needham successfully established the basic homologies and devised a convenient system of nomenclature applicable to all insect wings. Although some of the older, unscientific methods of denoting the veins still persist—as, for example, the method of numbering those present in sequence from either the anterior or the posterior, regardless of homology—the Comstock-Needham system, with minor modifications based on more recent research, is almost universally used.

The so-called hypothetically primitive plan of wing venation (Fig. 4.3) is useful as a point of departure. It is a plan that includes all the principal elements, rather than a diagram of a true "ancestral" wing, and thus serves purposes of illustration rather than of phylogeny.

The principal longitudinal veins, in sequence from the anterior, are the **costa** (C), **subcosta** (Sc), **radius** (R), **medius** (M), **cubitus** (Cu) and the **anals** (A). The costa is unbranched. Except in the most primitive winged insects it lies along the front edge of the wing with no membranous area anterior of it. The subcosta may have two branches. Branches of the principal longitudinal veins are always indicated by subscript numerals; thus an anterior subcostal branch is Sc_1 and the posterior is Sc_2. The radial vein divides into R_1 and the **radial sector** (R_s), which in turn has four branches, R_2 to R_5. The medial vein divides into the **anterior** (MA) and **posterior** (MP) **branches,** each with sub-branches. Frequently either the anterior or the posterior medial branch is lost entirely and it is then customary to denote the existing branches and sub-branches simply as M_1 and so on, without indicating thereby whether it is the anterior or posterior branch that is present. The cubitus may divide into Cu_1 and Cu_2, the former with two branches, Cu_{1a} and Cu_{1b}. Comstock and Needham misidentified in some insect orders the lower cubital branch (Cu_2) as an anal vein. While the correct homologies are now recognized, it is customary to continue the original nomenclature. A com-

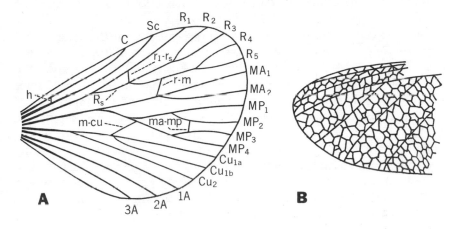

Figure 4.3. (A) A hypothetically primitive plan of wing venation, with nomenclature according to the Comstock-Needham system; (B) an archedictyonal wing. Abbreviations used on figure A are standard in entomology; longitudinal veins are abbreviated with capital initials, cross veins with small initials: C, costal veins: Cu_{1a}, Cu_{1b}, Cu_2, branches of cubital vein; h, humeral cross vein; MA_1, MA_2, branches of anterior median vein; MP_1, MP_2, MP_3, MP_4, branches of posterior median vein; m–cu, medio-cubital cross vein; ma–mp, anterio-posterior medial cross vein; R_1 to R_5, branches of radial vein; R_S, radial sector vein; r–m, radio-medial cross vein; r_1–r_S, sectoral cross vein; Sc, subcostal vein; $1A$, $2A$, $3A$, first, second and third anal veins.

plete cubital system is present in only a few insects and in such cases the full terminology must be used; generally only true Cu_1 is present and it then causes no difficulty to shorten the designations of Cu_{1a} and Cu_{1b} to Cu_1 and Cu_2. Posterior to the cubitus is a variable number of veins, the anals, usually separated from each other at the base; they are numbered, beginning with the anteriormost, $1A$, $2A$, and so on. Snodgrass renamed the anal veins "vannal veins," but this suggested change in nomenclature has nothing to recommend it and is rarely used.

Snodgrass pointed out the value of using the relationship between the veins and the alar sclerites to identify correctly the vein homologies in difficult cases. The costal vein proceeds from the **humeral sclerite** (Fig. 4.5A), which usually is small. The subcostal vein begins at the anterior arm of the **first axillary** (alar) **sclerite,** the radial from the anterior arm of the **second.** The medial and cubital veins begin at the **median plates** and the anal veins at the distal arm of the third axillary sclerite. It must be noted, however, that this method of identification becomes difficult or fails entirely where the full complement of alar sclerites is not present or when they are strongly modified.

The primitive wing probably had the areas between the longitudinal veins densely reticulated with an irregular network of veinlets. Such a reticulation was called the **archedictyon** (Fig. 4.3B) by Tillyard. It is typical of many of the fossil orders and is preserved in the wings of some of the more primitive of the living orders, reduced to a limited part of the wing. The archedictyal reticulation seems to have been supplanted gradually by a more economical and orderly system of **cross veins** placed more or less perpendicularly to the longitudinals. Numerous cross veins, and sometimes an archedictyon, are found in the Ephemerida, Odonata, Plecoptera, Embioptera, the orthopteriod orders except Dermaptera, and in Neuroptera and Mecoptera. The wings of these insects, when they are present, all give a reticulated appearance and are called "net-veined."

Cross veins are important to complete the circulatory pathways for the blood, so that it is not surprising to find them present in all but a few groups of insects. They are named according to the longitudinals to which they are connected and lower-case letters are used for their abbreviations (Fig. 4.3A); thus cross vein m–cu connects the medius and cubitus. When more than one is present between two longitudinals, the cross veins are numbered from the base of the wing outward using subscript numerals. Cross veins bearing the same designations in different wings are not necessarily homologous, but the nomenclature is convenient. Cross veins do not as a rule contain tracheoles or nerves.

The spaces between the veins (**cells**) are denoted by using the name of the vein forming the anterior boundary or by combining the abbreviations of the anterior and posterior bounding veins. Thus the space between the second and third medial branches can be designated either as "cell M_2" or as "M_2–M_3." The cells also may be designated by descriptive terms indicating position, such as "discal cell," "marginal cells."

For descriptive purposes the angles and margins of the wing are named as follows: the three angles are the **base, apex** and **anal angle** (also called **tornus**); the **humeral lobe** is generally more prominent on the hindwing, where it often serves to couple the wings; the front of the wing is the **costal margin;** the **outer** or **distal margin** runs from the apex to the anal angle and the posterior edge is the **anal** or **hind margin;** the central area of the wing is the **disc.**

A broad evolutional trend among insects is simplification of the venation, especially the strengthening of the leading edge and the reduction of the veins in the rest of the wing area to those sufficient to support the membrane efficiently without impairing blood circulation (see Fig. 13. 7C, E). Cross veins are reduced in number, generally to only one between each pair of longitudinal veins or the main dichotomies. Longitudinal veins are reduced either by outright loss or by the coalescence of adjacent veins and branches.

In certain insects a prominent sclerotized patch (**stigma**) lies at or near the costal margin toward the apex of the wing. The stigma is generally considered in connection with venation, but it is not a universal feature among insects. Even among those insects having it, it apparently is not homologous throughout. The Odonata have a stigma placed between the costal vein and the anterior branch of the radial vein on each wing. In Zoraptera and some Hymenoptera the stigma is similarly placed but is present only on the forewing. In other Hymenoptera the stigma lies between the subcostal vein and the anterior radial branch. In the Corrodentia it lies between two branches of the radial vein.

WING LINKAGE

For effective flight, the wings must be well coordinated, to which end two kinds of structural adaptations contribute: direct wing coupling and modification of the thoracic skeleton. The more obvious of these are the many kinds of devices for coupling the two wings (Fig. 4.4) on one side, so that they function as a unit. The simplest method is when the forewing overlaps the costal part of the hindwing, and in butterflies (Fig. 4.4A) there is nothing more to it. But in other insects with overlapped wings, the humeral lobe of the hindwing may interlock with a **jugal lobe** of the forewing, closely coupling the two wings in both the up and down strokes of flight (4.4B). More complex interlocking occurs in many modifications and variations. The hindwing may have a row of hook-shaped setae fitting into a fold on the anal margin of the forewing (Fig. 4.4C, D), or in other insects such hooks may engage similar hooks projecting from the hindwing, or hooks on each wing may engage the other wing (Fig. 4.4E). A long bristle-like seta or group of setae (**frenulum**) from the hindwing may be clamped to the under side of the forewing by special setae there (Fig. 4.4F).

None of these devices for coupling the wings would be sufficient alone to ensure unity of wing action were the thoracic skeleton not modified

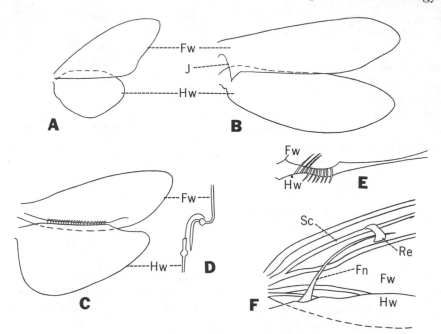

Figure 4.4. Wing linkage mechanisms. (A) Overlapping wings of butterfly (Lepidoptera); (B) jugum of forewing of *Rhyacophila* species (Trichoptera); (C) setal hooks of hindwing engaging a fold on the underside of the forewing of *Macronema* species (Trichoptera); (D) sectional detail of same, showing the upper edge of the hindwing, a setal hook and the lower edge of the forewing; (E) lower margin of forewing and upper margin of hindwing of *Panorpa nuptialis* (Mecoptera), showing setae of each wing engaged with other wing; (F) detail of base of wing of *Erynnis ello*, a sphinx moth (Lepidoptera). *Fn*, frenulum; *Fw*, forewing; *Hw*, hindwing; *J*, jugum; *Re*, retinaculum; *Sc*, subcostal vein. (Drawn from specimens in Carnegie Museum)

to prevent the fore- and hindwings from working in opposite directions. Such modification is especially evident in the orders Hymenoptera and Lepidoptera, where meso- and metathoracic tergal plates become fused, as do pleural elements, with the result that the major flight muscles operate the wings on one side in unison. Regardless of wing coupling apparatus, insects with poor fusion of meso- and metathoracic skeletal elements have weak flight; most such insects resort to a way of life not dependent upon aerial efficiency for success. Among these are the Isoptera and Neuroptera, in which thoracic fusion is incomplete and flight is quite awkward.

The Odonata present an excellent example of the importance of the skeleton in effective flight. Although the fore- and hindwings are uncoupled and independent, the Odonata have extraordinary skill in flight, being able to hover and to veer in any direction. In these insects the forewings swing up while the hindwings beat down, and vice versa—in fact, the Odonata are equipped with two "engines" instead of only one. Coordination is achieved by the complete fusion of the meso- and metathoracic terga into one plate. The primary flight muscles rock the tergal plate in a forward-backward seesaw motion and apparently the direction of flight is controlled by the angle of the wing planes.

The arrangement of the veins is correlated with flight. When the two wings on a side become a functional unit, the sole leading edge is then at the costal margin of the forewing, while the trailing edge is the anal area of the hindwing. Thus the anterior part of the forewing is generally strengthened by well-developed longitudinal veins placed close together, and the hindwing has fewer cross veins, thus allowing greater flexibility (see Fig. 13.6E). Where, as in Odonata, the wings work separately, or where only one pair is used in flight as in Coleoptera or Diptera, the venation is modified accordingly. Each wing of the Odonata has both a leading and a trailing edge, as is clear from the arrangement of the veins (see Fig. 13.2B, C). The beetle hindwing has a well-supported costal margin, providing it with an effective leading edge.

WING ARTICULATION

The wings are joined to the thorax by flexible membranous articulations, the integument of the upper surfaces being continuous with the tergites and that of the under surfaces with the pleural skeleton. Within these two membranous hinges, the upper and the lower, lie small but important sclerites, the **alar** (Fig. 4.5A) and the **subalar sclerites**, respectively. These sclerites serve to establish lines of folding when the wings flex, to provide attachment for certain specialized muscles and to augment the flight action.

The alar sclerites, located in the dorsal connective membrane, while variable, generally consist of seven elements. The **tegula**, a small scale-like sclerite at the extreme base of the costa, is rarely present on the hindwing. The **humeral plate** often intervenes between the tegula and the base of the costal vein; it is especially large and well developed in Odonata. The **first axillary sclerite** articulates with the **anterior notal process** of the dorsal skeleton and with the **second axillary sclerite** distally. The subcostal vein begins at the tip of the anterior arm of the first axillary sclerite. The second axillary sclerite rests on the alar process of the pleuron and articulates with the first axillary sclerite proximad, with the two **medial plates**

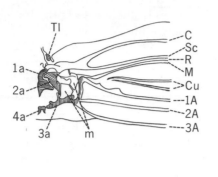

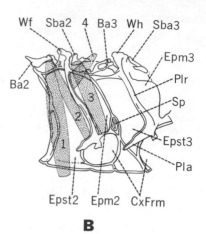

A   **B**

Figure 4.5.   Structures associated with flight in the grasshopper *Dissoteira*
(Orthoptera). (A) Base of forewing, dorsal view; (B) meso- and metathoracic pleura, seen from within. *Ba2, Ba3,* basalar sclerites of meso- and
metathoracic pleura; *C,* costal vein; *Cu,* first and second cubital veins;
CxFrm, coxal foramen; *Epm2, Epm3,* epimera of meso- and metathoracic
pleura; *Epst2, Epst3,* episterna of meso- and metathoracic pleura; *M,* median
vein; *m,* median plates; *Pla, Plr,* pleural arm and pleural ridge of apodemes;
R, radial vein; *Sba2, Sba3,* meso- and metathoracic subalar sclerites; *Sc,* subcostal vein; *Tl,* tegulum; *Wf,* mesothoracic wing process; *Wh,*
metathoracic wing process; *1,* first pronator-extensor muscle of forewing, originating (ventral) on sternum, inserted on first basalar sclerite; *2,* second pronator-extensor muscle of forewing, originating on coxal ring, inserted on first
basalar sclerite; *3,* depressor-extensor of forewing, originating on coxal ring,
inserted on subalar sclerite; *4,* flexor of forewing, originating on ridge of
pleural apodeme, inserted on third axillary sclerite (Fig. A); *1A, 2A, 3A,*
first, second and third anal veins; *1a, 2a, 3a, 4a,* first to fourth axillary sclerites. (Redrawn from Snodgrass, 1929, by permission of Smithsonian Institution)

distad and with the **third axillary sclerite** posteriorad. The radial vein begins at the anterior arm of the second axillary sclerite and the median and
cubital veins arise from the median plates. The third axillary sclerite,
articulating with the posterior notal process and with the second axillary
sclerite, has the wing flexor muscle inserted on it and the anal veins begin
at its distal arm.

The subalar sclerites lie in the ventral connective membrane, two on
the anterior side and one on the posterior side of the episternal wing
process of the pleuron.

MUSCULATURE

The primary muscles of flight are those which existed in the thorax before the development of functional wings and which probably are characteristic of the basic metamere. These "indirect" muscles serve to lever the wings up and down by moving the tergum, the pleurites serving as the fulcrum. The longitudinal muscles, attached to the anterior and posterior ends of the meso-metathoracic notal system, bow the tergites upward when they contract, thus sending the wing tips downward. Vertical muscles pull the tergal and sternal plates together, depressing the thorax and lifting the wing tips upward.

But simple up and down movement is not sufficient for flight. A set of "direct" muscles is inserted on the subalar sclerites and arises from the ventral part of the pleuron (Fig. 4.5B). The **first anterior extensor muscle** runs from the sternal margin to the anterior subalar (**basalar**) sclerites; the **second anterior extensor muscle** connects the anterior subalar sclerites with the base of the coxa, thus runs diagonally; the **posterior extensor muscle** runs from the coxal rim to the posterior subalar sclerite. In flight, the action of these muscles both imparts a "kick" to the wing strokes and gives a slightly rotary motion. A fourth "direct" muscle is a flexor inserted on the third axillary sclerite and originating on the pleural ridge; it is used in swinging the wing back over the abdomen into the resting position.

VARIATIONS IN THE WINGS

The primitive condition was four net-veined wings of equal size and the fore- and hindwings not being linked or coupled. The numerous phylogenetic lines leading to contemporary insects exhibited as many kinds of wing modification, among which a few major types may be mentioned.

Simple aerodynamic improvement involving wing linkage generally also alters the shape of the wings, leading to a pair of somewhat triangular structures on each side, with the forewings larger than the hindwings. One of the earliest versions of this alteration in shape is seen in the Ephemerida (see Fig. 13.2A). Similar alteration has occurred independently in many orders, including Lepidoptera and Hymenoptera, and commonly is accompanied by a reduction of venation. Among the insects with superior aerial skill, only the Odonata have preserved the primitive elongate-rounded wing shape (see Fig. 13.2B).

Other lines of development lead to emphasis on one or the other pair of wings in flight, the unused pair becoming markedly modified or even atrophied. Where the hindwings become the principal flight structures, the forewings often become heavily sclerotized and serve as protective covers for the hindwings and body at rest. Many of the orthopteroid orders have the wings modified in this way. In the grasshopper the forewings (see Fig. 13.4B, C, D), called the **tegmina,** are narrow, long and leathery, while the membranous hindwings are greatly enlarged. The venation of the tegmina is essentially similar to that of the hindwing, but lacks the strongly enlarged **jugal** (anal) **area.** When the forewings are of reduced importance in flight, they are apparently available for unusual modification, as in some orthopteroids. In certain Phasmida retaining wings, the tegmina may be leaf-like, contributing to the general illusion that the insect is part of the plant on which it rests. In the Dermaptera the tegmina are strongly reduced and very hard, serving only as a protective covering for the fan-like hindwings at rest.

In Coleoptera the forewings (**elytra**) are usually very heavily sclerotized, shaped to cover the top and part of the sides of the body when not in flight. Most beetles hold the elytra more or less horizontally when flying, and flight is typically clumsy. The elytra do not lose the functional hypodermal layers in the adult, the upper and lower layers being separated and supported by apodeme-like columns of cuticle. The lumen is richly supplied with blood and contains a well-developed system of tracheoles. The functions of the many glandular and receptor cells in the hypodermis have not been studied. In some beetles flight muscles are absent, although the hindwings are developed in an apparently normal fashion. In others the elytra are fused along the dorsal midline, making flight impossible. In Staphylinidae and related families, the elytra are shortened, covering only the anterior part of the abdomen. In the order Strepsiptera the reduced, heavily sclerotized forewing is a vestigial, poorly formed elytron (see Fig. 13.5G).

In the Heteroptera, one of the suborders of Hemiptera, only the basal part of the forewing (**hemelytron**) is sclerotized, the distal part remaining membranous. When the insect rests, the wings are folded back over the abdomen, the forewings overlapping and together covering the hindwings. The considerable variation in the form of the hemelytra is of value in identification. The membranous part may or may not contain veins, or it may be atrophied so that only the sclerotized basal part remains; in one family the entire hemelytron is membranous.

Many orders include some species in which one or both pairs of wings are short and abbreviated (**brachypterous**). The tiny but perfectly formed wings of some mantids and phasmids can only be decorative. The wings of Thysanoptera are peculiarly reduced, each consisting of a flattened rod heavily fringed with long setae (see Fig. 13.5E); many thrips are wing-less.

The Diptera use only the forewings in flight, the hindwings being re-duced to tiny articulating knobs (**halteres**) which apparently have im-portant functions. Since they are seen to vibrate during flight, an obvious function is balance, although just how they work in this respect is not clear. However, when they are removed, flight and even ambulation are impaired. The halteres receive the largest nerve supply in the thorax and have a well-developed system of chordotonal receptors with unknown function. Among wingless Diptera, *Braula*, a parasite in beehives, has no halteres, while Nycteribiidae, external parasites on bats, preserve per-fectly formed halteres.

The many kinds of wing reduction found in various insects generally are intermediate steps leading to forms completely without wings. Among the orthopteroid orders, some Orthoptera, many Phasmida, Dictyoptera and Dermaptera and all Grylloblattids are wingless. Social insects—ants, among the Hymenoptera, and the Isoptera, Zoraptera and Embioptera—frequently are wingless for other reasons. In these groups the adult sexual forms are winged, but after a mating flight and migration to a new colony site, the wings are lost. The lack of wings in termite worker and soldier castes is an embryologic phenomenon, since in these castes terminal de-velopment is suppressed and they never acquire wings and certain other adult structures.

Wingless species are found in nearly every order. Sometimes, as in the Psychidae (Lepidoptera), the Strepsiptera or the Hippoboscidae (Dip-tera), the males are winged, but the females are wingless, being in fact neotenic larvae. True adult winglessness is typical of parasitic groups such as *Braula* (Diptera) or the bedbug *Cimex* (Hemiptera) and all members of Anoplura, Mallophaga, and Siphonaptera. None of these in-sects has any need to fly. Their winglessness is secondarily acquired and they are descended from winged ancestors. Adult winglessness is also found in a few nonparasitic groups such as the Grylloblattodea.

FLIGHT

The upstroke of the wing results when the vertical ("indirect") thoracic muscles pull the notal elements downward. At the same time, the wing moves slightly rearward, so that the wing apex is somewhat behind the base at the top of the stroke. This is caused partly by the action of the "direct" muscles and partly by air pressure on the wing surface, the angle of which automatically alters according to whether pressure is applied above or below. On the downstroke the wing reaches forward as well as down, the motion being brought about by the action of the longitudinal ("indirect") thoracic muscles, which spring the flexible notum upward, enhanced by the "direct" muscles. The stationary insect thus describes a figure eight with its wing tips, while the wing tips of the insect in flight

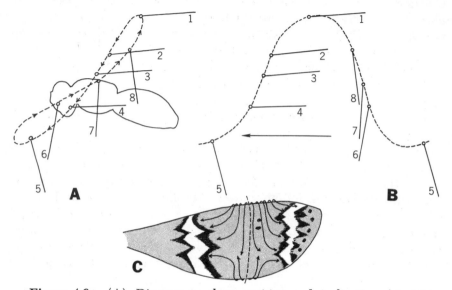

Figure 4.6. (A) Diagram to show position and inclination (straight lines) of the wing at eight successive instants during the stroke of flight, as recorded by high speed photography (the insect stationary); (B) same diagram projected as in flight (in direction of solid arrow); (C) course of spread of the influence determining the symmetrical wing pattern of *Ephestia* (Lepidoptera) imposed over the normal pattern resulting. (A redrawn (after Magnan) from Chadwick, *in* Roeder, 1953, by permission of John Wiley and Sons; C redrawn (after Kühn) from Wigglesworth, 1947, by permission of Methuen & Co.)

describe a series of steep curves (Fig. 4.6). Variations in the amplitude and angle of the stroke apparently account for changes in speed, for hovering and even for backward flight. The course must be steered by means of differential force applied by the wings on one side or the other, since the insect has no rudder.

Aerodynamic theory does not fully account for insect flight and its variations. It has been said that engineers discovered that it is impossible for the bumblebee to fly, but that the bee, knowing nothing of the theory, flies anyhow.

Among interesting statistics on flight, measurements of the rate of wing beat and separately measured flight speeds are summarized in Table 4.1, from which it may be seen that there is little relationship between them. Apparently the fly *Tabanus* must beat its wings five times as fast as the dragonfly *Aeshna* to attain the same speed. Similarly *Pieris*, the cabbage butterfly, can fly at about five miles an hour with far less effort than is expended by the housefly *Musca*. As to distance, the annual fall migration of the monarch butterfly carries clouds of them for hundreds of miles, while a great variety of insects have been captured when they settled on ships far out to sea. During World War II one of us, aboard a ship cruising in the China Sea approximately 150 miles from the Philippine Islands, watched a bird-wing butterfly (*Troides*) pass majestically by at masthead level. A cabbage butterfly (*Pieris rapae* (Linné)) in the Car-

Table 4.1 Rapidity of wing beat compared with flight speed in various insects [a]

Insect Genus (Order)	Wing Beats per second	Flight Speed, miles per hour
Musca (Diptera)	190–330	4.5
Apis (Hymenoptera)	180–250	5.6–8.3
Bombus (Hymenoptera)	130–240	6.7–7.8
Tabanus (Diptera)	96	9–31.3
Macroglossa (Lepidoptera)	72–85	11.2
Melolontha (Coleoptera)	46	4.9–5.7
Aeshna (Odonata)	20	9–22.4
Pieris (Lepidoptera)	9–12	4–5.1

[a] Data from various sources.

negie Museum collection was taken on shipboard by Rev. A. C. Good 75 miles off the coast of Liberia, West Africa; the nearest habitat of the species is North Africa. Anyone who has watched a hawkmoth hover before a flower while feeding or tried to net a dragonfly on the wing can attest to the maneuverability of those insects.

DEVELOPMENT

The wing first appears as a thickening of the hypodermal cells at the tergal margins of the meso- and metathorax. This first appearance is generally made during an early larval instar but may occur on the egg-enclosed embryo. The initial hypodermal thickening becomes a bulge and through successive instars gradually enlarges and flattens, assuming the wing-like shape. As this **wing pad** grows, it becomes spongy through elongation of the hypodermal cells, especially at their proximal ends where they become separated columns resting on basement membranes (Fig. 4.2A). The space between the layers is continuous with the hemocoel and is filled with blood. Near the completion of development the basement membranes of the two layers come to lie together, eventually to coalesce into a single median membrane, leaving the ramified pattern of veins. Tracheoles grow into the veins, as do neurons. Whether the tracheoles and neurons establish by their pattern the ramifications of the venation, or whether the reverse occurs, is debatable. Sometimes the tubular veins form around the pathways occupied by the tracheoles; Comstock and Needham thought this to be the basic procedure. But sometimes the veins form first, with the tracheoles and neurons then growing into them as if they were following lines of least resistance.

Two groups of tracheoles grow into each wing, an anterior **costo-radial** set and a posterior **cubito-anal** set. Both groups apparently arise as branches of the **longitudinal spiracular tracheal trunk** (but of the **dorsal trunk** in Odonata) and in close association with branches serving the middle and hindlegs. The nerve fibers found in the veins apparently are part of the peripheral system and probably they lead to the second and third thoracic ganglia, though this question has not been sufficiently investigated.

At the time of final ecdysis the wings are fully developed except for their size. The cuticle is laid down by the hypodermis and the wing is expanded to adult size by blood pressure in a comparatively short time. The wing and body cuticle then hardens. The hypodermis, having fulfilled its function and already disrupted during the expansion process, regresses.

The foregoing is necessarily a generalized account. The details of wing formation differ considerably among various insects. In general, two main types of growth have been observed. On hemimetabolous insects, such as orthopteroids, the wings develop externally and are easily seen during immature instars. From the outset they are quite obviously evaginations from the tergal margins. The rate of growth is more or less regular until the last immature instar, when accelerated growth leads to wings nearly as large as those of the adult.

Among holometabolous insects, such as Lepidoptera, the wing pads *in*vaginate at first, developing inside the integumental hypodermis, so that they are not externally visible on the immature form. Although the wing buds can be located on the egg-enclosed embryo and definitive wing pads generally can be found in the first instar larva, growth is very slow during the greater part of larval life. At the formation of the final larval instar (**prepupa**) there is a marked acceleration in the growth of all adult structures, including the wings. At this time a *temporary* tracheation is laid down in the wing buds, but its pattern has little in common with the later pattern of adult tracheation and it soon regresses. At ecdysis to pupation, the wings are everted to become external relative to the integumental hypodermis. A new group of tracheoles grows into the wing coincidentally with the formation of the venational pattern. The adult wing will contain lengths of these delicate, nonfunctional larval tracheoles in addition to the usual contents. The major part of wing development occurs during the pupal instar. At ecdysis to the adult, the wings are fully formed in miniature and it remains only to expand them to adult size.

A great deal of importance has been placed upon what seems to be two distinct and fundamentally different kinds of wing growth—*external* or *internal* wing pads, *evaginated* or *invaginated* growth. The pterygote insects have been divided into two series according to which procedure, external hemimetabolous or internal holometabolous development, is followed in an order. It is now apparent that this is an oversimplified view resulting from a misinterpretation of phylogeny and misinterpretation of embryogeny. This aspect is discussed further in Chapter Eight.

There are many steps and gradations between internal and external wing development. Certain hemimetabolous insects modify the process by first forming little depressions in the integument, into which the wings are evaginated, to become obviously external only at a later instar. A further step is found where the depressions beneath the developing wing are quite deep, almost sac-like, with only a small opening at the surface. Some of the holometabolous insects have an identical sac-like depression in which the wing develops (e.g., Coleoptera), to be freed finally at pupation. The series is a gradual one when all possibilities are considered and the distinction between internal and external development loses much of its force. Hinton (1948) brought forward evidence that holometabolism must have evolved polyphyletically. Grouping all holometabolous insects together results in associating some unrelated orders.

PATTERN AND COLOR

The arrangement of lines and spots of pigment on the wings is a prominent, often beautiful, sometimes grotesque feature of insects and is of the greatest interest to taxonomists. Nearly every species has its characteristic integumental pattern and coloring by which it generally may be distinguished from otherwise nearly similar species. In winged insects the pigmental differences are likely to be particularly noticeable. The wings present a large surface on which color and pattern are easily seen and often more readily studied than the minute differences on other parts of the body. By their very nature as greatly expanded but originally morphologically tiny areas of the skeletal integument, the wings represent a magnification of the integument.

Because they are part of the integument, wing color and pattern are part of the color and pattern of the entire body surface. The same pigments, as well as the same basic processes for producing pigments and distributing them, are found in all the integument.

PIGMENTS

Pigments affecting the color of insects are located both in the hypodermis and in the otherwise translucent cuticle. Where cuticular pigment is opaque or heavily colored the pigment in the underlying cells is not seen. But where the cuticle is not or only lightly pigmented, the hypodermal color determines or affects the apparent color of the insect. The precise chemical nature of insect pigments, their natural synthesis and source and the mechanics involved in distribution through the integument are incompletely understood.

The most frequently encountered and most important of the integumental pigments are the **melanins.** Colors resulting from them range from light yellow to deep black, depending upon the degree of oxidation of the basic molecule. Melanin probably is a by-product of metabolism derived from the amino acid **tyrosine** through a series of steps involving ring closure, oxidation and polymerization and depending on the presence of the chromogenous enzyme **tyrosinase** for final formation. A series of less commonly encountered pigments, also probably derived as metabolic by-products, are the **pterines.** They produce color ranging from flat white through yellow and orange to bright red. **Carotenoid** pigments are apparently ingested by the insect directly (indirectly by predators) from the plants which synthesize them. They appear in the insect integument with only minor alterations from the composition found in the food plant and produce colors in the yellow–orange–red range. A wide variety of pigments other than the foregoing has been found in insect integument, none of them frequently and most of them only in combination with others; few are understood chemically. The vermilion of certain aphids (Hemiptera) is probably an **anthocyanin;** the white on the wings of *Melanargia* (Lepidoptera) appears to be a **flavone.** Certain green colors in butterfly wings are the result of a mixture of **mesobiliverdin,** a blue pigment, with yellow carotenoids.

Not all the colors seen on an insect are due to pigment. Iridescence is produced by optical interference with reflections from a series of translucent microlaminations of varying thickness or of varying refractive index. Diffraction colors may be produced by microscopic striae on the surface placed one to two micra apart. Microscopic translucent particles in or on the cuticle may' produce colors by scattering the light (structural white) or by a differential scattering of the shorter wavelengths (Tyndall blue). True pigment coloring sometimes is overlaid by structures affecting the reflection, refraction or diffraction of light so that each color source contributes to the color effect, which varies with the angle of view.

The striae, laminations or particles producing nonpigmental colors are located at or near the surface of the cuticle or of the cuticular setae or scales. It has been shown that the ontogenetic determination of cuticular structures, notably the structure of scales, is a separate process from, though occurring coincidentally with, the determination of color and pattern of cuticular pigment.

PATTERN DETERMINATION

Much of our knowledge in this area is based on the studies of Kühn and his associates on the moth *Ephestia*, elaborated by subsequent workers using other insects. Experimental embryology has shown that the cell mass formed by proliferation of the zygote reaches a point where it is possible to identify the ultimate contribution to final structure that each cell will make. Before this point is reached, interference with the normal growth process results only in a kind of reorganization of the cells such that the end result is little impaired. Once the point of **determination** is reached, each cell has a definite, irreversible job to do; any interference with the process results in the failure of the structures involved to develop further. This physiological-developmental mechanism applies to the formation of most structures, including venation, pattern and coloring of the wing. By using mechanical interference—surgical blocks, cauterization points, temperature variations—at successive times during wing development, it has been demonstrated that the pattern on the dorsal surface of the *Ephestia* wing is *undetermined* during the first day of pupation, but that after the fourth day any interference results in pattern defects correlated with the time and place of interference. For a symmetrical pattern like that found in *Ephestia*, determination progresses during the second and third days of pupation along a pathway which leads from the wing base out to the pattern axis along both margins of the wing, then spreads out in both directions (Fig. 4.6C). Subsequent to pattern determination, pigments are transported to the wing sites by the blood and diffused by the hypodermis into the cuticle, are arranged according to the determined pattern, then through the action of catalysts and other agents assume ultimate color.

The determination of the development and shape of setae is a similar but independent phenomenon. After pattern in *Ephestia* and the butterfly *Vanessa* has already been determined, the shape and development of wing setae are still indeterminate. The independence and sequence of these two processes lead to apparent sexual dimorphism in certain Ithomidae (Lepidoptera). The males of many genera have a reduced pattern confined mainly to marginal elements, with the central areas of the wings transparent (Fig. 4.2C), but the females have scales on the central areas as well and exhibit a distinct, complete pattern. Examination of the transparent discs of the male wings reveals the presence of sparse hair-like but pigmented setae arranged in the same color pattern present in the female. Thus the sexes do not really differ in color or pattern, but rather in their respective scale shapes, and dimorphism, in these insects, is the result of differences in the process determining setal development.

In *Ephestia* the second and third days of pupation, while pattern determination occurs, are especially critical. Similar critical periods exist for every insect, constant for a species under similar external conditions such as humidity and temperature, but varying widely with different species. "Normal" phenotypes result from "normal" ecological conditions—that is, those ordinarily encountered in nature by the insect. Alterations in the environment, especially alterations of temperature or humidity, during the critical period or periods usually result in "abnormal" phenotypes. In parts of the world with distinct seasons, as in the temperate zones, or those tropics with distinctly contrasting wet and dry seasons, insect species with multiple generations during the year are generally exposed to more or less drastic environmental differences during the critical determinative periods of successive generations. The result is a series of phenotypic variations correlated with the season during which pupation occurs. Many temperate zone butterflies thus have recognizably differing spring, summer and autumn "forms." In Africa, dry season and wet season "forms" are prominent and often are dramatically different in appearance. But all such seasonal "forms" of the species are clearly identical genetically. The differences in pattern and coloring of seasonal "forms" are induced by environmental conditions. Similar or even more radical differences have been induced in the laboratory by manipulating the environment during critical periods.

Though comparatively little work has been done with pattern and color determination in insects other than Lepidoptera, the principles and processes of the development of integumental coloring as observed in moths and butterflies probably apply to all insects. Kühn and his associates found such to be the case in leafhoppers (Hemiptera), for example.

Maintenance Systems

Listening to the inner flow of things.
JAMES RUSSELL LOWELL

From the functional viewpoint the structures inside an animal fall into two groups—maintenance systems and control systems. The activities of the enteron and of respiratory and circulatory structures maintain the individual by supplying all tissues with materials convertible into energy and by removing excess and waste materials attendant upon energy production. The reproductive system of arthropods makes little or no direct contribution to the welfare of the individual, but is concerned solely with future individuals—it is the maintenance system responsible for the species itself.

The executive functions of control and coordination are vested in the nervous system, supplemented by the endocrine system. The external structures discussed in preceding chapters all function essentially in supplying materials for the furious and continual activity taking place within the body, while providing a protective insulation from the external environment and making possible a more or less constant internal environment conducive to effective physiological functioning. At the same time, the external structures are in turn dependent upon the internal maintenance and control mechanisms.

The internal structures vary from group to group, reflecting differences in food ingested, in external ecological conditions and in evolutional attainment. Variation is not only morphological; it is physiological as well. The following accounts are concerned primarily with common denominators rather than with variables. If morphology seems to receive more stress than physiology, it is because knowledge of the former is rather more complete. There is available a vast amount of detailed information on the chemical and physical aspects of what happens to certain specific molecules in certain specific tissues of certain specific arthropods under certain specific conditions. Some of these data are useful generally and some are not; some studies are well grounded and presented, while others give an impression of busywork. In any event, present knowledge of the comparative physiology of these animals is incomplete and it is difficult to find common denominators. Several excellent reviews of insect physiology are available (Roeder, 1953; Wigglesworth, 1947) and the interested student should consult them. This general area is one which proves rewarding to the competent investigator.

THE ENTERON

In all arthropods the alimentary canal has three main sections (Fig. 5.1A). The **foregut (stomodaeum)** and **hindgut (proctodaeum)** are tubular invaginations of the skeletal integument, thus of ectodermal origin; they open respectively at the mouth and the anus. The inner ends of these two sections are connected by the **midgut (mesenteron)**, which has an entirely different embryogenic source and histological structure from the two ectodermal sections. The weight of authority through the years has supported an interpretation ascribing the midgut to the endoderm, but this view is now frequently questioned. The fact is that the arthropod endoderm behaves in an eccentric manner—and quite differently from its well-known development in the frog and chick. Some students dispute its existence, or its contribution to the midgut, while others believe that the midgut is formed from either mesoderm or ectoderm. Certainly, the process of midgut formation is not clear-cut and seems to be subject to wide variation among the various species investigated. In any event, there is no definitive evidence that the midgut is *not* endodermal (see also Chapter Seven).

There is so much variation in the way the alimentary tract is subdivided into specialized structures or regions that no general plan applicable to all arthropods can be presented. The basic organs of excretion, the **malpighian tubules,** however, are present in all insects, myriapods and arachnoids except those which have apparently lost them secondarily.

THE FOREGUT

The epithelium, basement membrane and intima of the foregut are respectively continuous with the hypodermis, basement membrane and cuticle of the external integument. The cells tend to be cuboidal in the foregut, but both pavement and columnar forms sometimes are present. The layer often is wrinkled to form rings or ridges projecting into the lumen. The intima is generally thin, delicate and nonpigmented, but otherwise it does not differ from external cuticle and has the same properties. Two layers of splanchnic muscles surround the foregut, an inner longitudinal layer and an outer circular layer, the whole enclosed in a

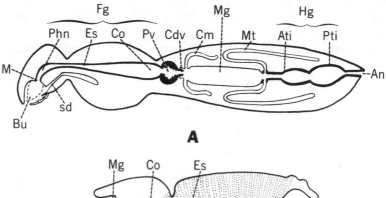

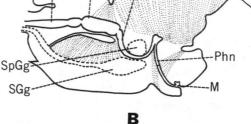

Figure 5.1. Diagrams of (A) the enteron of insects and (B) the anterior part of the enteron of a spider. *An,* anus; *Ati,* anterior intestine; *Bu,* buccal cavity; *Cdv,* cardiac valve; *Cm,* caecum; *Co,* crop; *Es,* esophagus; *Fg,* foregut; *Hg,* hindgut; *M,* mouth; *Mg,* midgut; *Mt,* malpighian tubules; *Phn,* pharynx; *Pti,* posterior intestine; *Pv,* proventriculus; *sd,* salivary duct; *SGg,* subesophageal ganglionic mass; *SpGg,* supraesophageal ganglionic mass. (B redrawn from Millot, 1949e, by arrangement with Masson et Cie)

delicate sheet of connective tissue. The primary directional arrangement of the muscle layers often is altered so that one or both layers come to be diagonal.

In ordinary terms the mouth is where food goes in: technically, it is the point where the foregut invagination begins, a point defined by the arrangement of the muscles and not always easily located. Thus in most of these animals the precise location of the *mouth proper* is not as obvious as it might seem. For example, the tip of the mouthparts of a hemipteron (see Fig. 3.18B) or a tick is not the mouth, nor is the space between the mandibles of the grasshopper or the chelicerae of the scorpion. The space between the mouthparts is the **buccal cavity;** the mouth is at its upper posterior surface.

Myriapods as a group have the simplest foregut, a straight tube leading to the midgut, with very little differentiation into regions, other than a slight enlargement of the muscular pharynx.

In arachnoids the pharynx generally has chitinous plates (**epipharynx, hypopharynx**) affording attachment to the well-developed musculature. The esophagus is usually small in diameter. In spiders and Phryneida it enlarges as soon as it passes between the circumesophageal connectives of the central nervous system, becoming the large "sucking stomach" provided with a powerful musculature (Fig. 5.1B), then narrows to a simple tube emptying into the midgut.

The structure of the foregut is generally more complex in insects, though the basic division into pharynx and esophagus is characteristic. In sucking insects the lower end of the pharynx becomes specialized into a pump, the **cibarium,** discussed in Chapter Three in connection with the mouthparts. The esophagus passes through the foramen magnum and enlarges in the anterior part of the thorax as the **crop,** which serves generally as a food reservoir. The crop, almost universally present, varies from a slight enlargement to a prominent diverticular sac, a condition especially characteristic of insects that take liquid food. The **proventriculus,** at the posterior end of the crop, may be developed as a valve, as in the honeybee, or may be a separate chamber, the **gizzard,** with heavy cuticular dentitions and well-developed musculature, serving to mascerate food particles, as in some orthopteroids.

The inner end of the foregut protrudes into the lumen of the midgut as the **cardiac valve.** Epithelial cells at this point secrete the chitinous **peritrophic membrane** in many, if not all, cases where it is present.

SALIVARY GLANDS

Though not derived morphologically from the enteron, the salivary glands are an essential functional part of the alimentary system. In insects the hypodermis of the midventral area of each of the three gnathocephalic segments of the embryo is potentially able to form a paired group of glandular cells. These cells become deeply invaginated, each pair drained by a duct opening on the ventral surface a little anterior of the appendages of the segment involved. Since the ventral areas of the three gnathocephalic segments contribute much of the buccal cavity, the ducts of the segmental glands come to open there in the adult. Frequently only one of the three potential pairs of glands develops while the other two atrophy, but in some insect groups more than one pair of salivary glands are functional. In some cases there is evidence that a single gland system actually consists of several pairs, the structures of one segment having "captured" the secretory cells of another segment during development.

As used in entomology the term "salivary glands" refers, as a rule, to the **labial glands,** the common duct of which opens at the base of the hypopharynx. The duct sometimes is strengthened by circular cuticular rings resembling the taenidia of tracheae. These glands are often so deeply invaginated that they lie in the thorax and when especially large they may extend into the abdomen. Their structure in the insects is quite diverse. In muscoid flies they are long, fine, undulate tubes and may be longer than the body; in mosquitoes they are a pair of sacs containing ramified lumens surrounded by secretory cells (Fig. 5.2A). A separate reservoir for the secretions is present in many orthopteroids, Hemiptera and other insects.

Maxillary glands develop into functional salivary structures in adult Collembola and Protura and in a few immature Neuroptera and Trichoptera. The **mandibular glands** are functional in all Apterygota and, among the Pterygota, in the Dictyoptera, Isoptera, Trichoptera and Hymenoptera —generally in addition to the labial glands. In adult Coleoptera *only* the mandibular glands are present. The labial glands of immature Lepidoptera normally produce silk and the salivary function is taken over by the mandibular pair. Near the end of larval development the labial glands of most Hymenoptera acquire the function of producing silk.

Four pairs of glands are present in chilopods (Fig. 5.2C). One pair opens at the base of the labrum, a second pair opens beside the hypopharynx and two pairs open into the anterior part of the buccal cavity. Probably these are the ventral glands of the labial, maxillary, mandibular and intercalary segments. It is interesting to find that the Diplopoda, despite the difficulty in homologizing their gnathal segments, also have four pairs of glands. The two anterior pairs open into the buccal cavity under the mouth, one pair behind the other, the third pair opens beside the hypopharynx. The fourth pair, opening at the base of the gnathochilarium, is long and tubular, extending well back into the trunk, and is quite similar to the labial glands of insects. The mandibular and maxillary glands are present in Pauropoda, but in Symphyla only a single pair of large glands, apparently the maxillaries, has been reported.

The number of salivary glands present in arachnoids varies with the group. Generally there are two pairs, the **rostral glands,** opening ahead of the mouth itself, and the **"maxillary" glands,** opening at the base of the

first legs (pedipalps) under the mouth (not homologous with maxillary
glands of insects).

The salivary secretions are typically weakly acid or weakly alkaline and
their main function is to lubricate food particles. In most insects and

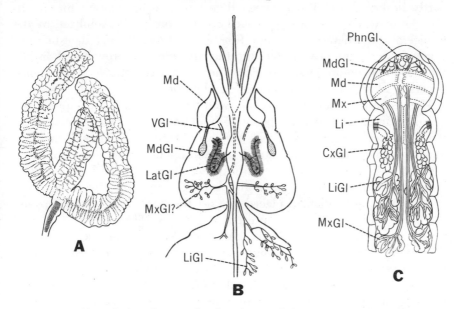

Figure 5.2. (A) Salivary glands of *Anopheles* species (Diptera), dissected and greatly magnified; (B) diagram of the salivary glands of the
honeybee (Hymenoptera); (C) ventral view of the salivary system of *Scolopendra* species (Chilopoda). *CxGl*, coxal glands (not salivary); *LatGl*,
pharyngeal (lateral) glands; *Li* labium; *LiGl*, labial glands; *Md*, mandible;
MdGl, mandibular glands; *Mx*, maxillae; *MxGl*, maxillary glands; *PhnGl*,
pharyngeal glands (probably homologous with "lateral glands" of honeybee); *VGl*, ventral pharyngeal ("circumoral") glands. (A from Russell, West
and Manwell, 1946, by permission of W. B. Saunders Company; B redrawn
from Wigglesworth, 1947, by permission of Methuen & Co.; C redrawn from
Verhoeff, 1902–1925)

myriapods the salivary secretions also include digestive enzymes related
to the food ingested. Amylase and invertase often are present; proteases,
lipases and even proteolytic digestive fluid have been reported in various
species. The digestive function of the salivary secretions can vary from
nothing to being a major source of enzymes. Malaria vector mosquitoes
(some species of *Anopheles*) secrete an anticoagulant along with enzymes;
in *Glossina* (tsetse fly) anticoagulant is present but no enzymes.

Digestion may occur before ingestion when the salivary secretions are rich in enzymes. Thus in many Hemiptera the salivary juice, which contains an enzyme that breaks down chlorophyll, is injected into plant tissue as a first step in feeding; the juices sucked in have already been partly broken down. Pre-ingestion digestion is usual among the arachnoids, nearly all of which are predaceous. The prey is immobilized by the chelicera and whatever legs may function in feeding, and digestive enzymes from the gut are injected into the tissues of the prey, liquefying its body contents before ingestion. Thus the salivary secretions of arachnoids generally play little or no direct role in digestion.

The cephalic glands are especially well developed in Hymenoptera, the mandibular and labial pairs being the minimum equipment present. In the honeybees (Fig. 5.2B) there are three systems—the labial, mandibular and pharyngeal. The labial system opens on the hypopharynx through a duct with four internal branches. Two of these branches lead back into the thorax to the labial glands proper, the other two lead to the "posterior cephalic glands" placed against the back wall of the capsule; the latter pair may be the captured maxillaries. The secretions of this system are said to be used in working the wax comb in the nest. Small mandibular glands open through separate ducts at the base of each mandible; their acid secretion has no proved function, and the best guess is that it may soften the cocoon and help the imago emerge from it. The pharyngeal system opens directly into the pharynx and takes over the true salivary function. In the worker bee "royal jelly" is secreted initially, but for only a short time. The pharyngeal glands soon become typicaly salivary; amylase and invertase have been identified in the secretion.

THE MIDGUT

The nonlaminated midgut epithelium includes three morphologic types of cells (Fig. 5.3B) and intermediates have been observed. The active, **functional cells** usually are columnar, but in some cases may be cuboidal. They rest on an enclosing basement membrane and do not form a cuticle. Their inner ends, lining the lumen, have a striated border composed of rigid rod-like elements or, more rarely, of filaments, but never of cilia. In insects and myriapods most epithelial cells probably perform both in secretion and in absorption, though in some cases individual cells may be specifically secretory *or* absorptive.

According to Millot (1949a), in the arachnoids both functions never reside at the same time in a cell, the secretory cells being morphologically distinct from the absorptive cells. Material absorbed always is in solution; phagocytosis of particles never occurs.

Goblet cells (Fig. 5.3B) occur in some insects interspersed among co-lumnar cells, from which they differ only in having the cytoplasm reduced and the striated border deeply invaginated. No function peculiar to them has been demonstrated, possibly because they function in the same way as columnar cells, the goblet-like invagination merely affording an in-creased working surface for fluid exchange.

Regenerative cells are small and generalized. They are present in one or more of three kinds of arrangements: they may be scattered among the columnar cells, resting on the basement membrane (Fig. 5.3B); they may be gathered into little clusters (**nidi**); they may be collected into larger masses that project through the muscle fibers into the hemocoel. Their function is to replace other epithelial cells as necessary. The functional epithelium is destroyed in various ways, sometimes *en masse* at ecdysis, sometimes cell by cell in the normal course of events. In either case, regen-erative cells undergo histogenesis to become new columnar cells.

In the midgut the arrangement of the muscle layers is reversed from that of the other two gut sections. The inner layer is circular, the outer is longitudinal. Because the muscles form only a loose lattice, the basement membrane of the epithelium is in direct contact with blood in the hemo-coel. Innervated from the visceral nervous system, these muscles supply both a churning and a peristaltic action.

The walls of the midgut may be deeply infolded and convoluted, af-fording a greater functional surface. In its simplest form, as found in myriapods and some insects, the midgut is a short, straight tube. **Divertic-ula (caeca)** (Fig. 5.1) are present in most insects and arachnoids, gen-erally placed at the anterior end of the midgut, but they may be scattered in various ways throughout its length. In Thelyphonida there is a pair of diverticula corresponding to each metamere in which the midgut lies. In other groups there may be only one diverticulum or there may be dozens. In form they may be merely shallow pockets, but more frequently they are digital and sometimes are much longer than the midgut itself. In some arachnoids they are highly ramified, forming masses which were called the "liver" or the "hepatopancreas" by early authors. Diverticula are en-tirely wanting in Lepidoptera, Collembola and all myriapods.

In adult orthopteroids, some beetles and many Hemiptera and Diptera the midgut is divided into regions each having its special function. The long coiled midgut of *Glossina* (Diptera), for example, has an anterior half, in which excess water is removed from ingested blood, followed by a somewhat enlarged second section where enzymes are secreted and di-gestion takes place, and finally a narrower posterior section where ab-sorption occurs. The midgut of many Heteroptera (a suborder of Hemip-

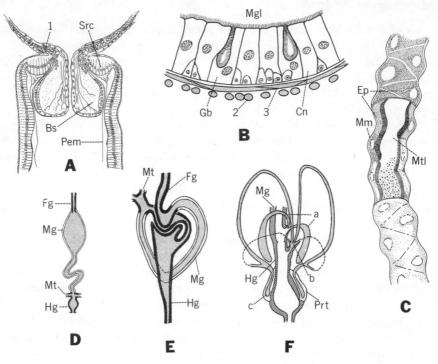

Figure 5.3. Structure of midgut and malpighian tubules. (A) Longitudinal section at the juncture of the fore- and midgut of a larval sawfly (Hymenoptera), greatly magnified; (B) the midgut epithelium of a larval butterfly (Lepidoptera), greatly magnified and diagrammatic; (C) histology of the malpighian tubule at the juncture of the upper (midgut) and lower (hindgut) sections; (D) diagram of the alimentary system as found in many Heteroptera (Hemiptera); (E) same, as modified in Coccidae (Hemiptera); (F) cryptonephridium, formed by the intimate relationship between hindgut and malpighian tubules in a chrysomelid beetle (Coleoptera). *a,* two short malpighian tubules opening into the midgut; *b,* four long malpighian tubules opening by a common duct lined with cuticle into the hindgut; *Bs,* blood sinus; *c,* malpighian tubules terminating in perirectal wall, which at these points is reduced to a thin layer; *Cn,* columnar cell; *Ep,* pavement epithelium; *Fg,* foregut; *Gb,* goblet cell; *Hg,* hindgut; *Mg,* midgut; *Mgl,* lumen of midgut; *Mt,* base of malpighian tubules; *Mtl,* lumen of malpighian tubule; *Mm,* "peritoneum"; *Pem,* peritrophic membrane; *Prt,* perirectal chamber; *Src,* ring of epithelial cells which apparently secrete the peritrophic membrane; *1,* sphincter muscle of the cardiac valve; *2,* circular muscles; *3,* longitudinal muscles. (Redrawn from Wigglesworth, 1947, by permission of Methuen & Co.)

tera) is divided into a sac-like "stomach" and a long, coiled "intestine" (Fig. 5.3D). Digestion apparently occurs in the "intestine," while the "stomach" is primarily a reservoir.

An unusual complication is found in the Homoptera (the other suborder of Hemiptera), insects that ingest large quantities of watery plant juice. The foregut and hindgut are in external contact with each other, leaving the midgut forming a loop (Fig. 5.3E); the greatest complexity is found in some Coccidae, in which the posterior esophagus and the anterior end of the midgut actually lie *within* the hindgut. Apparently the purpose of this arrangement is to facilitate the removal of excess water from food in the foregut and bypass it directly to the hindgut, a preliminary processing which concentrates food reaching the midgut for digestion.

Although no cuticle is formed by the midgut, the cells are protected from contact with food particles, in most insects, by the **peritrophic membrane** (Fig. 5.3A), a very thin sleeve of cuticle typically less than one-half micron thick. Two kinds occur: a continuous uniform tube, and a series of overlapping concentric laminae. In certain Hymenoptera and Diptera the peritrophic membrane is known to be generated by a collar of secretory cells located at the juncture of the mid- and foregut. These cells are derived from the embryonic stomodaeum, hence they are ectodermal. The membrane is formed continuously and moves down the gut aided by peristalsis, to be broken up in the hindgut and finally excreted, usually in pieces, with the feces. Food particles pass into it at the cardiac valve and it is permeable to enzymes and dissolved digested food.

Based particularly on observations on the honeybee and on immature dragonflies, a second theory of formation has been proposed. The peritrophic membrane is said to be delaminated from the midgut epithelium, mainly because both the striated border material and the hexagonal pattern of the surface of the cells have been observed on the membrane itself. Most recent students maintain that the cuticular secretions forming the membrane come from the foregut epithelium and in fact flow back over midgut cells.

It is not possible to list a standard set of enzymes: they vary with the kind of food normally eaten. Omnivorous feeders like the cockroach have a suitably diverse set—proteinase, lipase, amylase, invertase and maltase. Specialized feeders have only the enzymes particularly needed for their diet. Thus carnivores produce larger amounts of proteinase and lipase, the bee produces a quantity of invertase, the grass-eating Acrididae (Orthoptera) emphasize carbohydrases. Not all the digestive enzymes are localized in the midgut. Salivary secretions may initiate digestion; it seems probable that the process is continued in the blood or even in the ultimate utilizing cells. Enzyme for enzyme, little significant difference has been noted between those found in insects and those in vertebrates, although a few enzymes sometimes may be present in insects but not in vertebrates, and some vertebrate enzymes have not yet been identified in insects.

The role of symbiotic organisms presents a fascinating aspect of digestion. Most insects secrete antiseptic materials which exclude micro-organisms, but some do not and rely upon one or another symbiont for assistance in digestion. There is good evidence that in a few instances, at least, bacteria or yeasts produce the enzymes essential to the host. Leafhoppers (Hemiptera) are said to entertain yeasts that break down sucrose and starch. Certain cockroaches (*Panesthia*) feeding on wood, depend on bacteria in the crop to digest cellulose. Another wood-feeding cockroach (*Cryptocercus*) and a great many kinds of termites (Isoptera) harbor flagellate protozoa which secrete cellulase and break down wood fibers. The insect subsists partly on the cellulose hydrolyzed by flagellates, partly on their nutritive excretions and partly on the protozoa that have died. If the gut is experimentally sterilized, the insect derives no benefit from wood ingested and soon dies if no other usable food is made available.

Absorption of nutrients occurs, in general, in the midgut, especially in the posterior half, and, for certain materials, in the hindgut. The foregut plays no role in absorption except for fats in the cockroach. While it is possible that some fats are absorbed unchanged, probably most fats and all carbohydrates and proteins must first be degraded. These materials mostly pass into the midgut epithelium, where they may be stored temporarily or may enter the blood at once. Fats appear to be absorbed in specific, often limited regions. Proteins generally are absorbed in the posterior part of the midgut. Minerals may be removed from either the mid- or the hindgut; iron, sodium and chloride probably are absorbed almost entirely from the hindgut.

MALPIGHIAN TUBULES

In adult insects and myriapods the excretory tubules appear to be continuous with the hindgut, and traditionally they have been regarded as being part of it. They may be located at the juncture of the mid- and hindgut, but in many insects are clearly on the hindgut itself. It has been customary to state that the malpighian tubules form as evaginations from the hindgut. If this were true, they should have the characteristics of integument, including a cuticular lining, which is not the case. Both in structure and function the cells of the tubules resemble those of the midgut.

The functional lengths of the tubules originate in fact from undifferentiated cells lying between the embryonic mesenteron and proctodaeum, an area which could be mesenteronic but certainly is not ectodermal. However, it is probable that in some insects, at least, the mesenteronic tubules become attached to short hindgut evaginations, and in such cases both interpretations are partly true. In the arachnoids, the malpighian tubules unquestionably arise from the midgut material (Dawydoff, 1949).

Malpighian tubules are absent in Collembola, are absent or only primitively developed in Aptera and have been lost in Aphidae (Hemiptera). Otherwise they are present in all insects, normally in pairs. The primitive number is believed to be six, but fewer may be present due to loss, while many insects have more than six. Some Odonata and Orthoptera may have as many as 200, counting branches. When only a few tubules are present, they are generally long, sometimes longer than the body; when a great many are present they are often short. Regardless of number and length, their total surface area is of the order of 400 to 500 square millimeters per milligram of insect weight (Wigglesworth, 1947).

Myriapods have a single pair of long, tubular malpighian structures, located at the juncture of the mid- and hindgut. In arachnoids there are one or two pairs opening into the posterior part of the midgut. They do not lie free in the hemocoel, as is the case with myriapods and insects, but are enclosed by interstitial tissue, in which they produce extensive ramifications. The walls are syncytial and the lumen is said by Millot (1949a) to be ciliated.

In insects and myriapods the tubules have a pavement epithelium, the cells large with prominent nuclei (Fig. 5.3C). The perimeter of the lumen is formed by one to three or four cells at any given point, their internal surfaces lining the lumen being striated, with a border which is either brush-like, composed of numerous independent cytoplasmic filaments, or "honeycomb," in which numerous rod-like vesicles form a rigid palisade. The outer parts of the epithelial cells may also be striated against the basement membrane, which forms a sleeve around them. The whole is enclosed by a peritoneum—sometimes described as connective tissue—in which muscle fibers may be embedded and which usually carries a network of tracheoles. The arrangement of the muscles and muscle fibers is variable. Frequently they spiral around the tubule, sometimes they are found in circular and longitudinal sets, especially near the gut, and sometimes they are absent from a part or all of the tubule. The blind distal tips of the tubules are, in some insects, intimately associated with the rectum of the hindgut, an arrangement termed the **cryptonephridium** (Fig. 5.3F).

The primary function of the malpighian tubules is, as in the annelid nephridium and the vertebrate kidney, excretion—the regulation of the internal environment by controlling the ion and water balance in the blood and by removing nitrogenous wastes. The requirements and details of these processes obviously must vary with the food and water intake and with the external environment. Animals living in the water or in damp humus have little need for water conservation, but those exposed to sunlight and air are subject to desiccation and must conserve water. In insects and myriapods, the malpighian tubules, in direct contact with the blood, withdraw water, dissolved salts, amino acids and nitrogenous wastes. These materials pass down the lumen of the tubules into the hindgut. Some or all of the water, salts and nutritive substances are reabsorbed variously in the proximal part of the tubules or in the hindgut, while nitrogenous wastes pass out with the feces. Cryptonephridial tubules probably serve to conserve water by facilitating its removal from fecal material in the hindgut.

Precise measurements of the output of the tubules are hindered by contamination with the fecal material. In a general way, wastes excreted include large quantities of uric acid, small amounts of urea and ammonia, more rarely allantoin and other materials. Mineral salts and water are included in the feces in proportion to their not being needed to maintain suitable balance in the blood.

Secondary functions of the malpighian tubules are known in some insects. Modified cells in the tubules of some larval Chrysomelidae (Coleoptera) produce a sticky secretion that aids ambulation, while some females of the same family enclose the eggs in a similar secretion. The spittle surrounding immature Cercopidae (Hemiptera) is also a malpighian secretion. Many immature Neuroptera and the late larvae of several species of Coleoptera produce silk from specialized cells in the malpighian epithelium.

THE HINDGUT

The hindgut is basically similar to the foregut, both being invaginated ectodermal integument. On the whole, histological differences between the two regions are functional rather than structural. One exception is the formation of pads of epithelium in part of the hindgut of many insects. At the margins of the pads the cells are low, becoming increasingly higher toward the center. In advanced Diptera and a few other insects these pads are invaginated or infolded into the gut lumen to form papillae. Another exception is that an additional layer of circular muscles is sometimes present outside the longitudinal layer.

The hindgut of most insects (Fig. 5.1) begins with a well-marked constriction, the **pyloric valve,** provided with a sphinctor muscle, followed by a variable length of tubular gut, the **anterior (small) intestine.** The malpighian tubules often (but not always) arise at the extreme anterior end of the hindgut. The anterior intestine may be short and straight or long and coiled. It may be divided into two sections differing slightly in function, an anterior **ileum** and a posterior **colon.** In solpugids the entire anterior intestine is enlarged as the **cloacal sac.**

The **posterior (large) intestine**—not necessarily larger than the "small" intestine—bears the **rectal pads (papillae)** in its first region (**rectum**), whence a short, unspecialized length of tube leads to the anus. Where division of the hindgut into sections is marked, various valves with sphinctors are present at the boundaries. The hindgut has little or no differentiation in the myriapods. In ticks, it often is rudimentary and ends in a cul-de-sac with no external passage.

Material entering the hindgut includes water, but becomes increasingly dense as it is moved back. It is thus clear that water absorption is an important function and this may be the primary purpose of the rectal pads. Some nutrients and dissolved salts are absorbed from the hindgut, particularly from the anterior part.

In larval Scarabaeoidea (Coleoptera) a sac-like enlargement of the hindgut apparently serves as a fermentation chamber in wood-eating species. Particles of wood are retained there for some time while cellulose-fermenting bacteria digest them; protozoa feed on the bacteria and midgut secretions collect in the chamber. The beetle thus subsists on fermented wood, dead bacteria and protozoa, and the hindgut in this case becomes the chief site of digestion and absorption. A similar situation is found in the termites with symbiont flagellates in the hindgut.

THE CIRCULATORY SYSTEM

The circulatory system of Arthropoda is morphologically uncomplicated and in insects, myriapods and arachnoids it tends to become reduced and even more simplified. Blood circulates freely in the general body cavity (hemocoel), which extends into all appendages, so that the organs and most cell layers are in direct contact with it. This does away with any need for a system of veins and arteries. Definitive blood vessels are present only to the extent necessary to accomplish some pumping and elementary routing. These structures are often described as being "poorly developed." In a sense this is true, but the implication that they are insufficient and ought to be better is certainly incorrect. Functionally the blood system in these animals is physiologically similar to and just as efficient as the blood systems of other higher phyla, including the Chordata.

The tracheal system, present in all myriapods and nearly all insects and arachnoids, takes over the major transport of gases to and from the cells. Consequently this function is of quite secondary importance for the blood system, though it is not entirely eschewed. In effect, there are two circulatory systems, one for gases and the other for everything else. Relieved of responsibility for primary transportation of gases, the blood is also relieved of the necessity for constant, directional circulation at a given rate. The animal readily survives situations which, in the vertebrate, would lead to sudden death by "heart failure."

In summary, the functions of the blood system are: (a) the transportation of the nutrient products of digestion from the gut to the tissues; of metabolic products to sites of use, storage or elimination; of special materials such as hormones, buffers and enzymes; (b) the maintenance of the internal environment within acceptable ranges of osmotic pressures, pH and electrolytic concentration by transporting salts and water through the tissues and to the excretory sites; (c) limited transportation of gases exchanged (especially in the wings and at certain tracheal networks) and carried both in direct solution and tied to either hemoglobin or hemocyanin; (d) extension of appendicular parts by hemodynamic action and the splitting of the cuticle at ecdysis aided by the same action.

The morphological elements involved are: (a) the blood vessels, diaphragms and pulsating structures; (b) the blood cells; (c) the fat body, a tissue system conveniently considered with the blood and only partly entering the circulation picture.

THE BODY CAVITY

A great deal of emphasis has been placed on the view that the body cavity of arthropods is not a coelom—hence the word "hemocoel." The value and significance of this distinction and the stress laid upon it are not always easy to understand. To the purist "coelom" is reserved to the segmental cavity that forms within the embryonic mesoderm; an adult animal can have a coelomic cavity only if the embryonic coelomata enlarge, coalesce and eventually enclose the organs. The arthropods, a very ancient group indeed, have introduced many sophisticated short cuts into their ontogeny. One of these is the formation of the hemocoel. Segmental mesodermal coelomic vesicles appear in the embryo (but even this step has been eliminated in the highly evolved insect order Diptera), generally coalesce serially, and are said then to regress. What actually happens is that the internal walls of the vesicles break down so that the coelomata become continuous with the **epineural sinus**—the space between them formed by the withdrawal of the yolk from the developing central nervous system. This space, combining the two coelomata and the epineural sinus, presently is enclosed by embryonic tissue of the **lateral plates**—the coelomic mesoderm underlaid by ectoderm—the edges of which fold back and around, eventually to meet and to form the animal's dorsal surface. The coelomic mesoderm fails to keep pace with this development so that it specifically lines only a *part* of the resultant cavity (see also Chapter Seven).

This method of forming the body cavity is not a *fundamentally* different procedure from that leading to a true coelom, but it appears to be a variation of considerable practical value, one which, it is true, signalizes a major phylogenetic line branching from what is anthropomorphically viewed as the main trunk of evolution.

In the adult arthropod, the hemocoel is lined by the outer somatic mesodermal derivatives, the body muscles, and the inner splanchnic mesoderm, the gut musculature. Neither of these muscle systems forms a continuous layer, no peritoneum develops; the blood thus is in direct contact with all muscles, the hypodermis, the gut, the nervous system, and the reproductive system. In short, the blood reaches all functional tissue without need for an extensive system of blood vessels—an unusually efficient system.

BLOOD VESSELS

The principal and often the only blood vessel is a mesodermal tube, the **dorsal blood vessel** (Fig. 5.4A, B), running the length of the body between the gut and the dorsal wall. From its ventral margin a sheet of tissue extends laterally to the body wall to form the **dorsal diaphragm,** separating the **dorsal sinus** from the main blood cavity (Fig. 5.4C). An analogous diaphragm sometimes occurs in the ventral part of the hemocoel, partitioning off the **ventral sinus** in which the nerve cord lies.

The dorsal vessel is divided into two regions. The anterior portion (**aorta**) is tubular and leads blood into the head. The posterior portion (**heart**) has muscular walls and fibers or bundles of muscles radiate in various ways to the body wall; it is the principal pulsating organ. The heart has segmental dilations separated by intersegmental constrictions. Each segmental chamber has a pair of lateral slit-like apertures (**ostia**) connecting the dorsal sinus with the lumen of the heart. The chambers are not separated by valves at the constrictions, but the flaps of the ostia serve a double function in most cases, preventing back flow in the heart during systole and flow into the sinus during diastole. Functional valves

also occur at the ends of the aorta and such other blood vessels as may
be present.

The aorta may be a simple tube ending in the cephalic hemocoel, or
it may have branches and ramifications. Ordinarily it has no segmental
dilations, but segmental **afferent arteries** have been described in the

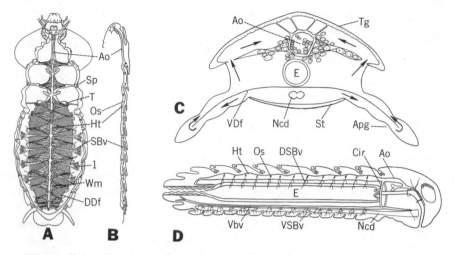

Figure 5.4. Diagrams of circulatory systems. (A) *Blaberus trapezoideus*
Burmeister (Dictyoptera), dissected, ventral view; (B) same, parasagittal
section beside dorsal blood vessel; (C) schematic transverse section through
an insect thorax; (D) parasagittal view of *Scutigera* (Chilopoda). *Ao*, aorta;
Apg, appendage; *Cir*, circular connective vessel; *DDf*, dorsal diaphragm;
DSBv, dorsal excurrent segmental vessel; *E*, enteron (midgut); *Ht*, heart;
NCd, central nerve cord; *Os*, ostium; *SBv*, excurrent segmental vessel; *Sp*,
spiracle; *St*, sternite; *T*, trachea; *Tg*, tergite; *Vbv*, ventral blood vessel; *VDf*,
ventral diaphragm; *VSBv*, ventral excurrent segmental vessel; *Wm*, "wing"
muscle of dorsal diaphragm; *1*, tergo-sternal muscle. (A and B redrawn from
Nutting, 1951; C redrawn from Wigglesworth, 1947, by permission of
Methuen & Co.; D redrawn from Verhoeff, 1902–1925)

heart region in many myriapods, arachnoids and in a few insects. In addition to the ventral diaphragm, a ventral blood vessel with segmental
efferent branches is found in some myriapods and some arachnoids, but
not in insects.

The basic scheme of blood flow is forward in the dorsal vessel into the
head, back through the hemocoel and into the dorsal sinus at the caudal
end, into the dorsal vessel through the ostia. Many structural variations
lead to modification in details of the flow plan. When the ventral dia-

phragm is present, it serves in part to direct circulation into and out of the legs and perhaps to maintain the ordered backward flow in the main cavity (Fig. 5.4C). The ventral vessel of myriapods apparently contributes to the same end, as its segmental branches collect blood returning from the leg cavities and route it directly to the caudal end where it is collected into the dorsal sinus.

Propulsion of blood in the dorsal vessel is brought about by waves of peristalsis running forward from the posterior end of the heart. These waves are rhythmic and regular, but vary greatly in speed from group to group. They may be so rapid that the entire heart seems to contract at once, or they may be slow enough that several waves can be observed moving along at the same time. Surrounding the delicate membrane (often overlooked) lining the dorsal vessel lie longitudinal muscle fibers and then a heavier layer of semicircular fibers. Contraction of the vessel is easily understood, being obviously brought about by the circularly arranged muscle fibers. Dilation is not always so obvious. In arachnoids and many myriapods (Fig. 5.4D), muscle fibers and bundles radiate from the vessel dorsally and laterally, and their action in conjunction with that of the longitudinal fibers enlarges the chambers. But in many groups, including most insects, the radiating fibers are few or absent, except those in the dorsal diaphragm and in the dorsal suspension of the vessel. In such cases it is difficult to visualize how dilation occurs and the problem is not entirely solved.

Propulsion is not supplied by the heart alone. The dorsal diaphragm, as well as the ventral when it is present, is supplied with muscle fibers which bring about an undulatory motion that contributes to propulsion and certainly helps avoid puddling of the blood. Accessory pulsating organs are variously located in various groups. In many insects such a structure at the base of the antennae boosts blood movement in that appendage. Propulsive structures have been described at the base of the wings of some insects, in the thorax or legs of others. In all arthropods, the normal movements of the body and appendages unquestionably contribute to keeping the blood in motion.

BLOOD SYSTEM OF INSECTS

Though there is evidence that the heart primitively extended into the prothorax, in most insects it lies entirely in the abdomen (Fig. 5.4A, B). In Aptera, cockroaches and certain immatures, heart chambers with lateral ostia extend into the mesothorax. Usually the heart ends in the first or second abdominal segment and is shortened posteriorly. At most there are nine chambers in the abdomen, so that the heart begins approximately at the genital segments, but in insects there ordinarily are fewer. Coalescence of chambers is frequent, along with shortening at the caudal end. In Mallophaga and Anoplura the single large heart chamber has two or three pairs of ostia, for example. A similar development is present in immature Odonata and some of the Hemiptera. In the former case it probably is a phenomenon of ontogeny, in the latter of evolution. The dorsal vessel is always held close against the inner side of the tergites by short strands of tissue in which muscle fibers are usually embedded. Small lateral excurrent blood vessels leading from the heart chambers into the main cavity and excurrent ostia have been described for many orthopteroids; such structures may be of wide occurrence but overlooked in insects; they are usual in myriapods and arachnoids.

The dorsal diaphragm is best developed in the abdomen, continuing into the thorax in a reduced condition. It consists of two sheets of connective tissue enclosing transverse muscles. In most insects these muscles form a triangle in each segment, the apex on the body wall and the broad base inserted on the ventral part of the wall of the dorsal vessel. The shape leads to the term **wing muscle** (Fig. 5.4A). Doubtless the primitive arrangement of these muscles is parallel rather than wing-like, but such a condition is not usual. The diaphragm is not always a continuous sheet. Often it is attached to the hypodermis only where the wing muscles originate, so that lunate apertures across the intersegmental divisions allow return of the blood into the dorsal sinus all along its length. In other cases the diaphragm consists of a network or mesh and sometimes it is present only as the covering for the muscle bundles.

The ventral diaphragm is essentially similar to the dorsal in structure but is rarely as well developed. Frequently it is only a layer-like series of separate muscles enclosed in connective sheathing, but in some grasshoppers and in the Hymenoptera it is a continuous sheet extending from the front of the thorax back into the seventh abdominal segment.

The importance of circulation through the wings is emphasized by the presence of special pulsating organs in the wing-bearing segments of so many Pterygota, accessory hearts ensuring a continual flow. In some Hemiptera and Diptera additional pulsating organs are present in the wings themselves. Blood enters via the costa, flows through the anterior veins and returns to the body through the posterior veins. Since the major veins also contain tracheoles bathed in flowing blood, the possibility of gas exchange in the wings cannot be excluded. As the blood leaves the wing it passes into a sinus formed between the dorsal body wall and a muscular plate. This sinus has a valve at its mesal opening so that the pumping action of the organ draws blood out of the wing and forces it either directly into the hemocoel or, as in some Sphingidae (Lepidoptera) and Dytiscidae (Coleoptera), through a special blood vessel leading to the aorta and thence to the head.

Circulation in the appendages is not left to chance. In grasshoppers and many other insects blood is led from the head cavity out into the antennae by tubular pulsating vessels beset with ostium-like valves. Thus blood flows outwardly through this organ, reaches the antennal wall by passing through the valves and is returned along the walls. Two kinds of devices in the legs have been described. In some cases there are tubular organs, more or less similar to those in the antennae, which pump blood to the tip of the leg, whence it returns along the walls, bathing the muscles and hypodermis en route. The second type involves the separation of an anterior and posterior appendicular sinus by a wall of muscle and membrane, the two sinuses being connected at the tip of the appendage, so that blood flows out through the anterior sinus and returns in the posterior. This arrangement sometimes also has a muscular "exhaust" pump near the appendage base which aspirates the return flow and sends it into the ventral sinus.

BLOOD SYSTEMS OF MYRIAPODS

The Chilopoda and Diplopoda have well-developed blood systems. The dorsal vessel extends the length of the trunk, with a chamber in each segment, though the segmental dilations are not well marked. Each chamber has a pair of lateral ostia entirely similar to those described above for insects and a pair of tiny excurrent vessels with two branches (Fig. 5.4D), one leading to the sides of the main cavity, the other to the fat bodies and midgut. The aorta is short, lying entirely in the head itself. It immediately branches to distribute blood throughout the cephalic sinus. A pair of semicircular vessels in the posterior part of the head connects the aorta with the ventral blood vessel. Ahead of these connecting vessels a short length of the ventral vessel leads also into the head where it branches around the gnathal nerve ganglia. Posteriorward, the ventral vessel extends to the caudal extremity. Tiny efferent vessels in each segment carry blood into the legs and to the segmental ganglia. The dorsal diaphragm is well developed and the muscles are arranged in triangular bundles in each segment, as in most insects. The dorsal sinus extends as far as the head.

Blood flows forward in the dorsal vessel, some of it being diverted into the segmental arteries; most either enters the head sinus or passes through semicircular connectives to the ventral vessel. In the ventral vessel, blood flows away from the connecting vessels, some going forward into the ventral part of the cephalic sinus, some flowing back toward the caudal end of the hemocoel. In each segment some blood is diverted through the lateral vessels. Blood reaches the hemocoel by several routes: directly from the lateral vessels of the dorsal and ventral vessels, or from the cephalic sinus. Below the dorsal diaphragm the flow is posteriorward and blood enters the dorsal sinus at its caudal end, thence into the heart by way of the ostia.

It is interesting to note that the system in Symphyla appears to be a simplified version of the chilopod-diplopod plan, with a pair of semi-circular vessels in the head connecting the dorsal and ventral vessels, rather than the insect plan, which does not include a specific ventral vessel.

The Pauropoda have neither blood vessels nor tracheae. Gas exchange must be cutaneous and circulation must depend on activity of the somatic musculature. Such an organization is feasible only for a tiny animal, like the pauropod, living in damp situations. It probably is not a primitive condition, but rather the result of loss during evolution.

BLOOD SYSTEMS OF ARACHNOIDS

In this class the development of the circulatory system varies from the comparatively complicated arrangement present in the exclusively pul-monary forms, where blood transports gases and must accordingly flow along definite, directionalized routes, to the complete atrophy of any organized system in some of the tiny species. Neither extreme is the primary condition. The greater number of arachnoids have tracheal sys-tems and the blood is involved very little if at all in gas transport; es-sential structures are similar to those found in insects.

The dorsal vessel is divided into a pulsating heart (Fig. 5.5A), generally confined to the anterior part of the abdomen, and an anterior aorta. In one family (the more primitive) of Thelyphonida and in the solpugids the heart extends into the last two cephalothoracic segments. The number of pairs of ostia, which varies from order to order, probably coincides with the number of segments that contribute to the pulsatile part of the dorsal vessel.

The dorsal vessel is held in place by a rather complete set of radiating muscle bundles which serve as ligaments and, by their contraction, to expand the heart chambers in diastole: a pair each of dorsal, dorso-lateral, lateral and ventral (Fig. 5.5A). The dorsal diaphragm is not developed into a flat sheet as in insects, but tends rather to be tube-like, enclosing the heart in a pericardial sinus, which is sometimes supplied with slit-like valves corresponding in position to the ostia. Below each ostium a small lateral efferent blood vessel generally is present, leading blood from the heart chambers into the main cavity outside the pericardial sinus. The aorta leads into the cephalothorax and, especially in pulmonate forms, may be quite complexly branched. Unlike the situation in insects where the posterior end of the dorsal vessel is said as a rule to be closed, in arachnoids it is open, dividing into right and left **posterior aortae** that lead blood into the caudal part of the abdominal hemocoel. Excurrent valves are placed at the ends of all arteries.

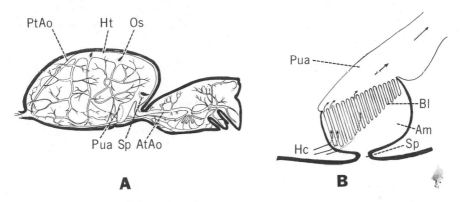

Figure 5.5. Circulation in spiders. (A) Schematic section of *Agelena labyrinthica;* (B) detail of book lung showing the route of the blood. *Am,* atrium; *AtAo,* anterior aorta; *Bl,* laminations of book lung; *Hc,* haemocoel; *Ht,* heart; *Os,* ostium; *PtAo,* posterior aorta; *Pua,* pulmonary artery; *Sp,* spiracle. (A redrawn from Millot, 1949e, by arrangement with Masson et Cie)

Thus the usual blood route in the dorsal vessel is in all directions from the middle: forward in the anterior aorta, caudad through the posterior aorta, lateral and ventral through the segmental arteries—all at the same time. In tracheate arachnoids blood returns to the pericardial sinus through its apertures, thence into the heart through the ostia.

The orders Pseudoscorpionida, Solpugida, Ricinuleida, Phalangiida and Acarida all have typical tracheal systems. The orders Scorpionida, Thelyphonida and Phryneida have **book lungs,** hence are pulmonate. The spiders are transitional in that some have tracheae only, some book lungs only, and most have both. Pulmonate respiration leads to certain complex modifications of the circulatory system, basically because the book lungs become a localized site for exchanging gases, and oxygen must then be distributed by the blood.

Book lungs are modified tracheae, confined to not more than four segments and more often to only two. They are hypodermal invaginations forming pockets (Fig. 5.5B) with deeply wrinkled and folded walls, thus presenting a comparatively extensive surface area where air and blood are separated only by thin tissue walls.

The scorpions, with four pairs of book lungs, possess a highly developed system of blood vessels. The anterior artery ramifies extensively, leading blood specifically into all appendages, to the nerve ganglia and eyes, to

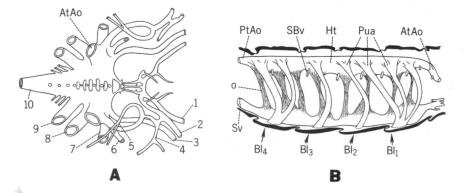

Figure 5.6. Circulatory system of *Buthus occitanus*. (A) Dorsal view of the arrangement of branches of the anterior aorta, all vessels cut through; (B) lateral view of cephalothoracic vessels associated with the book lungs. *AtAo*, anterior aorta; *Bl₁, Bl₂, Bl₃, Bl₄*, book lungs; *Ht*, heart; *0* subcardial median ligaments; *Pua*, pulmonary vessels; *PtAo*, posterior aorta; *SBv*, excurrent segmental vessels; *Sv*, sinus venosus; *1*, premaxillary artery; *2*, cheliceral artery; *3*, maxillary artery; *4*, tegumentary artery; *5*, ophthalmic artery; *6, 7, 8, 9*, arteries leading to the legs; *10*, spinal artery, leading into dorsal abdomen. (Redrawn from Millot and Vachon, 1949a, by arrangement with Masson et Cie)

the muscles and foregut; the eight pairs of lateral arteries from the heart proper service the midgut and other viscera; the posterior artery leads into the telson with tiny branches into the tail muscles (Fig. 5.6). All arterial ramifications empty into interstitial sinuses from which the blood is collected into a venous system. Two longitudinal ventral venous vessels lead to the entad part of the book lungs, where the blood must flow outward among the laminations, to be re-collected next to the integument and led by paired pulmonary sinuses into the pericardial cavity. The arrangement of the venous system is such that blood from the cephalothorax passes through the anterior book lung, blood from the tail passes through the posterior book lung, and blood from the midgut region passes through either of the two middle book lungs. The scorpion has, for practical purposes, a closed blood system "inferior" to that of the vertebrates only in that the venous part is made up of sinuses rather than true blood vessels.

THE BLOOD

Extensive data have accumulated on physical and physiological characteristics of blood, but they represent observations only on a random sample of species; much remains to be done before our understanding of arthropod blood is placed on a broad comparative basis. Variations in techniques and in validity of interpretation of data hamper attempts to reconcile published results, but much of the apparent inconsistency reflects the enormous diversity of the animals themselves.

Two classes of cells are present in insect blood: those properly part of the system and those belonging to other tissues and floating in the blood more or less accidentally. True blood cells, furthermore, are found both free in the **plasmolymph** or attached to various tissues in and around the circulatory system. The same cell type presents one aspect when free, another when attached. Phagocytes become variously disguised depending upon the material ingested. These factors help to account for the lack of an adequate system for classifying insect blood cell types. On the whole, the many systems proposed are more confusing than useful.

Insect blood cells probably can be reduced to three basic types, **proleucocytes, phagocytes** and **oenocytoids.**

Proleucocytes (Fig. 5.7A) are small, the proportionally large nucleus lying in a small volume of basophilic cytoplasm; they have often been observed in mitosis and may well be the lineal ancestors of other types; they are never phagocytic. The phagocytes (Fig. 5.7B) are extremely variable in size and shape, but generally have lightly basophilic cytoplasm. Because of their function, all sorts of inclusions may be present— foreign bodies, invading bacteria, fat globules, hydrolyzed tissue in transport. The inclusions often affect the descriptive characteristics of these cells and some workers have tried to classify and name the apparent variations. Oenocytoids (Fig. 5.7D) have been observed in Coleoptera, Lepidoptera, Hemiptera and Diptera, but have not been found in orthopteroids or in Hymenoptera. These are small cells (8–12 micra in diameter) with large nuclei and acidophilic cytoplasm; when present, they are never more than a small proportion of the total count.

For arachnoids, Millot has devised a much simpler system than is usually adopted by students of insect blood cells. He recognized three basic types which probably are homologous with the types listed in the preceding paragraph. Roughly fifty per cent of the blood cells are small

(7–20 micra in spiders, 6–8 micra in scorpions) with large nuclei and a small volume of basophilic cytoplasm (Fig. 5.7E). Millot (1949) used the term "hyaline leucocyte" for them; probably they are comparable with the proleucocytes found in insect blood. Phagocytes (Millot's "granular leucocytes") are eight to fifteen micra in diameter when free in the blood and undistorted by inclusions (Fig. 5.7G, H). The lightly basophilic

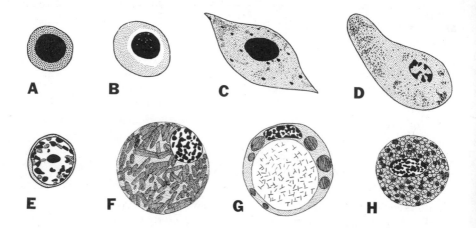

Figure 5.7. Blood cells of *Tenebrio molita* (Coleoptera) (A–D) and of the spiders *Tergenaria domestica* (E–G) and *Amaurobius similis* (H). (A) Proleucocyte ("prohemacytoid" of Jones); (B), (C) phagocytes ("smooth-contour chromophilic cell" and "granular plasmocyte"); (D) oenocytoid ("oenocyte-like cell"); (E) proleucocyte ("hyaline leucocyte" of Millot); (F) phagocyte ("acidophilic leucocyte"); (G) hemocyte with a phago-cytized vacuole enclosed; (H) phagocyte ("granular leucocyte"). (A–D re-drawn from Jones, 1950; E–H redrawn from Millot, 1949e, by arrangement with Masson et Cie)

cytoplasm contains numerous acidophilic granules. They make up forty to fifty per cent of the total cell count. The third type (Fig. 5.7F), "large acidophilic leucocyte," is about twenty-five micra across, with acidophilic cytoplasm. They account for not more than five per cent of the total and are not always present. Except for their size, these cells seem to resemble oenocytoids and likewise are of unknown function.

Concordant with the difficulty in identifying the germ layers of the embryo, hemocytes have been variously ascribed to the endoderm, meso-derm and ectoderm, with the consensus of opinion favoring the meso-derm. No blood-forming tissue has been identified in adult insects;

apparently new blood cells arise by mitosis from the pre-existing blood cells.

At the approach of ecdysis the number of hemocytes increases markedly, suggesting rather obviously that phagocytosis plays an essential role at this time. Increases also occur in connection with infection and parasitism. Because hemocytes are not necessarily floating free in the blood, differential counts probably are not significant.

The blood itself is essentially colorless, but usually pigments or other materials present lend it a hue typical of a species or even of a sex of a species. Green or yellow blood is most frequently observed, though almost every color does occur. It has not been proved that chlorophyll or its fractions color the blood of phytophagous insects, as was formerly believed; in fact, the agents lending color to the blood have not been identified. Insect blood is slightly acid (pH 6.2–7.2). Compared to human blood, insect blood has a generally higher total molecular concentration, a lower colloidal osmotic pressure, a protein content ranging from the same (6.6%) to as little as one per cent, and a significantly higher concentration of uric acid.

Buck (1953: 147) put it neatly, "The blood is the meeting place for the raw materials and products of nearly every physiological activity of the body." The raw materials and products are all found in it; their exact nature and the quantities present reflect the species, the individual's growth, age and health and to some degree local peculiarities of the environment. Buck concludes that "the concept of an 'average' insect blood has no validity." While the proteins present have not been fully or properly identified, several albumins and globulins have been found. Steinhaus (1949) showed that in at least some instances antigens produce an antibody response. Amino acids are present in an unusually high concentration, as much as fifty times as high as found in human blood, but only a few have been identified. Uric acid generally is present in a high concentration and urea normally in small quantities. Fermentable sugar, glycogen and unidentified nonfermentable reducing substances are present, but are extremely variable. Lipoids make up as much as one per cent of the blood volume. Hormones and enzymes are transported constantly. The inorganic constituents are exceedingly variable, but include acid-soluble nucleoprotein and lipid phosphorus; sodium, potassium and calcium (frequently as chlorides); sulfur and various trace elements including copper, iron, aluminum, zinc and manganese among others.

It has already been emphasized that in tracheated forms the blood system is not required to transport oxygen in the way necessary to vertebrates; the complex ramifications of the tracheal system delivering oxygen to or close to all employment sites make practical a much simpler circulatory system. Nevertheless the blood of these animals does make some contribution, minor but probably essential, by distributing oxygen in solution for short distances. This process may be partly direct diffusion, but at least the blood offers a facile medium. Nothing similar to an erythrocyte ever is present, but in certain cases gas-carrying molecules are dissolved in the blood.

Arachnoids with book lungs depend on the blood system for oxygen transport, increasingly as the tracheal system is reduced. In scorpions, where no tracheae are present, oxygen must be distributed entirely by the blood stream. The usual transporting molecule in arachnoids is hemocyanin, which while not as effective as hemoglobin, apparently is effective enough for the purpose. The aquatic larvae of many species of *Chironomus* (midges, Diptera) and the internally parasitic larvae of *Gasterophilus* (botflies, Diptera), have a hemoglobin dissolved in the blood. This material is half the molecular weight of vertebrate hemoglobin, but has a higher affinity for the oxygen molecule and is effective at a lower pO_2 range. Carbon dioxide, being far more soluble than oxygen, is always present in the blood in a higher concentration than found in vertebrates. It is not clear whether this gas is present because it is so readily dissolved or whether it is actually en route to an exchange site (tracheal system or book lungs) and is being regularly replaced.

MISCELLANEOUS HEMOCOELIC STRUCTURES

The **fat body,** the **nephrocytes** and the **oenocytes** are conveniently considered in connection with the circulatory system, though strictly speaking they are not a part of it.

The fat body, derived from intercoelomic mesoderm, sometimes forms a loose, discontinuous lining in the hemocoel with a parietal layer against the body wall and a splanchnic layer around the gut and organs; alternatively it is found in loose strands with no suggestion of organized layers. A segmental arrangement may sometimes be noticed. During early stages the fat body cells are generalized and have round or somewhat oval nuclei. As development progresses the nuclei alter in shape to become ribbon-like or stellate and the cell walls become difficult to see. Ultimately two kinds of cells may be distinguished; **trophocytes** and **urate cells.**

The trophocytes seem to be storage loci and typically are vacuolated. When the animal is well fed, the trophocytes are enlarged; during periods of starvation they diminish in size. Many adults, particularly those that do not feed, rely on nutritive fats, proteins and glycogens stored in the fat body during immaturity. A certain histological relationship between trophocytes and blood cells must exist: young trophocytes are almost indistinguishable from young blood cells; some observers have reported that trophocytes are capable of phagocytosis and even that they may sometimes break away from the fat body and circulate in the blood stream as phagocytes. Conversely, blood cells filled with ingested nutritive material have been reported as incorporating themselves into the fat body.

Urate cells differ mainly by the fact that they contain deposits of uric acid or urates, concretions which accumulate during life. In Collembola, an order lacking malpighian tubules, urate cells probably provide a major part of the solution to the excretory problem by affording more or less permanent storage. Despite claims to the contrary, there seems little doubt that in some insects the urate cells temporarily provide for excretion while the malpighian tubules are out of service during molting.

Nephrocytes are cells present in most arthropods scattered in the hemocoel in various ways. Their principal claim to fame at present is that they take up certain dyes (trypan blue, ammonia carmine) not eliminated by the malpighian tubules, but other than this affinity for dyes, little is actually known about them. A row (**pericardial cells**) is present in the dorsal sinus on each side of the dorsal vessel and other nephrocytes are likely to be found almost anywhere, including in the appendages. The pericardial nephrocytes, at least, do not store excretory materials; it has been suggested that they absorb colloid substances, transforming them into crystalline forms to be excreted eventually by the malpighian tubules.

Oenocytes originate from the ectoderm near the abdominal spiracles and are found in most insects. Their ultimate arrangement is various: they sometimes remain against the hypodermis, sometimes form projections into the hemocoel, sometimes disperse through the fat body. The best guess as to their function is that they are involved in secreting the cuticulin layer of the epicuticle and in forming the grease layer in cockroaches.

THE RESPIRATORY SYSTEM

Among the animals of interest in this book there are three kinds of respiratory systems. A tracheal system, a network of thin-walled tubes bringing air directly to all or most tissues, is present in insects, myriapods and many arachnoids. Book lungs, integumental pockets where gas is exchanged with the blood, are found in many arachnoids. Both tracheae and book lungs are present in numerous spiders. The third type, with no special structure and with gas exchange taking place through the cuticle, occurs only in small forms living in damp environments and always is a secondary development.

Despite their very different appearance and the diametrically opposite requirements they place on the blood system for oxygen transport, book lungs and tracheae are essentially the same morphological structures. The question of which, in the literal and historical sense, developed from the other has been debated by zoologists for more than a century and cannot be separated from basic problems of the broad phylogeny of arthropods. Three views have been advanced.

The classic position is that the original arthropods were aquatic and that their respiratory structures were something like the branchiae found on the appendages of such forms as *Xiphosura* (Chapter Ten). Great weight of evidence from fossil forms supports this idea. According to this view book lungs and tracheal systems must be terrestrial modifications of branchiae, the former only a minor adjustment and the latter a logical, inevitable development.

Another theory assumes that arthropods evolved on land and that the basic respiratory apparatus was the tracheal system; physiological improvements led to the reduction of tracheal ramification, with the book lung as its ultimate development. Aquatic branchiae are thought to be only a minor adjustment of book lungs, and the fossil "aquatic" scorpions are said to show that such an adjustment can easily be made.

The third school may be called "Head-under-Wing" or "Objective." In effect, its adherents say, "All this controversy is somehow undignified, and the evidence is all so confusing. We cannot interpret it, therefore it cannot be interpreted." This school views as parallel or convergent evolution any detectable similarity among branchiae, book lungs and tracheae, and holds that various phylogenetic lines happened to develop identical structures independently.

MYRIAPODS AND INSECTS

The tracheae form from invaginations of the lateral ectoderm in each metamere of the embryo. As these invaginations grow, they ramify until nearly all tissues of the segment are reached. Here the terminal cells of the tracheal hypodermis become flat and stellate. They enclose some tissues, grow between others, and in some cases are said to penetrate tissue cells. Within these terminal tracheal end cells (**tracheoblasts**) the **tracheoles** form—tiny intracellular cuticular tubules of the order of a tenth of a micron in diameter, connected with the ends of the tracheae and being, in effect, respiratory capillary systems.

The walls of the tracheal system thus are continuous with the integument and are histologically similar. The hypodermal cells become cuboid to pavement in shape (see Fig. 2.2B) and secrete a thin cuticle, the **intima,** strengthened by thickenings which generally are spiral. Richards and Korda (1950) used the electron microscope to demonstrate that similar helical strengthenings are present even in the tracheoles. Since it is part of the integument, the intima of the tracheal system is shed and replaced during each ecdysis.

In Diplopoda the tracheal system retains a simple, generalized arrangement despite the many specialized modifications of the skeleton and the wealth of variation achieved by that class. Characteristically each leg-bearing diplosegment, sometimes excepting the first and last in certain groups, has a right and a left tracheal system opening latero-ventrally on what seems to be the sternite. The opening itself (**spiracle, stigma**) is protected by a pair of lips having muscles that provide a valve-like action. The spiracle opens into an enlargement of the trachea, a pocket-like **atrium,** from which a number of tracheae branch into the segment. The system on each side of a diplosegment is independent, connected neither with the system on the opposite side nor with the systems of adjacent segments; there are no lateral trunks or transverse connectives.

Chilopods exhibit a wide range of variation in the development of the respiratory system. In a few genera the segmental systems are entirely separate; in a few other genera the right and left systems of each segment are connected with each other but not with the systems of neighboring segments. In most species longitudinal trunks and anastomoses integrate the systems on both sides of all segments into a unified whole. The number and arrangement of the spiracles vary from a pair (one on each side) on every leg-bearing segment except the first and last, to as few as only six pairs.

The tracheal system of the Symphyla resembles that of the Diplopoda, and preserves a pair of spiracles on the head, a very primitive feature. There is no anatomic respiratory system in the Pauropoda.

The apterygote insects possess tracheal respiratory systems which, on the whole, are predictably similar to myriapod systems.

The Collembola are small enough that they are able to rely on cutaneous respiration and the majority have lost the tracheal system. Only in *Sminthurus* is a complete, functional system preserved. Between the head and prothorax is a pair of spiracles, from each of which tracheae reach into all parts of one side of the body, but the right and left systems are not connected.

Two of the three families of Protura also have no tracheal systems. The

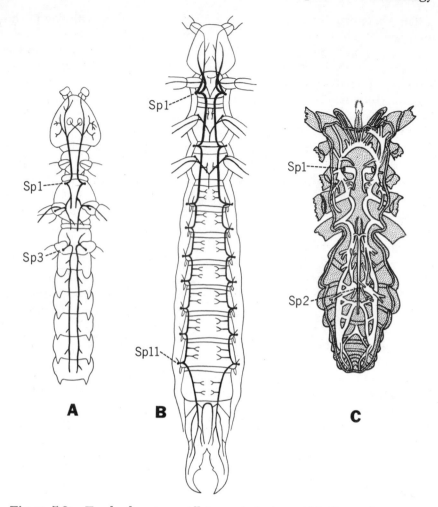

Figure 5.8. Tracheal systems, all in ventral view. (A) *Campodea* species (Aptera); (B) *Japyx* species (Aptera); (C) *Galeodes* species (Solpugida). *Sp1*, first spiracle, to *Sp11*, eleventh spiracle. (A and B redrawn from Grassi, 1887; C redrawn from Millot and Vachon, 1949b, by arrangement with Masson et Cie)

third family, the Eosentomidae, has two pairs of spiracles, respectively on the second and third thoracic segments. Here too the system on one side is entirely separate from that on the other.

Among the Aptera, members of the family Campodeidae have three separate systems on each side (Fig. 5.8A). The trachea servicing one side of the head opens through a spiracle placed at the anterior margin of the mesothoracic pleuron. A spiracle farther back on the mesothoracic pleuron leads to the tracheae of one side of the thorax. The system servicing one side of the abdomen opens through a spiracle on the metathorax. The other two families of this order always have a pair of spiracles on each of the first seven abdominal segments, and from two to four spiracles on the last two thoracic segments (Fig. 5.8B). A longitudinal trunk runs along each side, connecting the consecutive systems. Various degrees of right-left connections are found: in some cases there is only a small transverse connective at the posterior end between the eighth and ninth abdominal segments; in other cases there is a well-developed connective in each segment.

In the Thysanura, the bristle-tails (Machilidae) have spiracles on the second to the eighth abdominal segments, a spiracle on the mesothorax and one between the pro- and mesothorax. Each opens into an independent local system of tracheae, almost never connected with other systems. The silverfish (Lepismatidae) have spiracles on the last two thoracic and on the first eight abdominal segments. Longitudinal trunks are present on each side and there are transverse connectives in every segment.

In previous chapters it has been pointed out that, as a general principle in structural evolution in arthropods, the morphologic elements tend to become more simplified as the result of fusion or loss of parts. This principle—perhaps it is only a useful working hypothesis—was found to be true of leg segmentation, of mouthparts and of wing venation, for example. There is reason to believe that the same principle applies also to the evolution of the tracheal system. Thus the original tracheal system probably was made up of a series of systems, one on each side of each segment, with no system connected with any other and each having its own spiracular opening. Along most phylogenetic lines of tracheated arthropods two series of events have occurred: (1) Tracheal connectives, both longitudinal and transverse, formed; ultimately all the segmental systems are fused and become a single functional unit. In the Chilopoda the first step was to join by transverse connectives the two systems in a segment, later to develop longitudinal trunks; in most groups the reverse sequence seems to have occurred. (2) As the segmental systems become united, it becomes practicable to reduce the number of spiracles, a process logically associated with the formation of specialized body regions. The development of the ultimate, unified tracheal system is brought about by *fusion* of some of the original parts, by the *loss* of others; the net result is greater physiologic efficiency through morphologic simplification. Another evolutional trend is the complete *loss* of the tracheal system found in some members of many groups, but only possible in very small creatures.

It is never safe to evaluate the evolutional level of an animal by the modification of only one system, since one set of structures may undergo marked change while another system retains a primitive configuration. For example, in Diplopoda the skeleton is highly modified, but the tracheal systems on each side of each segment remain unconnected. The tracheal systems found among apterygote insects present some interesting phylogenetic problems. Certainly the respiratory structures both in *Sminthurus* (Collembola) and in the Eosentomatidae (Protura) are well evolved, although transverse connectives or anastomoses are lacking. A much more primitive condition is present in the supposedly more advanced Machilidae (Thysanura) and, in a different way, in the Campodeidae (Aptera). It is worth noting that while some members of both the Aptera and the Thysanura have well-developed tracheal systems which resemble the integrated system typical of pterygote insects, neither order attains the degree of evolution found in certain Collembola and Protura!

Despite numerous variations and modifications, the tracheal systems of Pterygota follow a generalized plan of organization. The spiracle opens into a short **spiracular trachea** which sends out three branches, one to the dorsal somatic region of the segment, one to the ventral somatic region with a branch into the appendage and one to the visceral tissues. Anterior and posterior branches of the spiracular, dorsal, ventral or visceral tracheae in adjacent segments may anastomose forming the main longitudinal trunks. Accordingly, there may be as many as four trunks on each side, but the visceral trunk is encountered somewhat infrequently and one or two of the others may be absent or incompletely developed. Transverse connectives form in all or most segments when principal branches of the dorsal or ventral tracheae of each side anastomose. The dorsal connective (**tracheal commissure**), when present, lies above the dorsal blood vessel, and the ventral connective runs beneath the nerve cord. All tracheae, trunks and connectives give off subsidiary branches which sometimes become larger and more impressive than the primary tracheae.

In many insects there are expansions of the tracheae, the **air sacs,** which lack the taenidia characteristic of usual tracheal walls and thus are quite delicate and flexible. There is no standard arrangement of air sacs in insects. There may be a great many small sacs or a few large ones, they may be scattered throughout the body or localized. When present they serve to increase the volume of air circulating in the system. Although air sacs are never provided with muscles, it is evident that normal movement of the body walls and even variation in blood pressure would force them to act as bellows. When filled, the sacs serve to decrease the animal's specific gravity—an advantage in flight; they are used by certain aquatic forms to control depth and vertical movements in the water.

Since the tracheal system is segmental, it would be supposed that every metamere should develop a pair of tracheal invaginations, at least in the embryo. Of the head segments, only the labial is known to form such invaginations. A functional labial spiracle is present in Symphyla and a few Collembola (*Sminthurus*). The tracheal invagination of the labial segment of the honeybee larvae gives rise to the cephalic tracheal system, but the spiracle is obliterated before the embryo hatches and the tracheae become part of the thoracic system. The Pterygota have a maximum of ten spiracles, a pair each on every segment from the second thoracic to the eighth abdominal. Prothoracic invaginations in the embryo have been reported for some insects and may be temporarily functional in the larva, but a true prothoracic spiracle never is present in an adult pterygote, although the mesothoracic spiracle sometimes migrates as far as the prothoracic pleuron and may be found in the membrane between the two segments. When fewer than ten spiracles are present in an adult insect, it may be assumed that some degree of evolutional advance is involved. Lost spiracles sometimes are represented by scars on the pleuron, but often they leave no trace. When an immature insect has fewer than ten spiracles, as frequently is the case among larvae of Diptera and other advanced orders, it is generally because they have not yet developed. Many Diptera hatch at an early embryonic level and lack, among other structures, a tracheal system. The tiny first instar larva respires cutaneously. The tracheal system may develop, often a bit at a time, during successive instars, or it may first appear only in the pupa.

Through the years a body of terms classifying tracheal systems on the basis of the functional spiracles present has been developed. Although widely used in introductory texts, these terms are of little value in connection with adult systems, but Keilin (1944) found them useful for the variations found in dipterous larvae. His system was:

A. **Polypneustic:** 8 or more pairs of functional spiracles
   1. **Holopneustic:** 2 thoracic and 8 abdominal spiracles
   2. **Peripneustic:** 1 thoracic and 8 abdominal spiracles
   3. **Hemipneustic:** 1 thoracic and 7 abdominal spiracles

B. **Oligopneustic:** 1 or 2 pairs of functional spiracles
   1. **Amphipneustic:** 1 thoracic and 1 "postabdominal" pair of spiracles
   2. **Metapneustic:** 1 pair of "postabdominal" spiracles only
   3. **Propneustic:** 1 pair of thoracic spiracles only
C. **Apneustic:** no functional spiracles

It must be emphasized that these arrangements of larval spiracles are special cases in embryology, not special kinds of tracheal systems. For most people, sets of terms like the foregoing are more likely to obscure than to elucidate a problem.

Among adult insects, two thoracic and eight abdominal spiracles are usual in almost every order. Even in those orders where adults of some or most of the groups have fewer spiracles, the basic number is often present at some stage of ontogeny and in adults of the more primitive genera. In the Isoptera, the queen termite has only six abdominal spiracles, but immatures, workers and soldiers have all eight. The metathoracic spiracle is never present in Lepidoptera or Hymenoptera and frequently is wanting in Mallophaga, Anaplura, Hemiptera, Coleoptera and Diptera. The first and last few abdominal spiracles may be missing in the larger and more advanced orders, as well.

Aquatic insects solve the respiratory problem posed by their chosen environment in several different ways. Adult Coleoptera and Hemiptera that dive beneath the water surface—and some of them stay under water for comparatively extended periods—carry respiratory air with them, both in the tracheal system and as a film around the body, this latter made possible by the clothing setae. Mosquito larvae and related groups must come to the surface of the water from time to time to replenish the air supply in the tracheae. In effect, all these insects "hold their breath" and are aquatic only to the extent that a man is aquatic when diving. *True* aquatic adaptations are present in the immatures of Ephemerida, Odonata, Plecoptera, Trichoptera and some Neuroptera and Diptera. In most of these cases, richly tracheated integumental evaginations are present during the aquatic instars—the adults are terrestrial and revert to a normal tracheal system—and the gills of these immatures are morphologically nothing more than modifications of the tracheal system. In some cases larval gills are direct evaginations at the spiracles, but often they are formed from other loci on the body wall. The branchial basket of immature dragonflies (Odonata) is the modified rectum, well tracheated, into which water is circulated. All these gills take in dissolved O_2 which is then distributed in the usual manner by the tracheal system. Certain aquatic larvae utilize cutaneous respiration. So-called "blood gills" are finger-like body wall evaginations containing hemolymph but not necessarily tracheae. They are present in a few immatures (e.g., *Chironomus* in the Diptera). They do not necessarily function in respiration, but more probably exchange water and ions (Wigglesworth, 1933).

The most elementary spiracle, as found generally in Apterygota and in a few primitive Pterygota, is just an opening of the trachea through the body wall, with no special arrangement present to prevent water evaporation or the entrance of foreign particles. A great diversity of modification is found among insects correcting these two shortcomings of the simple spiracle. The primary step is the formation of a pocket, the **atrium**, with the tracheal opening proper lying at its inner end. The walls of the atrium frequently are beset with interlacing setae or other kinds of processes which act as a filter for the entering air. The many different kinds of valve-like structures for controlling the aperture fall roughly into two categories: those placed at the outer end of the atrium and those at its inner end. Lip-like flaps are the commonest device of the former category, and they may be provided with muscles. Closing (and opening) structures placed at the inner end of the atrium sometimes are folds projecting from the atrial wall and moved up (opened) and down (closed) by a set of muscles, or may be a more complicated arrangement of muscles which serves to squeeze the aperture shut.

ARACHNOIDS

As previously noted, two different respiratory structures are present in the arachnoids. In three orders, Scorpionida, Thelyphonida and Phryneida, only book lungs are present. In five orders, Pseudoscorpionida, Solpugida, Ricinuleida, Phalangiida and Acarida, only tracheae are found. Of the spiders (Araneida) some have only book lungs, some have only tracheae and the rest have both at the same time. The tenth order, Palpigradida, have lost respiratory structures, as have some of the smaller Acarida.

Physiologically, these two kinds of structures are quite different indeed. Since tracheae carry oxygen to all parts of the body and directly service all the tissues, the presence of a well-developed tracheal system relieves the blood of most responsibility for oxygen transport. Book lungs set just the opposite physiological requirement. Gas exchange takes place only at a specific, localized site and the blood must transport oxygen to the tissues. It is natural and easy to regard these two kinds of structures as representing profoundly different structures. Yet the morphologic evidence shows that book lungs and tracheal systems are but variations in the development of the same lateral metameric invaginations of the embryonic ectoderm. Possibly the key to which of these two possibilities develops lies in whether or not the blood itself is *capable* of oxygen transport.

Vandel (1949) thought that tracheae in terrestrial arthropods were developed independently by the several major groups. Millot (1949a), agreeing, noted that book lungs must have preceded tracheae because scorpions and primitive spiders have them, though at the same time he acknowledged the essential homology between book lungs and tracheae. These conclusions on evolution are based on certain assumptions which may not be sound. It might help if it were recognized that (1) nearly all metameres (head and terminal metameres excepted) can produce ectodermal respiratory invaginations; (2) these invaginations may become tracheae or book lungs, depending upon the ability of the blood to transport oxygen and upon the size of the animal; (3) there is no reason to establish segmental homologies with the branchial evaginations of living Crustacea; (4) living arachnoids all are highly evolved, no synthetic form survives and the scorpions are not strictly a primitive order (as Snodgrass emphatically recognized). Finally, since the arachnoids do not and have not received a fraction of the attention that has been devoted to insects, our knowledge of them remains at a far more elementary level.

A book lung (Fig. 5.5B) is an invaginated pocket in which the integument is deeply infolded to form numerous respiratory surfaces arranged like the separated leaves of a book or, in cross section, like the teeth of a comb. The number of **lamellae** varies from five to several hundred. They are thin-walled and little columns of cuticle keep them apart to ensure air circulation among them. The blood circulatory system is modified to ensure that all blood passes through the internal surfaces of the lamellae as part of a determined route. The spiracle leading to the lung has a pair of lips under muscular control, serving to determine the size of the aperture. The atrium itself often has muscles arranged so that a pulsating inhalation and exhalation occur. Differences in structure of book lungs among the various arachnoid groups are amazingly slight. These organs are similar in all forms having them, and are always located latero-ventrally.

The scorpions have four pairs of book lungs located on the fourth, fifth, sixth and seventh abdominal segments. The Phryneida and the suborder Holopeltidea (Thelyphonida) have two pairs of lungs placed on the second and third abdominal segments. The other suborder of the Thelyphonida, the Schizopeltidea, have only one pair, those of the second abdominal segment.

Solpugids have a highly developed tracheal system (Fig. 5.8C) entirely comparable with that of the insects. Spiracles are located between the third and fourth and between the fourth and fifth abdominal segments, and in some members a third pair is placed between the fifth and sixth segments. Of considerable interest is the presence, on the ventral side of the cephalothorax, of another pair of spiracles placed between the coxae of the third and fourth ambulatory appendages (between the fourth and fifth cephalothoracic segments). The system penetrates the appendages and directly services all tissues; large longitudinal trunks run the length of the body and transverse connectives occur in nearly every segment.

Despite their name and appearance, the Pseudoscorpionida are not closely related to the scorpions. A pair of spiracles on the third abdominal segment opens into a pair of anterior tracheal trunks which branch into the forward part of the body. The other pair of spiracles, on the fourth abdominal segment, leads to the posterior trunks which service the abdomen. The two sides of the anterior and posterior systems are poorly connected and there are, in effect, four separate systems.

Phalangiida have a spiracle on the second abdominal segment and the tracheal system is well developed. The family Phalangiidae ("daddy longlegs") have auxiliary spiracles on the tibiae of the legs.

Acarida have tracheal systems, except a few groups that depend exclusively on cutaneous respiration. Spiracles are located somewhere on the cephalothorax and their position is one of the more useful taxonomic characters. They may be on almost any segment (cephalothoracic segments are almost impossible to identify and number in this order) and may be ventral, lateral or dorsal, or some combination of positions. There may be from one to four pairs. Similarly, the tracheal system may be very well developed or it may be so elementary as to be of little real use.

The small, aberrant order Ricinuleida have a single pair of spiracles on the dorsal side of the fifth cephalothoracic segment. Each opens into a relatively large **atrium** equipped with several sets of muscles which enable lung-like inhalation and exhalation. A large number of minute, unbranched tracheae lead directly from the atrium into all tissues.

In spiders there are two pairs of ventral spiracles respectively placed on the second and third abdominal segments. While these openings generally are at the anterior end of the abdomen, segmental modification in a few families separates them so that the posterior pair is near the tip, fused into a single median spiracle. Each spiracle opens into an atrium (**pulmonary chamber**) which either has its walls folded into the lamellae of book lungs or gives rise to two main tracheae. Both book lungs and tracheae are found in diverse levels of development. There may be as many as 150 lamellae in a book lung, or as few as four or five. The main tracheae may ramify richly into all parts of the body and appendages, or they may have only a few branches and reach only a very limited part of the abdomen. The tracheal intima has helical taenidia in members of only one of the fifty-seven families and in two genera of another family. In all other spiders with tracheae, the intima bears erect little spines with ramified tips collectively forming a network in the lumen. In brief, the book lungs of spiders are just like book lungs present in other arachnoids, while the tracheal system is entirely similar to that of insects except for the different method of internal support in the tubes.

The two primitive suborders, Liphistiomorpha and Mygalomorpha, have only book lungs The Araneomorpha, the third suborder, comprising ninety per cent or more of living spiders, include two families with book lungs only, two families with tracheal systems only, and forty-two families in which the anterior pair of spiracles opens into book lungs while the posterior pair opens into tracheal systems. It is among these spiders with both systems present that the widest variations in anatomic development are found. One would expect that where the book lungs are poorly developed, having few lamellae, the tracheal system would be well developed in functional compensation, but such is not necessarily the case. Sometimes both are very well developed; in other cases, both are poorly developed.

Arachnologists are far from unanimous in interpreting all this variation in respiratory systems. Petrunkevitch (1933) relied heavily on the combinations of book lungs and tracheae and their development in erecting a major reorganization of the Araneida, but Millot (1949e) maintained that Petrunkevitch's system was unjustified and misleading because (in his opinion) respiratory systems in living spiders are the result of a great many separate lines of evolution. It does seem clear, however, that book lungs and tracheal systems are essentially homologous, representing in the arachnoids two more or less interchangeable ways of developing the same basic structure. If this is so, the respiratory system of insects, myriapods and arachnoids probably all are homologous in that they represent metameric invaginations of the lateral ectoderm and there is no evidence that these invaginations form anywhere but at the same morphologic loci.

REPRODUCTIVE SYSTEM

Unlike other organ systems, the reproductive system plays no role in the physiological activities of the individual and contributes nothing to the individual's survival *as* an individual. Secretion of hormones by the gonadal structures, a characteristic function in Chordata, has not been demonstrated in insects; on the contrary, the hormones affecting secondary sexual characters appear to originate at other sites. Neither castration nor the transplating of gonads of the opposite sex into the individual appears to have any effect on either secondary sexual characters or behavior. The reproductive system thus is simply the production line for sperms or eggs and the mechanism for getting them together. It looks only to the next generation and maintains only the continuity of species. In a sense, all other systems and structures exist for the support of the reproductive system, receiving nothing directly in return.

The parts of the reproductive system may be subsumed under four categories: (a) the germ cells, (b) the gonads, (c) the ducts, (d) the external structure of copulation and oviposition.

Early in embryonic development certain cells cease to contribute to developing tissues. These primordial germ cells (see Fig. 7.1) become associated with the mesodermal genital ridge and eventually are enclosed by the gonads, which develop from the ridge. The primordial germ cells are thus apart from and precede the germ layers. Whether the first primordial germ cell is self-determined—that is, a cell which appears at an early cleavage stage and is destined to be the lineal ancestor of the gametes *because* of its inherent internal organization—or whether germ cell determination is vested in a specific position in the egg cytoplasm, into which a generalized cleavage cell happens to migrate, thus becoming the primordial germ cell, in no way reduces the validity of Weismann's germ-plasm theory as a basic concept (discussed in most introductory zoology or biology texts).

The gonads themselves are essentially metameric, but segmentally arranged gonads are present in only a few living forms—most immatures and a few adults of Thysanura, for example, where six or seven segmental gonads open into the duct system. The usual arrangement is a pair of gonads, right and left, representing the result of migration and coalescence of segmental elements, or the proliferation of one segmental structure, or sometimes some of both. Each gonad consists of a tube or a group of tubes (follicles in the testis, ovarioles in the ovary) in the hemocoel and lying above, beside or under the enteron. The female gonad is suspended by a ligament from the dorsal hemocoel wall; in the male these ligaments are generally (but not always) lost during development. A mitotic descendant of the primordial germ cells lies at the apex of each follicle or ovariole. At maturity, proliferation of the apical cells, a process involving both mitosis and meiosis (see Chapter Seven), leads to the formation of

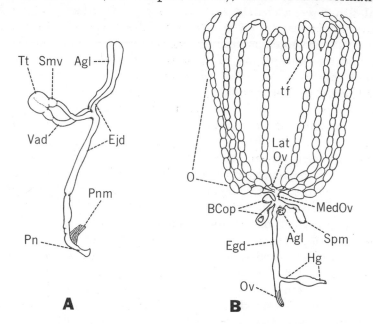

A   **B**

Figure 5.9. Reproductive systems of *Fumea casta* Pallas, a bagworm moth (Lepidoptera). (A) Male; (B) female. *Agl,* accessory gland; *BCop,* bursa copulatrix; *Egd,* egg exit duct; *Ejd,* ejaculatory duct; *Hg,* hindgut; *LatOv,* lateral oviduct; *MedOv,* median oviduct; *O,* ovary; *Ov,* ovipositor; *Pn,* penis; *Pnm,* penis muscle; *Smv,* seminal vesicle; *Spm,* spermathecal duct; *tf,* terminal filament; *Tt,* testes; *Vad,* vasa deferentia. (Redrawn from Williams, 1947)

sperms and eggs, each step of the process taking place, as the cells move down the tubes into the ducts, at a regular point. This in turn leads to modification of the gonadal tubes into frequently recognizable segments, especially in the female. Thus an ovariole (Fig. 5.9B) has three generally distinct zones: (a) The terminal filament is the dorsal prolongation of the epithelium and forms the suspensory ligament which is almost always attached to the dorsal hemocoel wall, though sometimes the filaments lie free. (b) The apical section of the tube itself is the **germarium** where the primordial cells proliferate, as do the nutritive cells when they are present. (c) The rest of the ovariole, usually the greater length, is enlarged and contains the developing egg cells (see Fig. 7.3). In the testes (Fig. 5.9A) regional differentiation is less marked, except by the stage of development attained by the germinal cell within. Terminal filaments ordinarily are not present, though in a few groups they form suspensory ligaments or lie free in the body cavity. The apical zone, where the primordial germ cells proliferate, is the **germarium;** the region of spermatogonial proliferation is the **zone of growth;** the region of meiosis is followed by the **zone of transformation** (see Fig. 7.2). None of these zones normally presents variation in external appearance. Each gonadal tube consists of an epithelial layer resting on an outer basement membrane, outside of which is connective tissue forming a peritoneum abundantly penetrated by tracheoles and often containing muscle fibers. Infolding of the inner epithelial layer forms cysts enclosing groups of developing male gametes, or a female oöcyte, as the case may be.

The gonadal tubes come together distally, all those on one side opening into a duct. The paired ducts join to form the common duct, which in turn leads to the external genital aperture. These parts are known respectively as the paired **vasa deferentia** and the median **ejaculatory duct** in the male, the **paired oviducts** and the **median oviduct** and **vagina** in the female. The proximal parts of the paired ducts are continuuous with the gonadal tissue and are mesodermal. The common duct and usually the distal part of the paired ducts are ectodermal, formed by a tubular invagination of the integumental material. The ectodermal part has a cuticular intima, absent in the mesodermal parts. The exact point where the ectodermal part of the ducts stops and the mesodermal part begins is subject to considerable variation. In general, advanced forms show a greater contribution from the ectoderm and a proportionate shortening of the mesodermal tubes. Various special structures such as glands and diverticula form on the duct system. In the male these glands secrete fluids ejected with the spermatozoa as a seminal medium, or form the **spermathecal sac.** The **accessory glands** of the male system usually are derived from the ectodermal part of the ducts, but may sometimes be derived from the mesodermal part. Diverticula, the **seminal vesicles,** may be present on the ectodermal section of the paired vasa deferentia, serving as storage pockets for matured spermatozoa.

In the female system, the accessory glands are located near the terminus and function in connection with egg laying. The secretions serve to glue the egg in place or to clothe the egg mass in a protective coating, as appropriate. Where the egg is retained for hatching and the larva develops internally, as in viviparous Diptera, the **colleterial glands** supply nutritive material. It will be recalled that the sting of Hymenoptera is the modified ovipositor (female external genitalia); in these insects at least one of the accessory glands is modified to secrete the toxic or irritating material injected by the sting. Diverticula found in the female duct system include the **egg calyces,** in which matured egg cells are stored, the **spermatheca,** in which sperms are stored after copulation, and the **bursa copulatrix,** which serves as a copulatory pouch.

Both presumed phylogeny and embryonic development suggest that the segmental gonads originally opened laterad through short ectodermal genital pores on every gonad-bearing segment. This condition is found in living arthropods only in the highly problematic class Pycnogonida. In all myriapods, insects and arachnoids—even in the rare instances where the gonads themselves seem to be segmentally arranged—paired longitudinal ducts always are present and almost always lead to a single ventral position. In some of the more primitive forms—the Diplopoda and, among the insects, Ephemerida and male Dermaptera—there are two genital openings side by side.

In arachnoids the median ventral genital opening is on the second abdominal segment; in diplopods it is between the second and third legs on the anterior part of the third trunk segment; in symphylids it is on the fourth evident trunk segment; in pauropods it is on the posterior edge of the second trunk segment. Whether the anterior placement of the genital opening shows any relationship between the arachnoids and the other groups mentioned is very doubtful, but along with a good many other structures, it helps establish a close connection among the three myriapod groups. The fourth myriapod group, the Chilopoda, like the Insecta, have the genital opening at the posterior end of the abdomen. This has often been interpreted as establishing the relationship between the two, but is of doubtful value for the purpose; their relationship is better supported on other grounds.

The duct system of male insects (except Collembola) opens on the posterior side of the ninth abdominal segment. An intromittent organ is not always present; when it is, its tip is usually taken to be the external opening of the ejaculatory duct. While this is true for practical purposes, Snodgrass (1935) emphasizes that a secondary invagination, which he called the **endophallus,** may be present in many insects, and that the endophallus should not be confused with the ejaculatory duct, which opens into it.

In female insects (again excepting the Collembola) the developing paired lateral oviducts open originally into an ectodermal pouch between the seventh and eighth abdominal sternites, but among adults, only the Dermaptera have this condition. Since intersegmental membranes are derived from the segment behind them, the basic invagination probably is derived from the eighth segment; in most insects the female ectodermal pocket is clearly a derivation of the eighth segment. The accessory glands around this pocket come to be drawn inside the genital chamber when it enlarges, a condition typical of most advanced orders. Near its terminus the ectodermal part of the median common oviduct widens to form the **vagina** or **genital chamber,** of which the spermatheca is the inner part, while the outer part may become the bursa. The modifications of appendicular and scleritic structures to form the ovipositor and the external genitalia were discussed in Chapter Three.

Control Systems

The nervous system is the primary mechanism of co-ordination and control in the body. But as in the better known vertebrates, internal secretions—either regular or periodic in occurrence—supplement and complement the nervous system in arthropods.

THE NERVOUS SYSTEM

As in all animals, **receptors** are placed on the arthropod body surface in such a way that activity or change in the environment can be detected. In complexity, receptors vary from simple tactile setae to the multi-cellular, highly organized eyes. Each receptor or receptive unit is associated with a **dendron.** The external stimulus—light, heat, sound, chemical activity, touch—is translated into an impulse which travels through the **sensory neuron** to a **ganglion.** Here the stimulus is identified and interpreted. If the external event initiating a nerve impulse is of such a nature as to lead to some response on the part of the animal, an impulse then travels from the ganglion to an **effector**—generally a muscle or set of muscles, though sometimes a gland—by way of a **motor neuron.** The result is muscular (or glandular) activity.

This is what occurs in principle, though the statement of it is a gross oversimplification. Even the most elementary activity of the nervous system is impressively complex, and almost nothing is found in its most elementary form in the arthropods under review.

The histologic unit is the **neuron** (Fig. 6.1A), a specialized ectodermal cell having a small quantity of cytoplasm surrounding the nucleus and giving off slender cell extensions which may be of considerable length.

The essential characteristic of the neuron is the ability to receive an impulse at the end of one of these extensions and transmit it past the nucleus (in the central cell body) to the tip of another extension. In all neurons the impulses travel only in one predetermined direction. The nervous system as a whole, consisting of a series of connected neurons, may be roughly compared with a direct current electrical system. An extension of a neuron transmitting impulses toward the central cell body is called a **dendron** (dendrite, afferent fiber); an extension transmitting impulses away from the central cell body is an **axon** (axone, efferent fiber). A neuron may have several dendrons but only one axon, although an axon may have one or more large branches called **collaterals.** The tips of dendrons, axons and collaterals are ramified, forming **arborizations.** When a neuron has two cell extensions it is said to be **bipolar;** when more than two are present, the cell is **multipolar.**

Motor neurons, with their central bodies in ganglia, extend axons to effector organs. Sensory neurons have their central bodies near the receptor, usually in or against the hypodermis, or sometimes gathered into subsidiary ganglia; their axons transmit impulses to central ganglia.

The point where the axon of one neuron contacts the dendron of another is called a **synapsis** (Fig. 6.1B). Synapses may be likened to solder joints between two electrical wires, but they are more complex than that, in fact. Under certain circumstances they may act as filters or as relays. Particularly at the **internuncial neurons,** which connect sensory and motor pathways, it is possible for impulses to arrive simultaneously from several points of origin, so that filter and relay mechanisms are necessary to avoid confusion. Although neuronic synapses in terrestrial arthropods have been insufficiently investigated, it may be inferred from studies on other animals that here, too, the synapses serve to select and route multiple impulses.

A ganglion (Fig. 6.1B) has a central mass of medullary tissue (**neuropile**) consisting of the intermixed axons and dendrons of motor and internuncial neurons and the terminal arborizations of sensory dendrons. Motor and internuncial cell bodies with their nuclei form a peripheral zone around the medullary material. There are two sheath layers, both derived from ectoderm: The inner is made up of **neuroglial** cells, which have their cell bodies in the ganglion and send branching extensions out along the nerves and nerve trunks. The neuroglia supports the neurons both mechanically and physiologically. The outer sheath is a very thin, delicate sheet, the **neural lamella,** also found around the nerves and trunks. It is said to serve as an insulation, especially against potassium ions in the blood.

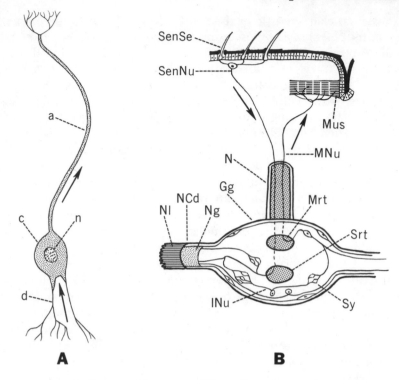

A   **B**

Figure 6.1. (A) General structure of a neuron; (B) diagram of a central ganglion showing relationships with sensory and motor elements. In both figures the arrows indicate the direction of impulses. *a*, axon; *c*, central body of the cell; *d*, dendron; *Gg*, ganglion; *INu*, internuncial neuron; *MNu*, motor neuron; *Mrt*, motor root of a segmental nerve; *Mus*, muscle; *N*, segmental nerve; *n*, cell nucleus; *NCd*, central nerve cord; *Ng*, neuroglia; *Nl*, neural lamella; *SenNu*, sensory neuron; *SenSe*, sensory seta; *Srt*, sensory root of a segmental nerve; *Sy*, synapsis.

The term **nerve** is commonly applied to bundles of ensheathed neuronic extensions leading from ganglia to various parts of the body. A nerve generally includes both motor and sensory cell extensions, though some nerves contain exclusively one or the other. Axons are surrounded by a layer of protein molecules (Richards, 1943, 1944) probably similar to, if not identical with, vertebrate myelin. A **nerve trunk** is a larger nerve, particularly the unbranched segment near a ganglion.

The **central nerve cords** are two longitudinal nerve trunks running side by side connecting the ventral chain of segmental ganglia. Their medullary tissue includes mainly fibers from internuncial and motor neurons, and frequently sensory fibers as well.

The nervous system is ordinarily divided into the **central, peripheral** and **visceral systems.** These are not coequal parts; all are interconnected and interrelated. The peripheral system designates inclusively all of the central system except the ventral ganglia and cords. The visceral (**sympathetic**) system possibly qualifies better for separate consideration, but it must be kept in mind that it too is closely connected to and interrelated with the central system.

CENTRAL NERVOUS SYSTEM

Every metamere basically has a pair of ventral ganglia connected with each other by a **transverse commissure,** and with the ganglia of adjacent segments by the paired ventral nerve cord. From each ganglion nerve trunks lead to all parts of one side of the segment, including the appendage when it is present. Trunks containing both motor and sensory fibers have a double origin at the ganglion. A dorsal root carries motor fibers only, a ventral root sensory fibers only (Fig. 6.1B); the two roots immediately fuse into the trunk.

The annelid–arthropod central nervous system is fundamentally made up of a connected series of separate, serially identical units (Fig. 6.2A) in which each unit provides only for the structures in its own segment. The numerous modifications of the central system seem to tend toward overcoming segmental independence, effecting improvements in coordination by centralizing the control of certain activities. Such functional modifications are correlated with morphologic modifications. The extent that an arthropod has departed from the simple, prototypic arrangement of the central nervous system may be taken as one clue to its degree of evolutional progress.

Some primitive adults, a certain number of immatures and most embryos have the paired ganglia well separated in a segment; progressive development leads to fusing each pair into a single mass with the transverse commissure embedded within; further, the paired ventral cords may lie so close together that they appear to be a single cord.

Beginning with the head, there is a persistent trend to bring together ganglia of adjacent segments to form functional centers—brains and subbrains. Only in arachnoids does this serial fusion result in a single superganglion fairly designated the "brain" (Fig. 6.2D). In insects and myriapods there are two centers in the head, one above and one below the esophagus; the trunk ganglia of myriapods (Fig. 6.2B) are rarely collected into functional "sub-brains," but in pterygote insects (Fig. 6.2C) the thoracic ganglia tend to form a third center, to which abdominal ganglia are sometimes added. Division of the body into specialized regions is followed by a parallel development of regional control centers in the nervous system.

In insects (Fig. 6.3) and myriapods the head capsule contains two ganglionic masses, one above and one below the anterior end of the foregut. The **supraesophageal mass**, often called the "brain" for convenience, has three parts, the **protocerebrum** (**forebrain**), the **deutocerebrum**

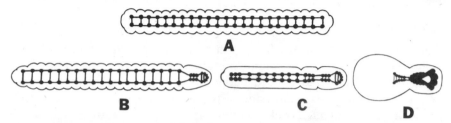

Figure 6.2.   Diagrams of (A) the ventral (central) nerve "ladder" characteristic in principle of Arthropoda and Annelida; (B) modification characteristic of Myriapoda, in which the anterior three ganglia form the supraesophageal mass and the three ganglia associated with the mouthparts form the subesophageal ganglion, but the trunk ganglia maintain their segmental positions; (C) further modification characteristic of Insecta, in which the three thoracic ganglia tend to fuse into a mass and the posterior ganglia tend to form a genital mass; (D) the extreme "cephalization" characteristic of Arachnida, in which segmental relationships of the ganglia become completely obscured.

(**midbrain**) and **tritocerebrum** (**hindbrain**), the whole roughly shaped like an inverted **V**, the last two parts dividing into right and left halves which straddle the esophagus. From the two tritocerebral halves the main nerve cords pass down- and backward on each side of the esophagus to the **subesophageal mass,** a second "brain" formed from the ganglia of the mandibular, maxillary and labial segments.

The protocerebrum has a central mass which is derived primarily from the closely fused ganglia of the first (preantennal) segment and which encloses a system of commissures and chiasmata. From the central mass, neural tracks lead to the visual receptors and to the **mushroom bodies** (**corpora pedunculata**); within it, numerous fibers converge from other ganglia. The corpora pedunculata especially are responsible for making the protocerebrum the most important association center in the head, but since the neurons are sensory, the corpora may have been originally olfactory (Vandel, 1949). That the mushroom bodies are derived by

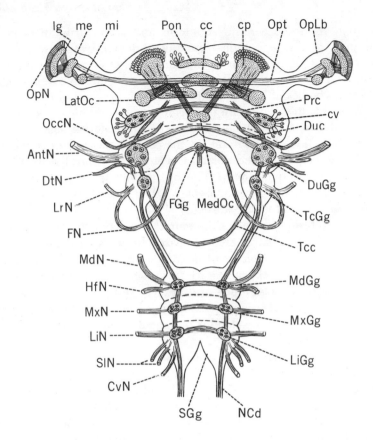

Figure 6.3. Cephalic part of the central nervous system of insects, diagrammatic. *AntN*, antennal nerve; *cp*, corpus pedunculatum; *cc*, corpus centrale; *cv*, corpus ventrale (probably the true procerebral ganglion); *CvN*, cervical nerve; *DtN*, dorsal tegumental nerve; *Duc*, deutocerebral commissure; *DuGg*, deutocerebral (antennal) ganglion; *FGg*, frontal ganglion; *FN*, frontal nerve; *HfN*, hypopharyngeal nerve; *LatOc*, lateral ocellar lobe; *lg*, lamina ganglionaris; *LiGg*, labial ganglion; *LiN*, labial nerve; *LrN*, labral nerve; *MdGg*, mandibular ganglion; *MdN*, mandibular nerve; *me*, medulla externa; *MedOc*, median ocellar lobe; *mi*, medulla interna; *MxGg*, maxillary ganglion; *MxN*, maxillary nerve; *Ncd*, central nerve cord; *OccN*, occipital nerve; *OpLb*, optic lobe; *OpN*, optic nerve; *Opt*, optic tract; *Pon*, pons cerebralis; *Prc*, protocerebral commissure; *SGg*, subesophageal ganglionic mass (in outline); *SlN*, salivary nerve; *Tcc*, tritocerebral commissure; *TcGg*, tritocerebral (intercalary) ganglion. (Based on Snodgrass, 1935, modified and reinterpreted)

delamination from the acronic ectoderm and secondarily incorporated into the mass of the preantennal ganglia is demonstrated by the early embryogenesis of many myriapods and primitive insects. Thus Holmgren, Hanström and others were probably correct in assuming a homology in the mushroom bodies of both Annelida and Arthropoda, but erred in concluding from this that the entire protocerebrum is acronic.

The **optic lobes,** from which emerge the **optic nerves** leading to the compound eyes, lie anterio-lateral on the central mass; the **ocellar lobes** and **ocellar nerves** lie on the dorsal aspect of the central mass beneath the ocelli they respectively serve. The size and complexity of these lobes are correlated with the development of their receptors; the lobes are absent when the receptors are absent.

The deutocerebrum consists of the paired ganglia of the second (antennal) segment. The two halves are only partly fused as a rule, the posterior parts being separated and each half bearing a prominent lateral **antennary lobe.** The large nerve track leading to the antennal lobe and a smaller one to the central body (**dorsal lobe**) are sensory. Motor nerves to the antennae are either contained in an **accessory antennal nerve** or incorporated into the antennal nerve. The slender **tegumentary nerves** from the dorsal lobe service the vertex.

The tritocerebrum, lying behind and beneath the deutocerebrum, is a pair of small ganglia belonging to the third (intercalary) segment, which bears no appendages in insects and myriapods. The only trunks from the hindbrain are the paired **labrofrontal nerves,** each with two branches; one leads to the labrum and clypeus, the other to the **median frontal ganglion,** the anteriormost element of the visceral system. The segmental commissure between the tritocerebral ganglia loops back and under the esophagus (**subesophageal** or **substomodaeal commissure**); in some groups it may be incorporated into the two nerve cords and the anterior part of the maxillary ganglia, and thus is not discernible as a separate structure. Its position beneath the esophagus indicates that the tritocerebrum—hence the intercalary segment—is primitively postoral and that it has assumed its position above the esophagus secondarily, either because the esophagus has moved posterior or because the intercalary ganglia have been drawn forward. Neither theory has been proved.

The subesophageal mass is always completely fused, hence it is not clear from adult structures just how many pairs of ganglia really contribute to it. Paired trunks supply the mandibles, maxillae and labium; smaller nerves service the hypopharynx, the salivary glands and some of the cervical muscles. Most of these nerves contain both sensory and motor fibers.

In the myriapods the ventral chain of ganglia extends back into the penultimate segment. From each segmental ganglion three pairs of nerve trunks emerge, two of which lead to the body wall, the third to various visceral structures. These ganglia remain associated with the segments to which they belong, with no serial fusion; complete lateral fusion, both of the ganglia in each segment and of the ventral cords, is usual.

Insects have the ventral chain arranged in a basically similar fashion, but the primitive condition is present in adults only of Thysanura and Aptera. Fourteen trunk ganglia have been observed in many embryos, both of primitive and of specialized groups, located in the three thoracic and the eleven abdominal segments. The pair in the eleventh abdominal segment fails to appear in other insect embryos. The last three or four pairs of ganglia soon coalesce into a terminal center, so that in many adults no more than eight or nine pairs can be counted.

Regional specialization of the insect trunk leads to the concentration of segmental ganglia and the shortening of the ventral chain—a trend not possible in the myriapods, where the trunk ganglia are committed to servicing the many pairs of legs. In winged insects an additional pair of nerve trunks leads from the meso- and metathoracic ganglia and controls the flight muscles. Frequently the first few abdominal ganglia are added to the metathoracic ganglia; sometimes the second and third or all three thoracic ganglia fuse, forming, in effect, a special control center for locomotion. In the more advanced families of Diptera and Hemiptera all the abdominal and thoracic ganglia are fused into a single mass in the thorax. The extreme of centralization is attained by scale insects and plant lice (Hemiptera), where this thoracic mass is coalesced with the subesophageal mass.

The central nervous system of arachnoids is basically the same as in all other arthropods. Differences in its arrangement in adults as compared to insects and myriapods are the consequences of (1) differences in the identity and number of segments and their arrangement into regions and (2) the high level of evolutional modification present in all living arachnoids. Unlike the situation noted in myriapods and insects, no truly primitive arachnoid survives today.

It will be recalled from Chapter Two that in arachnoids the preantennal and antennal segments, although they begin to form in the embryo, regress early in embryogenesis and contribute nothing to the adult skeleton (see Table 2.1). It might be expected, then, that both the protocerebrum and deutocerebrum would disappear along with the segments from which they are derived: only the deutocerebrum completely regresses. The protocerebrum, involved as the optic center of arthropods, is retained for the same function in arachnoids, and in some orders the acronic contribution also is present. In the class as a whole, there is a strong tendency toward reduction of the size and importance of the protocerebrum as compared to its development in other arthropods. The corpora pedunculata are completely wanting in the more advanced arachnoid orders, and sometimes the two halves of the protocerebrum remain separated, connected only by the commissure, and appear to have no function except in connection with the visual receptors.

The tritocerebrum, as has been noted, may have two functions: innervation of the appendages of the intercalary segment and connection with the sympathetic system by way of the frontal ganglion. The tritocerebrum is seen to be small in insects and myriapods, since the intercalary segment bears no appendages, and perhaps is preserved because of the relationship with the sympathetic system. In Crustacea, in which the intercalary segment bears the second antennae, and in arachnoids, in which it bears the chelicerae, the tritocerebrum is much larger and more important. The frontal ganglion (**rostral ganglion**) is present also in arachnoids and is connected by a pair of trunks to the tritocerebrum.

The "brain" of arachnoids thus consists of only two pairs of ganglia and in some groups is clearly divided into two loosely connected halves. The tritocerebrum is part of the supraesophageal mass and, as in other arthropods, its transverse connective loops around and under the esophagus, though it almost always is incorporated into the longitudinal cords and the subesophageal mass so that it cannot be found by superficial dissection.

Each metamere of the arachnoid embryo gives rise to a pair of ganglia, as in other arthropods, but early in development some or all of the segmental ganglia migrate forward, either fusing into the subesophageal mass or forming a subsidiary center in the abdomen. In the adult the number of ganglia constituting the subesophageal mass varies from order to order. The most generalized condition—though certainly not the primitive arrangement—is found in scorpions, in which the subesophageal mass includes nine pairs of ganglia, those of the five leg-bearing segments plus those of abdominal segments two to five. In this order the first (**pregenital**) abdominal segment is atrophied along with its ganglia. Abdominal segments six, seven and eight, which make up the terminal part of the stout part of the abdomen (**mesosoma**), each have a single pair of ganglia. The "tail" (**metasoma**), consisting of five segments and the telson, has four pairs of ganglia, the last of which is double, representing the fusion of the terminal two pairs. Like the acron, the telson does not give rise to ganglia of the ventral chain.

In the order Thelyphonida two kinds of coalescence are found. Members of the family Schizomidae have nine subesophageal ganglia; a second center in the anterior part of the abdomen includes eight ganglia. Thelyphonids have twelve ganglia in the subesophageal mass and five coalesced in the posterior part of the abdomen. In the Phryneida and the most primitive of the spider suborders, the Liphistiomorpha, all seventeen ganglia have been drawn into the subesophageal mass, from which their nerves run back in branching trunks to all parts of the body. In the rest of the spiders the subesophageal mass consists of twelve pairs of ganglia and the five terminal ganglia regress in the embryo soon after forming or, in some cases, fail to appear at all. In pseudoscorpions, phalangids and mites, all ganglia are fused into a subesophageal mass, but coalescence is so complete that it is difficult to determine how many pairs are present or how many have atrophied.

SYMPATHETIC NERVOUS SYSTEMS

Certain ganglia, with their motor and sensory fibers, appear to be set apart from the central nervous system functionally, though connected with it. These sympathetic systems are primarily concerned with conditions *inside*, rather than *outside*, the body. Three such systems have been found in some insects—the stomodaeal, the ventral and the caudal—but only the stomodaeal appears to be standard equipment.

Although present in virtually all arthropods, the stomodaeal system (Fig. 6.4) exhibits a wide range of variation. It innervates the muscles and receptors of the gut and heart, sometimes also of other organs. Its essential feature is the **frontal ganglion** (**rostral,** in arachnoids), apparently the control center for peristalsis, placed on top of the anterior end of the esophagus and connected by a pair of trunks to the tritocerebrum. In insects and myriapods it clearly is separate from the supraesophageal mass, lying ahead of it and nearer the mouth. In arachnoids the connecting nerve trunk, shortened so that the ganglion is drawn back between the tritocerebral lobes and appears to be part of them, has sometimes been interpreted (incorrectly) as a preoral tritocerebral connective. Nerve fibers from the frontal ganglion service the clypeus, and the **recurrent nerve** (**rostral nerve**) leads back along the top of the foregut.

In myriapods, apterygotes and most arachnoids, the recurrent nerve sends fibers directly to the gut, aorta and heart, there being no other ganglia in the system. This situation is usually described as being "reduced" or "incomplete," suggesting that in these groups the stomodaeal system has been debased, but the opposite interpretation is likely to be the correct one. These arthropods have the primitive system without elaboration. The more complicated systems in spiders and pterygote in-

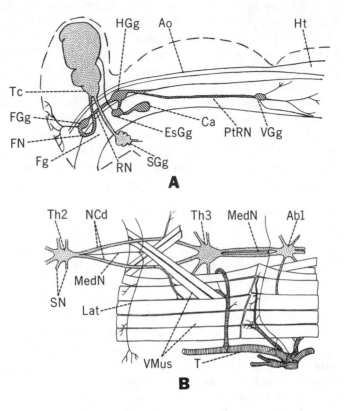

Figure 6.4. (A) Diagram of the sympathetic nervous system of insects in lateral view, the body outlined by broken lines; (B) detail of meso- and metathoracic and first abdominal central ganglia of an immature *Malacosoma americana* (Lepidoptera). *Ab1*, first abdominal ganglion; *Ao*, aorta; *Ca*, corpus allatum; *EsGg*, esophageal ganglion; *Fg*, foregut; *FGg*, frontal ganglion; *FN*, frontal nerve; *HGg*, hypocerebral ganglion; *Ht*, heart; *Lat*, lateral branch of median nerve; *MedN*, median nerve; *NCd*, central nerve cords; *PtRN*, posterior recurrent nerve; *RN*, recurrent nerve; *SGg*, subesophageal ganglionic mass; *SN*, segmental central nerves; *T*, trachea; *Tc*, tritocerebrum of central system; *Th2*, mesothoracic ganglion; *Th3*, metathoracic ganglion; *VGg*, ventricular ganglion; *VMus*, ventral skeletal muscles. (A derived from various sources; B redrawn from Snodgrass, 1935, by arrangement with McGraw-Hill Book Co.)

188

sects are manifestly evolutional developments in which the basic "incomplete" system receives certain additions.

In pterygote insects (Fig. 6.4) as many as six distinct ganglia may be present in the stomodaeal system, and they may be fused in various ways. The recurrent nerve from the frontal ganglion leads back to the **hypocerebral ganglion,** placed just behind the supraesophageal mass. A pair of lateral trunks connect the hypocerebral ganglion with the **esophageal ganglia (pharyngeal ganglia, corpora cardiaca)** which flank it dorsolaterally on the foregut, and which are connected by a pair of small trunks to the protocerebral lobes. Other nerve trunks lead back to the **corpora allata,** important endocrine bodies. The hypocerebral and esophageal ganglia are sometimes fused into a single mass, to which may be added the corpora allata. The **ventricular ganglion**—sometimes a median structure, sometimes paired—lies further back on the foregut and is connected to the hypocerebral ganglion by the **posterior recurrent nerve** (or nerves, when the former ganglion is paired).

In arachnoids the frontal ganglion is embedded in the ventro-posterior part of the tritocerebral (cheliceral) ganglion. Nerves leading forward from it service the anterior pharynx and the clypeolabral (rostral) area; nerves leading posteriorward service the gut and dorsal vessel. The most advanced system is found in spiders, in which the posterior nerves (recurrent) are in the form of a pair of trunks which emerge from the posterior aspect of the tritocerebrum, pass along the sides of the foregut and end in a pair of ganglia on the crop (sucking stomach). These ganglia, probably homologous with the ventricular ganglia of pterygotes, service the crop and the anterior part of the midgut. Trunks lead from the paired ganglia back to a median ganglion lying above the hindgut and which innervates the posterior half of the enteron.

Regardless of its degree of development, the stomodaeal system of all arthropods arises by delamination from the gut ectoderm—principally from the stomodaeum, except the posterior median ganglion of spiders, which arises from the proctodaeal ectoderm. Thus the stomodaeal system differs sharply from the central system in both function and origin.

The ventral sympathetic system, present in most pterygote insects, consists of motor and sensory tracts associated with the spiracles and tracheae and arises from the **median nerve** (Fig. 6.4B). The median nerve forms from the ectoderm between the two main ventral cords and in most insects it and its branches come to be embedded in the central system. Only in embryos and larvae which have not yet fused the ventral cords may the median nerve be found as a separate entity. The median nerve has been viewed as part of the central nervous system, with which it is closely associated in development and in position, but it appears to be essentially sympathetic rather than central in function and to be largely independent of the central system.

The caudal sympathetic system is modified from several pairs of ventral ganglia that fuse at the posterior end of the central system. In most pterygote insects nerves from this mass service the posterior enteron and the reproductive organs. It is functionally a sympathetic system, but is derived from and is a specialized part of the central system.

PHYSIOLOGY

In summary, the nervous system functions in principle very much like that of vertebrates, including at the cytological level. The exact mode of action of the synapses is not clear, and the neural cells do not react to fatigue or to drugs in the same way as do vertebrate cells, being more stable in these respects.

It may be noted from the discussion of sympathetic systems that innervation of the mid- and hindgut and of some of the organs was not detailed. In most cases this innervation is not known, though it generally may be assumed to be sympathetic. However, muscle fibers of the malpighian tubules in certain species which have been rather carefully investigated apparently lack any connection with the nervous system. Here contraction is thought to be **myogenic,** that is, induced in the muscle fiber itself in response to local non-neural stimuli. Theoretically, the generalized cell embodies all possible cell functions, including neural, but it is unusual to find a cell sufficiently specialized to be recognizably muscular also having the neural function, however low the level.

Richards and Davies (*in* Imms, 1957) point out that the nervous system of insects does not provide for as high a level of functional centralization as is found in vertebrates. Each segment, in insects, constitutes a fundamentally independent unit capable of autonomous reflex behavior. Nervous coordination, and thus behavior of the insect as a whole, is brought about by intersegmental mechanisms and by impulses from cephalic centers. In the absence of such coordinating impulses, local autonomy occurs. The classic example of this is afforded by copulation in mantids. The fact that the female eats the male during the act does not prevent the decapitated male from finishing his work. Also, the surgically removed abdomen of a female silk moth has attracted a male, stimulated copulation and been fertilized, after which eggs were laid.

All the standard investigative techniques have been applied to the insect nervous system and much has been published in recent years on experimental results. Only the groundwork has been completed thus far and a great deal remains to be done. For a summary of what is known of the physiology of the insect nervous system, the student should consult Roeder (1953). No similar monograph treating either arachnoids or myriapods is available.

SENSORY RECEPTORS

Sensory receptors serve as mediators between the environment and the nervous system, translating a stimulus into a nervous impulse. The stimuli known to affect receptors are of three kinds: (1) mechanical vibration or pressure, leading to the deformation of a protoplasmic membrane either by direct contact with an object or by movements of the environmental medium (air or water), including those resulting from sound; (2) contact with chemicals, stimulating taste, the olfactory sense or the common chemical sense; (3) light rays. Equilibrium is a sense no less well developed in insects than in vertebrates, but in only a few cases are there receptors specialized for equilibrium alone. It appears that equilibrium is sensed, along with motion and position, by the **proprioreceptors,** placed internally along most joints and flexible parts of the body. In some cases the eyes may contribute to perception of equilibrium.

Sensory receptors may be external (eyes, antennae, palpi and setae) or internal (proprioreceptors and the sympathetic receptors). **Exteroceptors** perceive external events, **interoceptors** react to internal stimuli. All external receptors involve modifications of hypodermal cells, sometimes as in the eyes, to a striking degree, sometimes almost imperceptibly. Any hypodermal cell, whether modified or not, probably serves in some way as a receptor if it is associated with a sensory dendron. The organs of perception generally involve some cuticular modifications contributing to the effectiveness of the organ.

PERCEPTION OF TEMPERATURE AND HUMIDITY

Particularly for a terrestrial arthropod, maintenance of acceptable levels of temperature and moisture is of prime importance for survival. The individual's body temperature is entirely dependent upon the environmental temperature and the temperature range within which the individual can function well is comparatively limited. Most vertebrates can survive heat that would be lethal to the majority of arthropods. Temperatures below the activity range only lead to inactivity in arthropods and are not lethal until very low temperatures are reached. Desiccation is an ever-present danger to terrestrial arthropods and the mechanisms for water conservation frequently are elaborate. The range of acceptable temperatures and humidity varies widely from species to species and group to group, but a fairly definite range exists for each. Innumerable observations and experiments have established beyond question that these animals respond quickly to variations in temperature and humidity, always seeking the conditions most favorable to survival and activity.

The persistent behavior of terrestrial arthropods with respect to variation in temperature and humidity seems to be compelling evidence that there must be receptors capable of detecting heat and moisture. Humidity receptors have been identified with several types of chemoreceptors in many different insects. Some of these receptors appear to respond to dry, others only to moist air. In general, the sense of humidity seems to depend upon the detection of water vapor as a chemical. Temperature receptors have not yet been identified as such, though there is experimental evidence that temperature is appreciated by way of the antennae, the palpi and the tarsi. The intimate relationship between temperature and water vapor in air suggests that, at least in some cases, temperature may be sensed secondarily through the detection of humidity and that the search for receptors responding *only* to temperature may not be fruitful. The possibility also exists that thermal sensation is widely vested in the general hypodermis.

TACTILE RECEPTORS

Articulated tactile setae (see Fig. 2.2B) associated with sensory dendrons are scattered generally over the whole body surface and often are especially dense on the antennae, cerci and tarsi. Movement of the seta in its membrane stimulates the nerve cell. When these setae are placed, either singly or in patches, at leg and body joints in such a way that they are touched or pressed as a result of movement of the appendage or body, they serve as proprioreceptors.

Tactile hairs are especially numerous and important in arachnoids, a class in which vision is never well developed. In most arachnoid orders many of the tactile setae are exceptionally long and fine, untapered and set in cup-like depressions (**bothriotrichia**), and are considered to be especially sensitive.

Campaniform sensilla (Fig. 6.5A), found in insects, apparently are a further development of tactile setae. A modified hypodermal cell or cells support a dome-shaped area of thin cuticle with which the sensory dendron is associated. Deformations of the dome, which may be above, below or on the level of the surrounding cuticle, stimulate the neuron. Thus these receptors may respond either to direct contact or to the stresses of body movement. Many minor variants have been recorded in the shape and size of the dome and in the number and size of the hypodermal cells involved. When suitably located, campaniform sensilla also may have proprioreceptive function.

Chordotonal organs, also based upon an association between modified hypodermal cells and a sensory neuron, are subcuticular and more complex. Berlese (1909b) saw them as a further elaboration of campaniform sensilla, though some more recent investigators disagree. The unit of the chordotonal organ is the **scolopophore** (Fig. 6.5B), composed of an **apical cap cell** attached to the body wall and an **envelope cell**; in the central part of the cap cell is a terminal ligament which forms a functional extension of the **sensory rod** (**scolops** or **scolopale**) in the envelope cell. The sensory rod is a vacuolated cylinder with walls strengthened by longitudinal ribs. The tip of a sensory dendron penetrates the envelope cell, reaching the sensory rod. The organ may consist of only one or a few scolopophores, but usually a number of them is gathered together and enclosed in ensheathing membrane. In most cases a chordotonal organ is attached to integument at each end, but sometimes it may be attached only at the cap cell end and thus lies free in the body cavity. Found in insects but not in arachnoids, chordotonal organs are most frequent in the abdomen and appendages and at the base of the wings. Responding to elongation and depression, these organs serve sometimes as proprioreceptors, sometimes as receptors for perceiving internal pressures or external vibrations; they are the essential parts of certain auditory receptors.

AUDITORY RECEPTORS

Low intensity disturbances of the air producing displacement of air particles along with a local pressure increase are interpreted by auditory receptors as sound. Sound may also be transmitted through solid and liquid media. In arthropods the auditory receptors are elaborations of tactile receptors, both articulated setae and chordotonal organs entering into their structure, but they never are as complex as those found in higher vertebrates.

Auditory setae are the simplest, and at the same time the least understood, of the sound-perceiving structures. No morphological characteristic has been found to distinguish them from purely tactile setae, and perhaps there is none; sound detection is, after all, only a refined variation of the sense of touch. Auditory setae, scattered over the body, have been noted in many different insects and arachnoids; quite probably they occur in all. Usually their existence has been revealed when the more obvious auditory structures have been experimentally removed or immobilized and the animal nevertheless continued to respond to sounds.

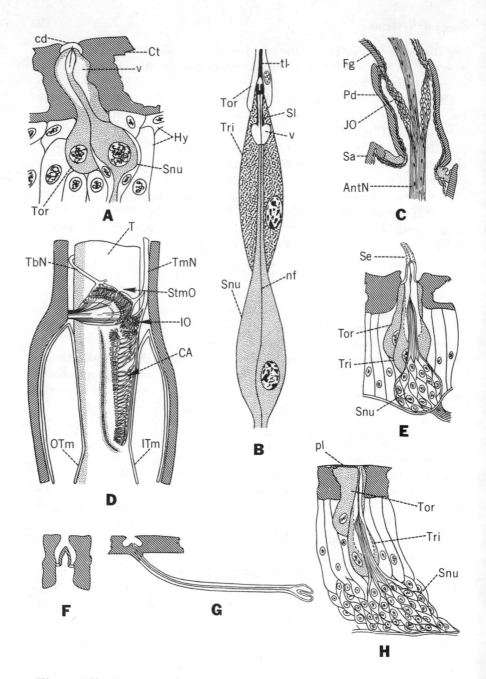

Figure 6.5. Structure of sensory organs in insects. (A) Campaniform sensilla; (B) an integumental scolopophore; (C) section through the pedicel of the antenna of *Melolontha* (Coleoptera) showing a simple form of Johnston's organ;

Johnston's organ (Fig. 6.5C), present in all insects except the most primitive, is a specialized chordotonal structure within the second antennal segment. The chordotonal sensilla extend from the membrane in the cup of the pedicel, where the flagellum is seated, to the wall of the pedicel, and sometimes fill the entire segment. The sensory fibers lead directly to the deutocerebrum through the antennary nerve, an arrangement suggesting that Johnston's organ responds to movements of the flagellum, but the sense involved varies among insects and quite possibly several kinds of stimuli may be perceived.

The whirligig beetle (*Gyrinus*) extends its antennae forward near the water surface, apparently perceiving wavelets and irregularities through changes in the position of the flagella; when the antennae are removed the beetle is unable to avoid collisions. It appears that the antennae of insects with well-developed Johnston's organs are quite sensitive tactile structures, even responding to light breaths of air. The auditory function is added in some insects, as has been shown by study of the mosquito *Aedes*. Sound vibrations set in motion the numerous setae along the flagellum, imparting to the whole segment a vibratory motion detected by Johnston's organ. The male mosquito responds to the shrill buzzing of the female in flight, as well as to vibrating tuning forks pitched in the same range or to amplified recordings of sounds in the same frequency.

Relatively complex, exclusively auditory organs are present in some insects, especially those with special sound-producing structures. Among the Orthoptera, the short-horned grasshopper has a pair of "ears" (**tympana**) on each side of the first abdominal tergum and the crickets and long-horned grasshoppers have auditory organs at the base of the fore tibiae (Fig. 3.6H). Cicadas (Hemiptera) have sound receptors at the

---

Figure 6.5 (*continued*)

(D) scolopophorous auditory organ in the fore tibia of *Decticus* (Orthoptera); (E) a basiconic chemoreceptor; (F) the cuticular part of a sensillum coeloconicum; (G) cuticular part of a sensillum ampulaceum; (H) cuticular and cellular parts of a sensillum placodeum. AntN, antennal nerve; CA, crista acustica (Siebold's organ); cd, cuticular dome; Ct, cuticle; Fg, flagellum of antenna; Hy, hypodermis; IO, intermediate organ; ITm, inner tympanal membrane; JO, sensilla of Johnston's organ; nf, nerve fiber; OTm, outer tympanal membrane; pl, cuticular placode; Pd, pedicel of antenna; Sa, scape of antenna; Se, seta; Sl, scolops; Snu, sensory cell; StmO, supratympanal (subgenual) organ; T, trachea; TbN, subgenual branch of tibial nerve; tl, end knob and terminal ligament; TmN, tympanal nerve; Tor, tormogen or cap cell; Tri, trichogen or envelope cell; v, vacuole. (A from Sihler, 1924; B redrawn from Hess, 1917; C, E–H redrawn from Snodgrass, 1924; D redrawn from Schwabe, 1906)

base of the abdomen, and in various Heteroptera they are on the second or the second and third thoracic pleura. Chordotonal tympanic organs are present in many Lepidoptera, placed on the first abdominal segment, on the metathorax or at the base of the wings. While these organs in some moths have been shown to appreciate sound, it may be a secondary function not always present; their basic function probably is proprioception.

These more complex auditory organs consist of tracheal air sacs separated from the outside by thin cuticular tympanal membranes; numerous chordotonal receptors are fastened to the tympanum or to the walls of the tracheal sac in such a way that they are stimulated by vibrations of the tympanum or by the resultant compression of air within the sac. The tympanal membrane may be exposed and visible, as in short-horned grasshoppers, or it may be sunk into a pit, which sometimes has only a slit-like opening, as in long-horned grasshoppers and crickets.

The greatest complexity is reached in some of the long-horned grasshoppers, where two tympana, a trachea, three chordotonal organs and two nerves are involved (Fig. 6.5D). A pair of longitudinal slit-like openings may be seen near the proximal end of the fore tibia. Each slit leads into an invaginated cavity lined with thin cuticle. These two cavities have their inner walls closely applied to the wall of an enlarged trachea, the common walls forming an inner (medial) and an outer (lateral) tympanum. Between the tympana the widened trachea is divided by a medial septum. The **supratympanal organ,** placed just proximal of the tympanal chambers, consists of a large number of scolopophores attached by their cap cells to the outer wall of the leg and at the other end to the tracheal wall; it receives sensory fibers from both the tympanal nerve and the tibial nerve, both of which lead to the prothoracic ganglion. The small **intermediate organ** is placed just beyond the supratympanal organ and at the proximal extremity of the tympanal chambers. Its scolopophores, serviced by the tibial nerve, are attached only to the tracheal wall and lie free in the hemocoel of the leg. The third chordotonal organ is the **crista acustica** (**Siebold's organ**), composed of a long series of scolopophores which diminish in size distad. They are attached only to the tracheal wall, but are held against it and supported by ligamentous bands.

CHEMORECEPTORS

A necessary characteristic of a chemoreceptor is that the cuticle overlying it must be thin enough and of such a nature as to allow the passage of at least some of the materials to be detected. Chemoreceptors in insects appear to be variations of tactile receptors and, in some cases, probably serve both functions. A number of different morphologic types have been described, but they seem to fall into two series of increasing modification, one series derived from the tactile seta, the other from the campaniform sensillum. The sensory dendrites penetrating chemoreceptors characteristically contain small refringent bodies.

Some innervated articulate setae have very thin cuticular walls, either entirely or only around the base, and are frequently set in cup-like depressions. This is the **trichoid** type (**sensillum trichoideum olfactorium**), and a variant with shorter, stouter hairs has been termed the **sensillum chaeticum**. Such receptors are found especially on the antennae, mouthparts and tarsi and have been studied in some Diptera and Lepidoptera. Where the setae assume a cone-like or peg-like appearance (Fig. 6.5E), the receptor is called **basiconic** (**sensillum basiconicum, sensillum styloconicum**), and principally occurs on the antennae and mouthparts. Where the setal cup is deepened so that the seta is below the general surface, the term used is **sensillum coeloconicum** (Fig. 6.5F), and an extreme form, where the seta lies in a chamber connected to the surface by a tube, is called **sensillum ampullaceum** (Fig. 6.5G); these types have been found on the antennae of many of the higher orders.

The **placoid receptor** (Fig. 6.5H) (**sensillum placodeum**) is a circular or oval plate of thin cuticle supported by a cap cell and an envelope cell and receiving a bundle of dendrites containing refringent bodies. It is thus somewhat similar to the campaniform sensilla detailed above.

In arachnoids, groups of placoid-type chemoreceptors arranged in long rows at the bottom of a slit-like depression are characteristic and are known as **lyriform organs**. These organs may be simple, with only one small isolated slit, or compound, with many slits grouped together; they may be scattered over the whole body surface or concentrated in various patterns characteristic of the order. Similar arrangements are not found in insects or myriapods.

Three kinds of chemical senses are recognized by physiologists. The *common chemical sense* requires a high concentration of an irritant, which must be volatile at ordinary temperatures. The sense of *taste* requires direct contact with materials that volatilize at physiological temperatures, but which need not be in such high concentrations. The sense of *smell* requires only very low concentrations of compounds volatile at ordinary temperatures. To these last two kinds, animals respond by choosing, either accepting or rejecting the substance. These three senses represent in fact *degrees* of sensitivity. No clear boundary separates one from another, and the distinction probably is of greater use to the experimenter than the animal.

In general, the common chemical sense serves as a protection against dangerous substances. No receptor specialized exclusively for the common chemical sense has been identified, but receptors responding to it are thought to be scattered over the whole body surface. The sense and its reaction may be the result of a violent assault on all chemoreceptors.

The sense of taste is employed in food selection. The receptors are primarily found on the antennae, on the mouthparts, in the preoral cavity and on the tarsi.

The sense of smell gives notice to the animal of something either desirable or undesirable in the environment, generally at a little distance. It is used not only in food selection, but also in locating a member of the opposite sex or the correct place for depositing the eggs. The sense of smell in insects has been rather carefully investigated because of the significance of sexual and ovipository activity, and especially because of our need for materials which repel or attract specific pest insects.

PHOTORECEPTORS

Photoreception is the appreciation of light, without regard to the formation of an image or the discrimination of wavelength (color). The term *light* is not restricted to the wavelengths to which the human eye responds, but includes wavelengths in the infrared and ultraviolet ranges.

A "dermal light sense" is said to exist in many insects (Collembola, roaches, immature Lepidoptera and Diptera) but the receptors concerned have not been identified. The existence of a dermal light sense has been inferred from the reactions to light by insects having their known light receptors experimentally rendered inoperative. It has been suggested that dermal sensitivity to light may be a reaction of tissues to ultraviolet rays, a reasonable possibility, since ultraviolet light often is especially stimulating to insects.

Photoreceptors sufficiently developed morphologically and sufficiently specialized physiologically to qualify as organs of vision are found in nearly all arthropods. There are two different sets of visual receptors, the compound eyes and the ocelli. The correct distinction between the two is with respect to differences between their neural tracts (Fig. 6.3), not with respect to the number of external facets. The **compound eyes** are always laterally placed on the head and they are not necessarily multifaceted; their neural tracts lead directly into the optic lobes. The two groups of **ocelli** are respectively placed dorso-medial and dorso-lateral; they are morphologically posterior of the eyes, though the dorso-lateral pair is shifted forward during the ontogeny of certain beetles. The neural tracts from the ocelli lead to small ocellar lobes, which in turn are connected to the optic tracks; the ocelli are never *directly* connected with the optic lobes.

A confusion in the correct identification of these two different sets of receptors exists in many entomological writings because the word *compound* has been widely used only to describe a multifaceted eye, while a single- or few-faceted receptor has been described as an *ocellus*. For example, the statement has sometimes been made that Collembola have ocelli but not compound eyes; this is not true, for the Collembola have, in fact, single-faceted compound eyes but no ocelli. The so-called *lateral ocelli* of certain immature insects are actually the transient representatives of the compound eyes and are more correctly called **stemmata**; they are not ocelli in the morphological sense.

There is every reason to believe that both compound eyes and ocelli are respectively homologous throughout all arthropods. It is evident that the compound eyes have been characteristic of the arthropods for a very long time; ancestral insects, ancestral myriapods and ancestral arachnoids all had them. The insects retained and even improved them. Among myriapods they are in various states of reduction and debasement, with only the Scutigeridae preserving them in multifaceted form. In the arachnoids, multifaceted compound eyes are never present, apparently having degenerated to single facets along all phylogenetic lines. Vandel (1949) thought that the optical system of chelicerates is not homologous with that of other arthropods, but studies of the optic tracts demonstrate the essential similarities. It should be recognized that the multifaceted condition so general among insects is actually a specialization rather than the basic feature of the visual receptors associated with the procephalic optic lobes. The ocelli, too, must have been ancient and are found on all phylogenetic lines. However, where the compound eyes are well developed, as in insects, the ocelli tend to become unimportant and to regress. In arachnoids, the ocellular system is retained and has importance equal to that of the few-faceted compound eyes.

OCELLI

The pedicels of the three ocelli of insects are placed on the dorsal aspect of the protocerebrum. Each of the **lateral ocelli** rests on an **ocellar pedicel** which is a smaller, simpler version of the pedicels beneath the compound eyes. The pedicel of the **median ocellus** contains two sets of nerve fibers. In a very few species (e.g., *Melanoplus femurrubrum*, Orthoptera, and certain beetles) the ocellus itself is double and the pedicel is bifurcate. It appears likely, as has frequently been suggested, that the median ocellus of insects represents a fused *pair* of ocelli. The ocelli are connected via the ocellar pedicels and intermediate association neurons to the optic center which lies in the intercerebral part of the protocerebrum between and above the corpora pedunculata and to which fibers from the compound eyes also eventually lead. It should be noted that the optic center receives fibers along two different routes on each side; those from the compound eyes enter it laterally, those from the ocelli from the rear.

There are many structural variations of the receptor organs themselves in the various insect groups, though the basic arrangement is always the same. Many of these variations concern the arrangement of the hypodermal cells and the cuticle (**cornea**). The cornea is translucent and convex and usually is thickened to form a lens (Fig. 6.6A). Either the underlying transparent hypodermis beneath (**corneagen layer**) serves only to support the cornea, or the cells may be elongated and so shaped as to supplement the corneal lens (**vitreous body**). In the Ephemerida, however, the cuticle is not thickened, though it is arched, and the primary hypodermis is made up of somewhat flattened cells which follow the corneal contour; a lens is formed beneath the primary hypodermis by cells proliferated from it.

The sensory layer (**retina**) is composed of numerous sensory neurons, each connected with a fiber of the ocellar nerve. These cells are arranged in groups of two or more (each group is a **retinula**) around a longitudinal rod (**rhabdom**). In some insects there are also pigmented cells lying between the retinulae, while in others the pigment is contained in the visual cells. The number of cells in a retinula and the arrangement of the pigment supply the basis for a great many variations.

COMPOUND EYES

The principal feature distinguishing compound eyes in the true sense is that they are innervated directly from the optic lobes of the protocerebrum. As fully developed ("typical"), the corneal layer is divided into numerous facets, each facet forming the outer end of an **ommatidium**, the structural unit of the eye

The ommatidium (Fig. 6.6B) consists of hypodermal cells, the cuticular cornea secreted by them, cone cells and pigment cells derived from the hypodermis and neural cells.

The primary hypodermis secretes the translucent lenticulate **cornea** externally identified as a **facet**. In some cases there are two primary hypodermal cells in each ommatidium, forming the **corneagen layer.** Beneath them lie four elongate **cone cells** which secrete a refractive body, frequently crystalline but sometimes liquid. In other cases there are four

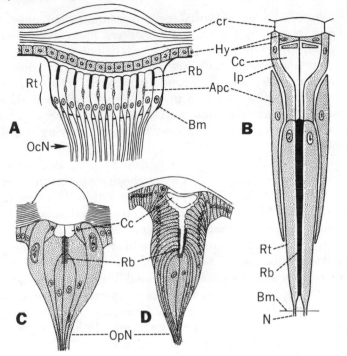

Figure 6.6. Histology of insect eyes. (A) Diagram illustrating the structure of an ocellus; (B) an ommatidium of the eucone compound eye of *Machilis* (Thysanura); (C) stemma of a caterpillar (Lepidoptera); (D) stemma of a larva of *Dytiscus* (Coleoptera). *Apc*, accessory pigment cell; *Bm*, basement membrane; *Cc*, crystalline cone cell; *cr*, cornea; *Hy*, hypodermis; *Ip*, iris pigment cell; *N*, sensory nerve fiber; *OcN*, ocellar nerve; *OpN*, optic nerve; *Rb*, rhabdom; *Rt*, retinal cell. (A and B from Comstock, 1940, by permission of Cornell University Press; C and D from Snodgrass, 1935, by arrangement with McGraw-Hill Book Co.)

elongated primary hypodermal cells in the group. They secrete the cornea, but there is no second hypodermal layer beneath them and the crystalline body (or fluid) is wanting; the primary hypodermis is both corneagen and cone. The hypodermal layer or layers are always surrounded by a ring of modified hypodermal cells, the densely pigmented **primary iris cells.**

Below the hypodermis is a **retinula** composed of a group—usually seven, but the number varies—of visual cells surrounding an optic rod. The **rhabdom** is formed by the clustered sensitive fibers (**rhabdomeres**) of the visual cells. In contact with the cone cells distad, the rhabdom emerges from the retinula proximad as a single nerve fiber. Surrounding the visual cells is a continuous ring of **secondary pigment cells** overlapping the primary pigment cells above, so that collectively the two rings of pigment cells wall off an ommatidium, preventing light rays which enter the facet from affecting surrounding ommatidia and making it an effective optic unit.

The ommatidia collectively are underlaid by the basement membrane perforated by the nerve fibers and by tracheoles which run longitudinally between the ommatidia and frequently are extremely numerous.

Four principal histological variations are found among insects. In **eucone** and **pseudocone eyes,** both the corneagen and the cone layers are present. In eucone eyes there is a crystalline cone, in pseudocone eyes the cone is semiliquid within the cone cells above their nuclei. The former type occurs very commonly and is found in Thysanura, Ephemerida, Odonata, Orthoptera, Trichoptera, Lepidoptera, Hymenoptera, some Neuroptera, some Hemiptera and some Coleoptera. The latter type occurs in the majority of Diptera. In **acone** eyes only the cone layer is present, serving also as the corneagen layer, and no cone, either crystalline or fluid, is formed; this type is found in Dermaptera, most Hemiptera and some Diptera and Coleoptera. In **exocone** eyes, found in some families of Coleoptera, the cone layer is present, but the cuticle is complex, there being an inner layer of crystalline cone material beneath the cornea proper.

The number of facets, one of the factors affecting the resolving power of the eye, is greatest in flying insects that depend heavily upon vision for the success of their daily activities. Each eye of the dragonfly (Odonata) may have 28,000 or more facets, in Lepidoptera there are 12,000 to 17,000, in the common housefly about 4000. An insect living in a more limited or more protected environment is likely to have fewer eye facets than related but more active species. Extreme reduction is reached in some of the external parasites, in cave dwellers and in permanently subterranean species. In Strepsiptera the winged males have protuberant eyes but only about fifty facets, while the immobile females lack eyes entirely. The genus *Basilia* (bat-tick flies; Diptera) is characterized by having only two facets in each eye (Fig. 6.7A). Lice (Anoplura) and fleas (Siphonaptera), when they have compound eyes at all, have only one facet. The Collembola have from one to eight separated facets on each side, the ommatidia being the eucone type; because of their appearance they are often miscalled "ocelli." A similar situation is found in Chilopoda and Aptera, where the compound eyes are reduced to one facet or to a few separated facets. The family Scutigeridae has retained a more or less typical multifaceted compound eye, and in some diplopods there are a dozen or so facets arranged in a group on each side.

The diameter of a facet is of the order of twenty-five micra, but even

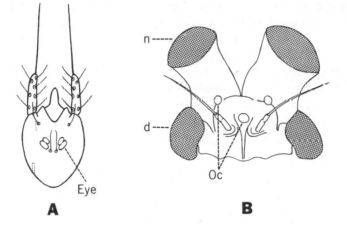

Figure 6.7. (A) Dorsal view of the head of *Basilia,* a bat-tick fly (Diptera) showing two-faceted compound eyes; (B) front of head of *Cloeon,* a mayfly (Ephemerida) with divided compound eyes. *Eye,* compound eye; *d,* part of compound eye adapted for day vision; *n,* part of compound eye adapted for night vision; *Oc,* ocelli. (A redrawn from Fox and Stabler, 1953; B redrawn from Comstock, 1940, by permission of Cornell University Press)

in the same eye the facets may vary in size in different areas, suggesting functional specialization. The males of *Tabanus* (Diptera) have larger facets in the anterior and upper parts of the eyes. In *Simulium* (Diptera) the eye is divided into two distinct areas, one of which has larger facets. The mayfly *Cloeon* (Ephemerida) has these two areas widely separated (Fig. 6.7B), so that it appears to have four eyes, a pair in the normal position and a ventral pair which is beneath the water surface when the insect swims. Some other species with divided eyes appear to use one set by day, the other by night.

Stemmata ("lateral ocelli") are lateral, but they are not correctly ocelli, since they are innervated from the optic lobes. They occur only in the larvae of some holometabolous insects. In structure they superficially resemble true ocelli or the single-faceted compound eyes of many apterygotes. While the stemmata are homologous with the compound eyes of the adults, they do not *become* the adult eyes but are discarded during terminal embryogenesis (see Chapter Eight). The numerous variations in structure (Fig. 6.6C, D) represent various stages in development toward the ultimate adult eye in correlation with the ontogenetic level of the particular larva. In *Musca* (Diptera), the larvae have only some light-sensitive photoreceptors not identifiable externally. Larvae of the Cyclorrhapha (suborder of Diptera) have photoreceptors which can be seen, and in some other Diptera the larval eyes have only a few retinulae and the corneal lens may be undeveloped. In larvae of Lepidoptera (Fig. 6.6C) and Trichoptera, and of nonparasitic Hymenoptera, Coleoptera (Fig. 6.6D) and Neuroptera, the eyes consist of many ommatidia underlying one or a few corneal lenses, though frequently the ommatidia may be incompletely developed.

VISION

Two kinds of images are projected by multifaceted compound eyes: **apposition images** and **superposition images**; the former is an adaptation for diurnal vision, the latter for nocturnal. In each case the image itself is a mosaic formed by numerous points of light, each point with its own brightness; such an image may be compared with a photograph in a newspaper or with a drawing composed entirely of stippling.

The image is formed by **apposition** when each ommatidium is fully isolated from surrounding ommatidia by pigment in the iris cells, thus preventing light rays from passing from one unit to another; each rhabdom thus is stimulated only by rays entering perpendicular to the lens system. The image is formed by **superposition** when pigment cells do not shield the individual ommatidia; light entering the eye will stimulate a *group* of rhabdoms and oblique rays are not excluded. The principle of mosaic vision was first proposed by Müller in 1826; the optical basis for the two types of images was discovered by Exner in 1891 and is well summarized by Wigglesworth (1947). Most diurnal insects, active in sunlight, have eyes that form images by apposition; most nocturnal insects, needing to receive stimuli from very dim light, form images by superposition. Some insects are normally active in both bright and dim light; the pigment in their iris cells migrates in response to brightness, expanding to form an optical barrier in bright light but retracting into basal clumps in the presence of dim light.

All insects with well-developed compound eyes discriminate form, movement, brightness and color, but color discrimination is not uniform among all insects and the image resolution varies. In general, insects are more sensitive than vertebrates to the shorter wavelengths and the spectrum visible to them extends well into the ultraviolet range. Only a few insects react to deep reds, while most respond best to green, violet and ultraviolet.

The ocelli of insects appear to be stimulatory and perhaps to a degree regulatory organs, supplementing and enhancing the visual reflexes of the compound eyes. It will be noted that the ocelli are reduced in number or absent altogether in many adult insects and are never present in larvae. They cannot be image-forming organs, since the focal length of the lens is always such that the image is projected beyond the sensitive cells.

ARACHNOIDS

Whether the eyes of arachnoids are actually compound eyes reduced to a few separated components or whether true ocelli are present does not seem to have been investigated; the question could be resolved only by tracing the sensory paths between each eye and the optic center. Since there are two optic centers in the supraesophageal mass, and since there are two sets of optic nerve trunks on each side, it appears likely that both the compound and the ocellar systems are present. Each eye has a single corneal lens never divided into facets. In general structure arachnoid eyes resemble those of Collembola and certain myriapods, though there are modifications in the structure of the visual cells peculiar to arachnoids.

Two types of eyes are generally distinguished, the **direct** and the **indirect**. The **direct eye** (Fig. 6.8A) has the visual cells normally oriented, with the rhabdoms in the outer and the cell nuclei in the inner parts. In the **indirect eye** (Fig. 6.8B) the visual cells are rotated in various ways so that the nuclei become outer and the rhabdoms assume an inner position and may be bent. A reflective **tapetum**, a postretinal crystalline layer, is present. The direct eye is better adapted for bright light, the indirect for dim light.

The cornea may be rounded and thickened into a lens or it may be flat; in some cases its inner layers are differentiated into a crystalline body. The hypodermis is often heavily pigmented around the periphery of the eyes and is translucent only in the center; the cells are often elongated, something like the cone cells of insects, and form a vitreous layer, but in less developed eyes they may be but little differentiated from the surrounding hypodermis. In any event they are directly underlaid by the basement membrane, *under* which are the sensory cells, a characteristic difference between arachnoids and insects.

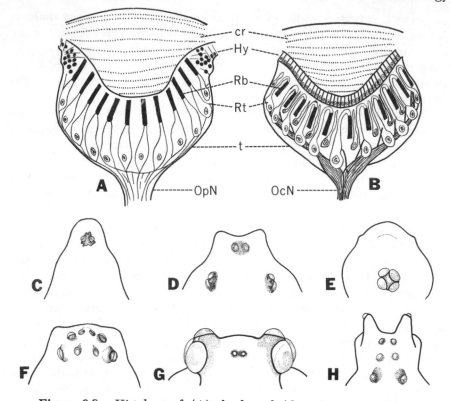

Figure 6.8. Histology of (A) the lateral (direct) eye and (B) the median (indirect) eye of a solpugid; (C–H) dorsal view of the heads (in outline) of various spiders showing arrangement of eyes: (C) *Nops*, (D) *Scytodes*, (E) *Tetrablemma*, (F) *Heteropoda*, (G) *Pholeus podophthalmus* (female), (H) *Euphrostenops*. *cr*, cornea; *Hy*, hypodermis; *OcN*, ocellar nerve; *OpN*, optic nerve; *Rb*, rhabdom; *Rt*, retinal cells; *t*, tapetum. (Redrawn from Millot, 1949a, by arrangement with Masson et Cie)

The visual cells may be grouped, two to eight cells in a group, around a common rhabdom, or they may remain individually distinct with the sensory rods of each cell (rhabdomere) acting independently.

Hunting spiders and solpugids have relatively good vision in the sense that reasonably resolved images are formed, but even with these animals objects only a few feet away are not clear. Other arachnoids distinguish only movement and light intensity. Poor vision in arachnoids is compensated for by their ultrarefined tactile sense, the development of which may help to account for the debasement of the eyes.

Eyes in arachnoids are generally designated according to position (Fig. 6.8C–H). It is of interest to note that when a pair of median eyes is present, they usually differ in structure from the lateral eyes. Some of the scorpions have twelve eyes, a median and five lateral pairs, the maximum number found in the class. Nearly every arachnoid order, however, has many eyeless members, and in three major groups all members are blind— the orders Palpigradida and Ricinuleida and the family Schizomidac (Thelyphonida).

ENDOCRINE SYSTEM

The delicate, incessant and vital role of the endocrine secretions in vertebrates is fully appreciated, if not fully understood. While there can be little question of the importance of hormones in insects and little doubt that they exert a basic control of many internal functions, the endocrine system has been explored mainly in connection with molting and metamorphosis. Sufficient information has been gathered from numerous suggestive experiments to make clear that hormones probably are involved in controlling many other functions as well.

Endocrine secretions are transported by the blood from the secretory site to the site of action. That the blood must be the distributive medium is deduced from the fact that these two sites are generally distant from each other. Proof is provided by an experiment in which the blood from an insect about to molt is injected into an insect that has just completed molting; the recipient insect molts precipitously. The out-of-cycle ecdysis must have been caused by hormones in the blood of the donor insect.

The known sites of hormone production in insects are all closely associated with the nervous system; it seems probable that an interrelationship between the two systems must exist. While there may be other sites, the principal known sites of endocrine secretion are the supraesophageal mass, the corpora cardiaca, the corpora allata, the prothoracic glands of certain immatures, the pericardial glands and the cephalic glands.

In the supracsophageal mass large non-neural cells have been found, embedded in the intercerebral part of the protocerebrum. Both their structure and their staining properties suggest that these cells are secretory and they probably are the source of certain hormones known to be produced by the "brain." It has been demonstrated experimentally that endocrine secretions arising from the supraesophageal mass affect molting or metamorphosis, induce the formation of yolk in maturing eggs and, in one species, cause expansion of integumental chromatophores.

The esophageal ganglion (corpora cardiaca) of the sympathetic nervous system contains both secretory and neural tissue. By means of the experimental removal of this structure and of experimental transplantation, it has been demonstrated that the esophageal ganglion is associated indirectly with control of the molting process because of the influence of its secretions on the activity of the prothoracic glands. It is also known that secretions from the "brain" induce the esophageal ganglion to produce in female *Calliphora* (Diptera), a hormone which promotes egg development.

Although connected with the sympathetic nervous system, the corpora allata are composed mostly of secretory tissue. The secretions have been shown to be concerned not only with molting and metamorphosis, but also with egg production, with the formation of enzymes in the alimentary system and with control of respiration through the regulation of oxygen consumption.

In immature Dictyoptera, Hemiptera, Lepidoptera, Coleoptera and Mecoptera, a pair of glands in the prothorax originates from the hypodermis of the labial segment and is associated with branches of the central nervous system. These prothoracic glands are cyclically active between molts; when stimulated by a hormone from the supraesophageal ganglion, they produce an endocrine secretion that precipitates molting. During larval life a secretion from the corpora allata is present and each ecdysis results in another larval instar; as the time for pupation draws near, the corpora allata cease to produce this hormone and apparently its withdrawal allows the secretion from the prothoracic gland to exert its influence by inducing the development of adult structures.

Pericardial and ventral cephalic endocrine glands have been found in walking sticks (Phasmida). These glands are probably homologous with the prothoracic glands of other insects and their secretions are similarly related to molting and metamorphosis.

In larval Cyclorrhapha (a suborder of Diptera), the corpora allata, the secretory part of the esophageal ganglion and the prothoracic glands are merged into a single structure (**Weismann's ring**) encircling the aorta just behind the "brain." This composite structure has been shown to be functionally homologous with its several components. In the suborder Nematocera (the most primitive Diptera), the component glands remain separate and are arranged much like those of other insects; in the intermediate suborder Brachycera, the arrangement and degree of fusion of these glands are intermediate.

The center for control of metamorphosis in *Sialis* (Neuroptera) is known to be in the metathorax and first abdominal segment, but has not been specifically located and identified. A pair of glands in the prothorax of immature dragonflies (Odonata) controls metamorphosis, and while these glands seem to be different from those found in other juvenile insects, they probably are homologous.

It is clear that hormones control and regulate the stages in the life history of an insect by influencing growth and by determining the events associated with ecdysis. In all insects investigated the process seems to be basically the same. Stimulated by secretions from the supraesophageal mass, the prothoracic glands—or their homologues—produce a **growth and differentiation hormone** (**ecdyson**) that leads to molting. Throughout immaturity the corpora allata produce a **juvenile hormone** (**neotenin**), in the presence of which the formation of adult structures is suppressed, and each ecdysis results in another immature instar and the successive instars progress only slightly toward adulthood. When production of juvenile hormone ceases, pupation occurs and development of the adult instar is initiated. One of the functions of the corpora allata is to maintain the juvenile condition by suppressing and retarding ultimate development.

The role of hormones in normal growth, aside from metamorphosis, has been studied by transplanting tissue from one insect to another under various conditions. When an eye is transplanted from a younger donor insect to a more developed host insect with larger eyes, the grafted eye will grow rapidly until it has caught up with the development of the host eyes in size, but subsequently will grow at the same rate. In experiments conducted with *Drosophila* (Diptera, Cyclorrhapha), growth control has been found to be localized in Weismann's ring. When the host insect receives transplanted Weismann's ring along with a grafted eye, accelerated growth occurs in the host, not just in the transplanted tissue.

Although enzyme secretion must be under secretory control, thus far no close relationship between enzyme activity and hormone production, such as has been found in vertebrates, has been demonstrated in insects. An interrelation between enzymes and hormones has been indicated by a few experiments. The hormone affecting egg production is secreted by the corpora allata; when it is present in *Rhodnius* (Hemiptera), the insect digests food more rapidly. A hormone apparently controls the number of mitoses in midgut regenerative cells in the adult mealworm *Tenebrio* (Coleoptera).

From the many studies conducted in recent years on the endocrines of insects it has become evident that the chemical control system is extremely complex and delicately balanced. The hormones are significant because of their essential role in controlling and regulating the life processes. The formation and activities of endocrine secretions must be given high priority in entomological research of the future.

CHAPTER SEVEN

Early Embryogenesis

A hen is only an egg's way
of making another egg.
SAMUEL BUTLER

Embryology, the *study* of the embryo, is sometimes
loosely used for **embryogenesis,** the *development* of the embryo. Exactly
what is embraced by embryology and embryogenesis depends directly
upon what is meant by an embryo. Entomologists often use the term
embryo to specify the insect only while it is within the egg; accordingly,
an insect would be an embryo from the moment the zygote is formed by
fusion of male and female gametes until the moment the animal hatches.
But there are certain difficulties in this interpretation. Some insects are
not the product of fused gametes: what is the starting point for such an
embryo? Some insects do not hatch from a previously laid egg: at what
point does such an embryo stop being one? Above all, the comparative
study of insect embryos demonstrates that hatching, when an egg *is* laid,
may occur in various species at such vastly different points in development that it cannot be used as a general milepost of developmental progress. The gamete-to-hatching definition of *embryo* is unrealistic; at best,
it is only a convention of convenience, a transference of ideas from the
lay vocabulary as applied to vertebrates and particularly to our own
species.

"The concept of an embryo should not be confined solely to that stage
of development which runs its course within the egg; in its widest application it covers all stages of immaturity," according to Hagen (1951),
who maintained that the definition of *embryo* from the basic biological
viewpoint places its termination either at that point when all adult
systems are well formed or when the reproductive system becomes potentially functional. Though an embryo begins with the formation of a
zygote (or an equivalent stage in parthenogenesis), the study of the

210

embryo (embryology) must reach further back and include the steps leading to it.

In view of Weismann's germ plasm theory, embryogenesis must begin with the formation of the gametes, so that embryology must embrace all events from the primordial germ cell to the potentially reproductive individual. In this more inclusive sense, *embryogenesis* becomes closely synonymous with *ontogeny*. One of the consequences of this viewpoint is that, with Berlese, one must regard the insect larva as an embryo, and the terms *nymph* and *larva* must be recognized as designating special kinds of embryos.

THE GAMETES

The general process of gametogenesis (Fig. 7.2) in animals is so well known and such an essential part of any introductory course in zoology that only a brief review will be presented here. Insects, notably the grasshopper and the fruit fly, have been favorite animals with cytogeneticists; it was from these animals that the basic pattern, widely applicable to all animals, was first derived in detail—another example of the excellence of insects as experimental material for basic research.

Very early in embryogenesis a certain cell is set aside, remaining in an unspecialized condition and not entering into the varied and complex histogenesis of other cells or contributing to the animal's somatic tissues (Fig. 7.1). This cell is the **primordial germ cell,** the ancestor of the gametes eventually to be produced by the individual. Primordial germ cells have been identified in some species quite early in cleavage and their subsequent fate has been demonstrated; in other species, investigators have not been able to find the primordial germ cells quite so early, but presumably the problem is only one of identification.

The primordial germ cells proliferate, generally forming a small mass which comes to lie near the posterior pole of the embryo. When the gonads form, each follicle receives one such cell (**primitive germ cell**), which remains near the follicular apex. The gonad is thus a protective, nutritive envelope of mesodermal derivation usually consisting of a large number of follicles, each of which harbors a primitive germ cell descended from the primordial germ cell. At maturity the primitive germ cell proliferates, forming **primary gametogonia** which, through a series of divisions, give rise to the **gametes**. The process is essentially similar in both sexes. The cells descended from the primitive cell move down the gonad while the events of their development take place, so that the gonad may be divided into a series of zones, sometimes recognizable externally,

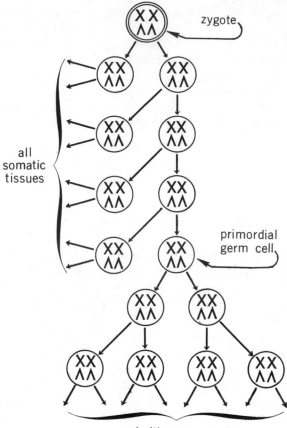

Figure 7.1. Diagram to illustrate the lineage of the primordial germ cell, the primitive germ cells and somatic tissues in an embryo. The heterosomes are indicated by *x* and *y*, the autosome complement by the inverted *v*'s. Solid arrows indicate division by mitosis.

each characterized by the stage of progress attained by the sex cells within.

The apical zone of the testis (see Fig. 5.9A) is the **germarium.** Here the primitive cell gives rise by mitosis to the **primary spermatogonia** (Fig. 7.2A), which in turn divide several or many times, producing a series of spermatogonial generations. The pressure of all this multiplication helps to push the developing spermatogonia into the **zone of growth,** where

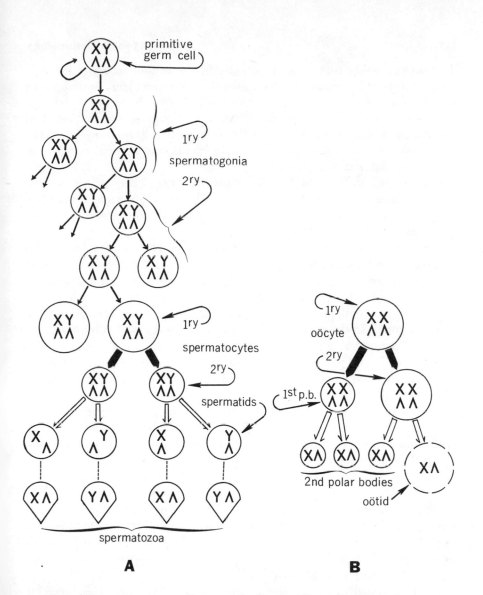

Figure 7.2. Diagram to illustrate the lineage of gametes from the primitive germ cell in the gonads of (A) the male and (B) the female. Steps leading to the primary oöcyte (B) are not illustrated and are similar to those of the male except that the *y* heterosome is replaced by the *x* heterosome and the intermediate stages are the primary and secondary oögonia. The relative sizes of cells are suggested by those of the circles. Male gametes are represented by kite-shaped figures, female gametes by large broken circles. Thin solid arrows indicate mitosis, heavy solid arrows meiosis without reduction and open arrows meiosis with reduction. *p.b.*, polar bodies.

they enlarge while continuing to divide. In the **reduction zone** the end-product cells of spermatogonial mitosis, the **spermatocytes,** undergo two successive aberrant divisions (meiosis) without growth, one of which is a reduction division, leading to the formation of haploid **spermatids.** The spermatids become **spermatozoa** in the **zone of transformation.** The vasa deferentia commonly have sac-like enlargements, the seminal vesicles, in which spermatozoa are stored.

As compared to spermatogenesis, oögenesis (Fig. 7.2B) presents some minor modifications, and because the female gamete normally becomes enclosed within an egg or equivalent membranes and materials, further complications attend the process.

The ovary (see Fig. 5.9B) is made up of a cluster of tubules, the ovarioles. The first functional zone of an ovariole is the **germarium;** as in the male, it contains the primitive germ cell. In most of the less evolved groups, notably the Odonata, Thysanura and orthopteroid orders, the primitive germ cell produces only **oögonia,** the female homologues of spermatogonia. In the majority of the advanced orders—Hemiptera, Coleoptera, Neuroptera, Lepidoptera, Diptera, Hymenoptera—some of the daughter cells lose gametopotency and serve solely as **nurse cells** for the oöcytes. When nurse cells are produced, the ovariole is said to be **meroistic;** when they are not produced, the ovariole is **panoistic.**

Most of the ovariole is the **vitellarium.** Here the gametopotent cells are enclosed (sometimes with nurse cells) within membranes, oögenesis proceeds and the eggs mature. The two meiotic divisions of the **primary oöcyte** lead to the production of only one functional gamete, the **oötid,** rather than to four gametes as in the male. The division of the primary oöcyte results in a large **secondary oöcyte** and a small, degenerate nucleus, the **first polar body.** When the secondary oöcyte divides, the products are the larger **oötid** and a small **second polar body.** Meanwhile, the first polar body may or may not divide, but if it does, the division produces two more second polar bodies. The bulk of the cytoplasm always goes to the oötid (this gamete should never be called an "egg").

In the "typical" process, the cytoplasm is filled with yolk and fat globules and other nutritive material; the entire system is then enclosed by an inner **vitelline membrane** and an outer **chorion,** thus becoming an ovum (egg). Both membranes apparently always are secreted by the epithelial lining of the ovariole, but in various ways. The epithelium may grow in and around the forming egg, enclosing it in a cellular sac and separating it from the wall, or the membranes may form without such a sac.

Variation in the ecologic situation into which the egg will be deposited is correlated with variation both in the chorion and in the nutritive contents of the cytoplasm. Eggs normally laid in more or less exposed places—on leaves or twigs, on or in the ground—usually have a thick, strong chorion (**shell**) frequently strengthened by sculptured patterns typical of the species and often inconspicuously colored. When a heavy shell-like chorion is present, sperm penetration is accomplished through the **micropyle,** a tiny trap door at one end, which closes after fertilization. Eggs deposited in more protected situations have a much thinner, more delicate chorion, as in the parasitic Hymenoptera, whose eggs are deposited within host tissues and thus need no shell. In viviparous species the chorion is entirely lacking. Nutritive contents also show variation, correlated with the requirements of the embryo before hatching and the situation in which the hatched larva will develop. A larger amount of yolk is present in the eggs of insects with young larvae that are free-living and self-sufficient from the outset. Much less is present when the young normally hatch into a highly nutritive environment, such as those of parasitic Hymenoptera. Virtually no yolk at all forms in the eggs of species that are viviparous—that give birth to embryos devoid of an enveloping chorion (Hagan, 1951).

FERTILIZATION

Except in the special cases of parthenogenesis (discussed later), the haploid male and female gametes unite within the egg to form a single diploid nucleus (**zygote**), normally the first cell of the new individual (Fig. 7.3A). The female obtains sperms through some form of copulation, often attended by complex behavior known as *courtship*. Fertilization proper occurs within the female genital tract in insects.

Sperms transferred to the female may continue to be functional for long periods of time. The honeybee presents an extreme example: a newly emerged virgin female mates with a male (drone) in midair, receiving and storing enough spermatozoa to fertilize all the eggs she will produce during her entire life—generally eight or more years. The adults of most species are much shorter lived, but apparently a single copulation is the rule rather than the exception, regardless of the number of eggs produced or the life span of the female.

SEX DETERMINATION

While other factors sometimes may be involved in the determination of sex, the chromosomes and genes play key roles. The number of chromosomes in the diploid complement varies from species to species and group to group (Makino, 1951). Each haploid gamete contributes to the zygote

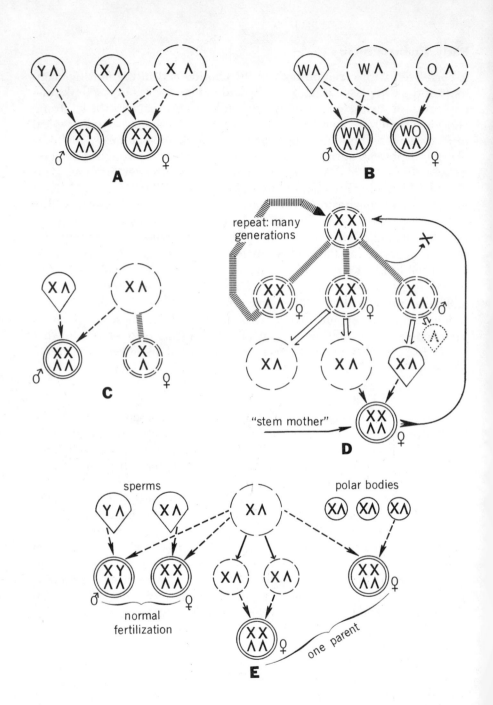

Figure 7.3. Diagrams to illustrate sex determination and parthenogenesis. (A) Normal fertilization in animals having two kinds of spermatozoa and one kind of oötid. (B) Normal fertilization in animals (Lepidoptera, Trichoptera,

a set of chromosomes, each chromosome differing from the others, but each with a homologue in one of the chromosomes in the set contributed by the other gamete. These chromosomes are the **autosomes**. In addition a few chromosomes—often only one from each gamete—form nonidentical pairs (**heterosomes, sex chromosomes**), or in some cases one parent contributes a heterosome having no counterpart in the other haploid set (Figs. 7.1, 7.2 and 7.3A). Sex determination is associated with the number and nature of the heterosomes.

Among insects, myriapods and arachnoids there are three principal types of sex determinative mechanics, each with different implications in the life histories of the various species. These types and their variations are more easily understood by use of chromosome formulae. Let n be the number of autosomes in the haploid set; a diploid cell would therefore be represented by $2n$. Let y represent the heterosome present only in males and x the heterosome present in both sexes when the male has the unique heterosome. When both heterosomes of the male are alike, the heterosome common to the sexes is represented by w. Th absence of a heterosome is represented by o.

In the basic type of sex determination the diploid male may be represented by $2n + xy$ and the diploid female by $2n + xx$. The oötids produced by such females are all alike, always $n + x$, but the males produce two kinds of gametes, either $n + x$ or $n + y$. The sex of any particular offspring is determined by which kind of male gamete fertilizes the female gamete. The majority of arthropods and other animals are of this

---

Figure 7.3 (*continued*)

Reptilia, Aves) having one kind of sperm and two kinds of oötids. (C) Sex determination in Hymenoptera, Mallophaga, some Hemiptera and a few mites, in which the normally fertilized oötid forms a zygote which becomes a diploid male, but the unfertilized oötid forms a hemizygote which becomes a haploid female (type I parthenogenesis). (D) Type II parthenogenesis in an aphid, in which the oötid becomes a pseudozygote and produces only parthenogenetic females for many generations; under certain influences, the pseudozygote may undergo reduction to form true gametes, but the offspring resulting from fertilization are always females. (E) Type III parthenogenesis, as found in a few insects, myriapods and arachnoids, occurs as an alternative to normal fertilization. The oötid may be fertilized by one of the polar bodies to form a parazygote, which always results in female offspring, or the parazygote may result from the fusion of two haploid cells formed by the mitotic division of the oötid. Thin broken arrows indicate fusion of two cells, whether by true or by false fertilization; heavy broken arrows indicate parthenogenesis without cell fusion; double circles indicate zygotes.

type. Since the y heterosome is present only in males, any genetic factors on y are phenotypically expressed in males (*white-eye* in *Drosophila, hemophilia* in man), but are rarely expressed in females.

A frequent variation of this primary type of determinative mechanics is the loss of the y heterosome, a condition found in many different species and groups. The male formula then becomes $2n + xo$; since o does not represent a chromosome, the diploid male has one less heterosome than the diploid female. Another variation is the duplication of the x heterosome, either with or without y present, leading to formulae like $2n + xxy$ or $2n + xxo$ for males and $2n + xxx$ for females. Duplication of x occurs in some of the Pseudoscorpionida, Araneida, Thysanura, Plecoptera, Dictyoptera, Dermaptera, Hemiptera and Coleoptera; in some species as many as five x's may be present in a single gamete. Still another variation, the duplication of the y heterosome, occurs in certain Orthoptera and Hemiptera.

In the second kind of sex determination (Fig. 7.3B), peculiar to Trichoptera and Lepidoptera among insects and characteristic of reptiles and birds among the vertebrates, the situation is reversed: males are $2n + ww$ and produce only $n + w$ sperms, but females are $2n + wo$ and produce two kinds of oötids, either $n + w$ or $n + o$. Sex is determined by the type of female gamete fertilized; phenotypes of sex-linked factors are therefore found in females instead of in males.

The third type of determination, characteristic of Hymenoptera, Mallophaga, some Hemiptera and several families of mites, is a form of parthenogenesis. A fertilized egg develops into a diploid female (Fig. 7.3C), but an unfertilized egg becomes a haploid male. All genetic factors are phenotypically expressed in males, behaving in general like the sex-linked factors in the other two types of sex determination.

These three different types have arisen independently and have little *general* phylogenetic significance. It is interesting, however, to note that the insect orders in which x and y duplication most frequently occurs (as in Hemiptera and Dictyoptera) are also the orders in which such irregularities as parthenogenesis are more common.

PARTHENOGENESIS

Parthenogenesis is often classified by entomologists as **obligatory,** when it is the sole method of reproduction, **facultative,** when ova develop whether they are fertilized or not, or **cyclical,** when parthenogenetic generations alternate with sexually produced generations. This approach has some value in the study of life histories, but it disregards the cytological bases for parthenogenesis—the real key to the whole problem. Three types of parthenogenesis, which are by no means respectively equivalent to the three classes listed above, may be distinguished on a cytological basis in insects and their relatives (Peacock, 1961): hemizygoid parthenogenesis, zygoid parthenogenesis and autogamous parthenogenesis.

Hemizygoid parthenogenesis, characteristic of Hymenoptera and a few other insects and mentioned above as the third type of sex determination, produces only males from unfertilized eggs (**arrhenotoky**) and only females by the usual process of fertilization (Fig. 7.3C); males are haploid, females diploid. To enable the unfertilized oötid to become a new individual, oögenesis must necessarily be modified so that the oötid (**hemizygote**) serves in place of a zygote and enters into cleavage without the stimulus of spermatozoa. Furthermore, spermatogenesis must also be modified: since all male cells in the germ line are already haploid, spermatogenesis cannot include meiotic reduction.

The other two types of parthenogenesis are found in species having both males and females diploid and normally are alternated with sexual reproduction.

Zygoid parthenogenesis occurs in aphids (Hemiptera) and some related families. The female gamete does not reduce the chromosome number during oögenesis (Fig. 7.3D) but remains diploid, becoming an equivalent of the zygote without being fertilized (**pseudozygote**). The extreme condition is found in many tropical species, in which this kind of parthenogenetic reproduction continues to produce females indefinitely (**thelytoky**) and males never appear. Temperate zones and certain tropical regions with marked contrast between wet and dry seasons periodically present unfavorable conditions to the animals living there, so that much of the fauna must suspend physiological activity in order to span the annual periods of food and water shortage and of extreme temperatures. In such regions aphid species reproduce parthenogenetically throughout the favorable season: generation after generation consists only of females, but with the advent of the unfavorable season males and females both appear. These are normal adults incapable of parthenogenesis and both sexes produce haploid gametes. Since all females are $2n + xx$ and all males are $2n + xo$ (Makino, 1951; J. Fox, 1956, 1957), it is supposed that the parthenogenetic mothers of males somehow eliminate an x heterosome during gametogenesis. The members of the sexual generation copulate and the females deposit overwintering eggs provided with protective chorions. At the beginning of spring (or the end of the extremely dry season) the eggs hatch, all becoming females (but what happens to the $n + o$ male gametes?) and parthenogenesis is resumed.

This type of parthenogenesis may be combined with viviparity and, in some species, with neoteny (precocious reproduction). In contrast to hemizygoid parthenogenesis, it produces under various circumstances parthenogenetic females, nonparthenogenetic females or males (**deutero-toky**); the first parthenogenetic female of each cycle is produced from a fertilized egg. It is true that temperate zone aphids cyclically alternate parthenogenesis with sexual reproduction, but since so many tropical species with the same cytological characteristics are exclusively partheno-genetic, it is incorrect to label this type of reproduction as "cyclical."

Autogamous parthenogenesis results from yet other deviations from normal reproduction. Females produce haploid gametes and they can be fertilized by male gametes, in which case the offspring are male or female in accordance with the mechanics of sex determination (Fig. 7.3E). Alternatively, however, the female gamete may be self-fertilized (**autog-amy**), then producing only females. This self-fertilization occurs in either of two ways. In some cases one of the polar bodies fuses with the oötid nucleus ("pseudofertilization"), producing a diploid **parazygote.** In other cases the same result is obtained when the oötid divides (this is not really the first cleavage division, as has been reported, though probably phylogenetically derived from it) and the daughter cells unite to form a diploid parazygote. Autogamous parthenogenesis is found in certain species belonging to several of the large insect orders—Hemiptera, Lepi-doptera, Coleoptera, primitive Hymenoptera, the orthopteroids—and in some Acarida and a few myriapods. It may occur normally but infre-quently (some Lepidoptera), or it may be somewhat more usual than bisexual reproduction. In a few species (several mantids and phasmids) it seems to have supplanted normal reproduction. It has been found in certain Hymenoptera combined with hemizygoid parthenogenesis. the females thus being produced either by two parents or by only one.

It will be noticed that all three types of parthenogenesis fundamentally are deviations from normal bisexual reproduction, each type effected by a specific modification of oögenesis or of fertilization. Experimentally induced parthenogenesis *simulates* fertilization and is an entirely different situation, being brought about by artificial stimulus (mechanical or chemical) never encountered under natural conditions. Its success in the laboratory, however, demonstrates that events leading to the forma-tion of the zygote are in delicate balance and helps one to appreciate why such diverse groups of insects have been able to devise different kinds of parthenogenesis. Minor upsets in the normal balance lead to profound effects.

THE EMBRYO

Although embryology necessarily includes a study of events leading to the establishment of an embryo, the embryo itself begins existence with the zygote or some equivalent cell (hemizygote, pseudozygote or parazygote). In general terms the zygote is a diploid cell having a nucleus formed by the additive fusion of the nuclei of a male and a female gamete, both haploid, through the process of fertilization.

The zygote is often enclosed by the egg, but sometimes the embryo has progressed beyond the zygote stage by the time the enclosing membranes form. Exceptionally the zygote may produce more than one individual. These questions are best deferred until normal—*usual* is a better word—events of embryogenesis have been reviewed.

CLEAVAGE

Cleavage is the process of mitotic proliferation of the zygote. It continues until the beginning of morphologic differentiation on the part of the cells or by the whole structure.

Holoblastic (total) cleavage (Fig. 7.4A) occurs in the absence of mechanical interference from a large volume of yolk, each generation of daughter cells dividing simultaneously, with each successive plane of division perpendicular to the previous plane so that a somewhat spherical mass (**morula**) of nearly identical cells is produced. About the time six divisions have been completed, cell differentiation begins. Because cleavage is never completely free of interference, perfect holoblastic cleavage is exceedingly rare.

As found in arthropods cleavage is modified by various degrees and kinds of interference. Perhaps certain parasitic wasps (Hymenoptera) come the closest to perfect holoblastic cleavage because only a comparatively small amount of yolk surrounds the cleavage mass; later divisions produce **blastomeres** (cleavage daughter cells) of somewhat irregular size. In some species not all blastomeres divide and in others some of the cells may migrate into the yolk. In the Strepsiptera, also internal parasites, the yolk is a tiny central mass which receives a blastomere at the sixteen- or thirty-two-cell stage and eventually is crowded to the periphery of the egg—otherwise cleavage closely approximates the typically holoblastic. Similar slightly modified holoblastic cleavage is found in a few mites and ticks, one phalangid and some scorpions.

Combination cleavage (Fig. 7.4B–F) begins as holoblastic. After a certain number of divisions, during which the yolk surrounding the embryonic cells also divides (sometimes only partially) into a series of

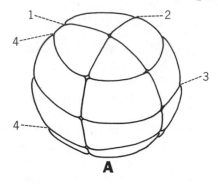

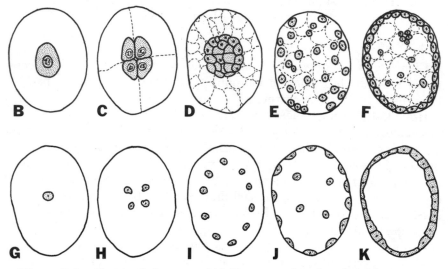

Figure 7.4. Types of cleavage. (A) Diagram of perfect holoblastic cleavage, the numbers indicating the sequence of the planes of division; (B–F) the stages of combination cleavage; (G–K) the comparable stages in peripheral cleavage. (B) and (G) are the one-celled stage; (F) and (K) are the blastoderm stage. (B–K redrawn from Johannsen and Butt, 1941, by permission of McGraw-Hill Book Co.)

pyramids with inwardly pointing apices, the blastomeres separate and move outward to the periphery, continuing to divide during migration. A few cells always remain within the yolk. Further division leads to the formation of a sphere of blastomeres enclosing the yolk. Combination cleavage is typical of most spiders, all pseudoscorpions and thelyphonids among the arachnoids, of Chilopoda, Symphyla and many Diplopoda among myriapods, and only of the Collembola among insects.

Peripheral (superficial) cleavage (Fig. 7.4G—K) is a further development brought about, in part, by a greater volume of yolk. The zygote begins division within, though not necessarily at the center of, the yolk. The blastomeres separate from one another as soon as they divide, migrating to the periphery where cleavage is completed. This procedure is characteristic of nearly all insects, some Diplopoda, certain spiders, many mites and ticks, all Phryneida and Solpugida.

Both the gametes move toward the center of the egg during fertilization, so that cleavage division begins there, though in some species with peripheral cleavage the movement of the gametes is incomplete. Where there is a very large volume of dense yolk, the gametes apparently are prevented from moving into it and remain at the periphery. The cleavage divisions are on two planes rather than on three, forming a disc of blastomeres at the anterior pole (the **animal**) of the egg. **Discoidal cleavage** among arthropods is found only in a few scorpions.

Whatever the manner of cleavage, the result is the formation of the **blastoderm (primary epithelium)**, a largely undifferentiated layer one cell thick. Unless the volume of yolk is so great as to prevent it—as is true when discoidal cleavage occurs—the blastoderm is more or less spherical and encloses the yolk.

Either during cleavage or as soon as the blastoderm nears completion, depending on the species, a few blastomeres move into the yolk (or are left behind during the migration to the periphery in combination cleavage) where they continue division. These cells are **vitellophages (yolk cells)** with an immediate function of beginning yolk digestion and making it available to the other embryonic tissues. Early investigators held that the vitellophages developed into the endoderm and became the midgut. Current opinion is that they either form a temporary mesoderm which is later broken down, or are destroyed and resorbed without forming any layer, but that in any case they do not contribute to the definitive midgut.

In many eggs a small area of specialized protoplasm near the posterior pole may be identified (**oösome, polar plasma, germ-track determinant, Kiembahn determinant**). Certain blastomeres pass through this protoplasm and add it to their own; they are then found congregated near the posterior pole, where the abdominal region will eventually develop. Ultimately these cells, the primordial germ cells, are enclosed by the gonads. The oösome simplifies, by its presence, early recognition of the primordial germ cells, but it is not always present. When it is absent, the primordial cells may be nevertheless found in some species clustered near the posterior pole, but in many other cases they cannot be surely identified until the gonad rudiments form, a situation that has led some cautious observers to claim that the germ cells are derived from somatic material, since they could not be found until after the germ layers had differentiated. However, there is little doubt that the primordial germ cells always differentiate before the somatic layers, whether or not they are readily identified morphologically, and indeed they represent the first definitively differentiated tissue of the new individual.

THE GERM BAND AND EXTRAEMBRYONIC MEMBRANES

Sooner or later the cells at one point on the blastoderm enlarge and crowd together, becoming somewhat columnar. This pad of thickened cells (Fig. 7.5A, B) is the beginning of the **germ band** and marks the ventral surface of the embryo. Sometimes a similar region of thickened cells (**primary dorsal organ**) appears on the dorsal side, but apparently is not needed and soon disappears. The germ band enlarges, while in the rest of the former blastoderm the cells gradually become pavement-like and well spaced. The blastoderm is thus differentiated into two regions, the germ band which is the embryo proper, and the **extraembryonic area.**

As it grows, the germ band may at first assume any of a variety of shapes—round, triangular, oval, somewhat elongated or greatly elongated —but in the end it becomes elongated. Also it may remain on the surface of, or sink completely into, the yolk, or first the posterior and then the anterior ends may flex down into the yolk with the middle remaining near or at the surface. In any event, with few exceptions, the margins of the embryonic area grow back over the germ disc (Fig. 7.5C, D) from all sides, finally meeting in the middle and coalescing. By this means *two* extraembryonic envelopes are formed. The inner one is the **amnion** and covers the embryo; the outer one is the **serosa,** which encloses both the yolk and the embryo.

The vast majority of insects form an amnion and a serosa in this manner, although there is quite a range of minor variation which need not concern us here. In the stinging Hymenoptera, the amnion is rudimentary or absent; in parasitic Hymenoptera and some viviparous insects and arachnoids the extraembryonic membranes become highly modified, both functionally and structurally.

In myriapods, Collembola, Aptera and most arachnoids the margins of the extraembryonic area do not overgrow the embryo and it remains uncovered, with no amnion or serosa forming. The yolk is enclosed by the embryos of these forms and an **amnioserosal membrane** is formed in the extraembryonic region by the residual blastoderm. That this may be a secondary adaptation is suggested by the presence of both amnion and serosa in scorpions and a few other arachnoids, though the majority of the class lack them.

The extraembryonic membranes of scorpions with discoidal cleavage develop in a manner quite similar to the procedure found in birds—the familiar example of discoidal cleavage. The margins of the extraembryonic disc grow outward from the embryo and eventually enclose the

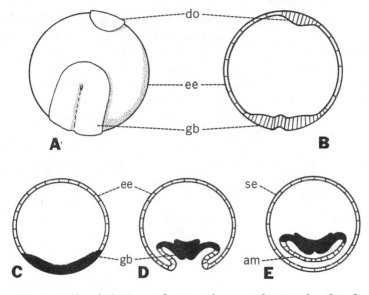

Figure 7.5. (A) External view of egg with germ band and dorsal organ; (B) diagrammatic cross section of the same egg. (C–E) Steps in the formation of the amnion and serosa by overgrowth (diagrammatic cross sections). *am,* amnion; *do,* primary dorsal organ; *ee,* extraembryonic area; *gb,* germ band; *se,* serosa. (C–E from Hagan, 1951, by permission of Ronald Press)

entire mass of yolk; meanwhile a fold forms at the periphery of the germ disc and gradually overgrows the embryo to enclose its ventral surface with the amnion, both embryo and amnion being enclosed by the serosa. The net result is exactly the same as in most insects, the variation clearly being caused by the great volume of yolk.

It will be recalled that in adult arthropods the ectodermal integument secretes the cuticle. It is interesting to find, therefore, that in many spiders, in myriapods and in Collembola and Aptera, two successive, ultimately concentric cuticles are secreted by the embryonic ectoderm and its topographical continuation, the amnioserosal membrane. Students of insect embryology designate these secreted envelopes as the **first and** second cuticles (Johannsen and Butt, 1941), while in spiders they are called the **deutovum** and **tritovum** (Dawydoff, 1949). The latter author calls attention to the similarity between the formation of these embryonic envelopes and the formation of the envelopes secreted by the early larvae of some Crustacea, of Xiphosura and of Chilopoda.

THE GERM LAYERS

Concurrent with the beginning of the formation of extraembryonic membranes, the germ disc develops a second, **inner layer** in one of several ways (Fig. 7.6). The most familiar method (Fig. 7.6A), found in most insects, involves a median longitudinal invagination of the germ band (involution), which first forms a trough. The lips of the trough grow back toward the midline so that the inner layer becomes somewhat tubular, then pinches off; finally the tube flattens against and grows out under the full width of the germ band. In a second method (Fig. 7.6B) a median longitudinal strip of cells separates from the rest of the germ band and draws in a little, the germ band then growing over it and joining on the midline to form continuous outer and inner layers (**overgrowth**). In the third method (Fig. 7.6C), found in many of the more primitive orders of insects, the inner layer of cells is proliferated from the inner side of the median longitudinal line of the germ band. In many species several of these methods may be combined, one occurring in one region, another elsewhere.

After the inner layer of cells becomes definitive, the residual germ band is the definitive **ectoderm** and the two solid **nerve cords** grow from its inner surface as longitudinal ridges, which come to lie between the two layers.

It is difficult to interpret the inner layer in terms of the classical concepts of endoderm and mesoderm, and a wide divergence of opinion is found among competent embryologists. Some believe that insects demonstrate the futility of the three-layer concept in embryology; others find both mesoderm and endoderm present in the inner cell layer. The problem hinges upon (a) how the midgut is formed and (b) the definition of endoderm.

The arthropod midgut (and its derivatives, if any) is the only structure that *can* be endodermal. Descriptions of the way the midgut forms in various embryos do not agree; unquestionably, the manner of formation differs from group to group. Are these differences merely variations of a theme, or is the midgut actually formed from one kind of material in one animal but from totally different material in another?

Dawydoff (1949) found no difficulty. In brief, his views were: the arthropod midgut is always formed from definitive endoderm, as are the malpighian tubules of insects and the hepatic organs of arachnoids and crustaceans. Two different endoderms always form. The first is provisional and nonmorphogenic and is represented by the vitellophages which function temporarily at early stages and do not contribute to the midgut. The

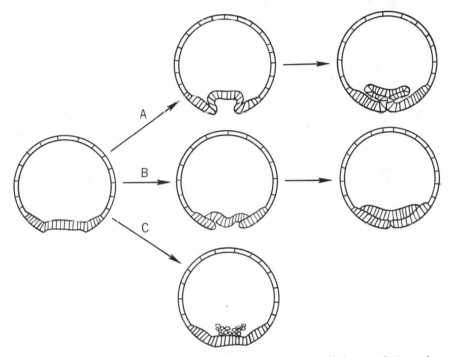

Figure 7.6. Diagram illustrating successive stages (left to right) in the formation of the inner germ layer by (A) involution, (B) overgrowth and (C) delamination. (Redrawn in part after Snodgrass, 1935, by arrangement with McGraw-Hill Book Co.)

second is the definitive endoderm, which differentiates as the **middle strand** of the inner cell layer, forming the definitive midgut in every case, but which may develop in a way difficult to trace correctly. Sometimes the middle strand cells clearly and directly become the midgut, as in scorpions; sometimes the middle part of the middle strand cells disassociates, and only the anterior and posterior remnants become the midgut, though the process is sometimes confused because these remnants become attached to the growing ectodermal invaginations of the fore- and hindgut. Either the disassociated cells are resorbed, or some of them are encompassed within other tissues, later to be freed and contribute to midgut development.

Many embryologists would take issue with Dawydoff's interpretation. It has been shown that in several insects (a grasshopper, some dragon-flies) the vitellophages do indeed contribute to the midgut by forming the epithelium of its middle part, though such a situation apparently is excep-tional. Further, the midgut of *Locusta* (Orthoptera) is believed to be formed entirely from the ectoderm of the fore- and hindgut invaginations. The explanation that these invaginations are tipped with endodermal cells receives little attention. Still further, the malpighian tubules in insects are commonly (but probably incorrectly) ascribed to the ectoderm. Whether or not ectoderm ever contributes anything to the midgut or malpighian tubules requires further investigation.

In any event, the germ layer theory has fallen into disfavor and has been under severe criticism. Certainly there is much to be said for think-ing in terms of an outer (ectodermal) and an inner layer, without attempt-ing to distinguish between mesoderm and endoderm. Endoderm is, in fact, frequently difficult to trace. It differentiates unequivocally only in a minority of animals. Part of the difficulty may lie in definitions. What is endoderm? Is it a third somatic layer which inherently differentiates from ectoderm and mesoderm, then goes on to form certain specific organs, particularly (in arthropods) the midgut? Or is it that tissue which forms the midgut, no matter what its apparent lineage or when or whether it first differentiated as a discrete layer?

SEGMENTATION[1]

Almost as soon as the germ band forms it begins segmentation—the process of dividing the body into definitive serial metameres and forming the basic structures in and on each. The earliest evidence of segmentation is almost always presented by the mesoderm, when it divides into seg-mental blocks in which the evanescent coelomic sacs begin forming. The ectoderm is affected soon after: internally, the paired ganglia of the ven-tral nerve cord develop; externally, transverse furrows appear at the inter-segmental points, superficially marking off the definitive metameres, and the rudiments of the paired appendages begin to grow.

These events do not occur simultaneously throughout the body. At first the germ band consists only of two tiny areas: an anterior part, usually the

[1] The word "segmentation" has two entirely different but equally correct meanings in embryology, referring either to cleavage or to the process described in this section and which sometimes is called "metamerization." We follow the usage more com-monly employed by students of insect embryology.

wider, representing the protocephalon, followed by a short, narrower piece representing the rest of the body (Fig. 7.7A). During rapid subsequent growth the posterior part of the germ band elongates, adding areas which will become the successively posterior segments (Fig. 7.7B, C). Keeping pace with growth, segmentation begins at the anterior end of the germ band as soon as it is formed and proceeds toward the caudal end, affecting each area as germ band material becomes available.

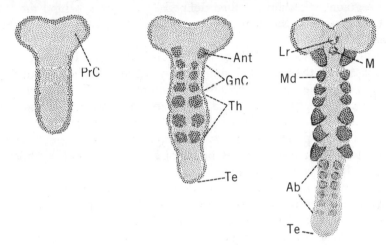

Figure 7.7. Ventral views of three stages of the embryo of the mantid *Tenodera sinensis* (Dictyoptera) showing general growth and the formation of limb rudiments. *Ab,* abdomen; *Ant,* antennal rudiment; *GnC,* gnathal segments bearing rudiments of the mandibles, maxillae and labium; *Lr,* labrum; *M,* mouth; *Md,* mandibular rudiment; *PrC,* procephalic lobe; *Te,* telson, preceded by a zone of growth; *Th,* thoracic segments bearing rudiments of the legs. (Redrawn from Hagan, 1917)

The transverse ectodermal furrows do not appear in the same sequence in all embryos and sometimes the body is first marked off into regions (**macrosomites**) which then divide into the definitive metameres. When this second process occurs, the macrosomites are equivalent to the basic morphologic sections of the body (**tagmata**), but not necessarily to the obvious body regions of the adult animal (which sometimes combine tagmata). To some extent the two processes are concurrent in most embryos. The protocephalon apparently is a macrosomite and is the first macrosomite to form in ontogeny; it was surely the earliest to form phylogenetically. In the protocephalon many of the embryogenetic processes have become compressed, bypassed or omitted during development. It never becomes clearly divided by the ectodermal furrows into its segments, but probably some of the incomplete longitudinal furrows found there represent vestiges of the original transverse divisions.

In insects it is more usual to find that the definitive segments form first, the macrosomites either not forming or forming without being easily recognized. In those embryos in which macrosomites appear, the gnathocephalon is first marked off by a transverse furrow behind the future labial segment; the thorax is then defined by a furrow behind the future metathorax and at the same time the three gnathocephalic segments appear.

The abdomen does not behave as a macrosomite, but forms in a different way. At first the telson lies immediately behind the thorax, but it does not enter into the elongation of the abdominal region. Abdominal segments are added just ahead of the telson, so that growth keeps pushing it further and further back. This behavior during segmentation, as well as the fact that the proctodaeum always invaginates from it, serves to identify the telson. In insects it has been miscalled the "twelfth abdominal segment," but it is not a metamere.

In myriapod embryos the macrosomites generally appear before the true segments are formed. As in insects, the protocephalic macrosomite forms first, then the gnathocephalic. In Diplopoda the first three trunk segments—those bearing only one pair of legs each in the adult—form as the third macrosomite and thus behave similarly to the thorax of insects. The telson is much better developed in myriapods than in most insects and is easier to identify during abdominal growth and segmentation.

In arachnoid embryos a segmental furrow usually first marks off two macrosomites (Fig. 7.8): an anterior region, which later divides into the cheliceral metamere and a cephalic part, and a posterior section made up of the growth zone plus the telson. Between the two original macrosomites the anterior few leg-bearing metameres appear first, followed by the posterior cephalothoracic and the abdominal segments. It is significant that the posterior leg-bearing segments develop serially with the abdomen; the five leg segments of arachnoids do not behave as a single tagma, but apparently consist of an anterior macrosomite plus abdominal material.

The paired segmental ganglia of the ventral nerve cords usually begin to form somewhat before the appearance of superficial transverse furrows. Two solid ridges (**neural ridges**) grow on the inner side of the ectoderm (Fig. 7.9). The cells (**neuroblasts**) of the ridges are neuropotent and are drawn into little groups or knots, one such group forming from each ridge in each metamere (see Fig. 6.2).

The procephalic ganglia develop at the same time as, and serially with, the rest of the nerve chain and there appears to be little reason to consider the "brain" as being other than a part of the whole ventral system. Whatever the eventual position of the supraesophageal mass, the three ganglia which contribute to it certainly begin developing on the ventral surface of the embryo. In myriapods the three procephalic ganglia are distinct at first but form close to one another and soon fuse; in insects the distinction among them is much less obvious. The terminal abdominal ganglia in both insects and myriapods tend to fuse, either after they have

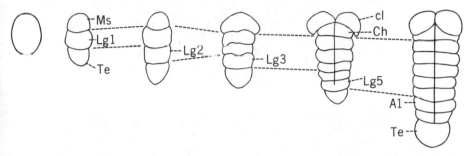

Figure 7.8. Successive stages in the segmentation of a scorpion. *A1*, first abdominal segment; *Ch*, cheliceral segment; *cl*, cephalic lobe; *Lg1*, first (pedipalpal) leg segment; *Lg2, Lg3, Lg5*, second, third and fifth leg segments; *Ms*, cephalic macrosomite; *Te*, telson preceded by zone of growth. (Redrawn from Dawydoff, 1949, by arrangement with Masson et Cie)

separately formed, or by developing together from the outset. Ganglia never form in the telson.

In view of the suppression of the protocephalon in arachnoids it is surprising to find that as many as four distinct segmental ganglia—not counting the optic and ocellular ganglia, which are not part of the ventral chain and become associated with the supraesophageal mass only secondarily—may form from neural ridge material ahead of the cheliceral (intercalary) segment (Fig. 7.10). These ganglia fuse very early and then degenerate. In spiders the trunk ganglia do not correspond with the apparent segmentation indicated by the ectodermal furrows. There seem to be not enough furrows or too many ganglia, but since the ganglion pairs correspond with the number of mesodermal coeloms, it may be assumed that abdominal furrowing has been modified.

The arthropods are coelom losers. The definitive body cavity (**hemocoel**) is formed from the enlarged **epineural sinus**, a space which first appears between the nerve cords and the inner cell layer at the early germ band stage. Coelomic cavities, when they develop at all, are added to the body cavity only after the latter is already well defined; they contribute only a small part of the hemocoel. In general, the coelomic cavities are more prominent and more consistently developed in primitive groups.

In the "typical" process, which tends to be suppressed in arthropods,

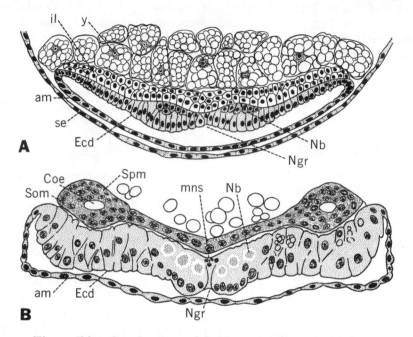

Figure 7.9. Cross sections of developing insect embryos through (A) the germ band after completion of the serosa and (B) a more advanced embryo after the formation of the coelomic cavities (serosa omitted). *am,* amnion; *Coe,* coelomic cavity; *Ecd,* ectoderm; *il,* inner cell layer; *mns,* median nerve cell strand; *Nb,* neuroblasts; *Ngr,* neural groove; *se,* serosa; *Som,* somatic mesoderm; *Spm,* splanchnic mesoderm; *y,* yolk cells surrounded by yolk material. (Redrawn from Johannsen and Butt, 1941, by permission of Mc-Graw-Hill Book Co.)

the two lateral sheets of the inner cell layer at the germ band stage are incontestably mesoderm (Fig. 7.9A). They form from a single layer of cells which soon becomes several layers thick and differentiates into the ventral **somatic layer** and the dorsal **splanchnic layer.** Early in segmentation this double layer of mesoderm divides into regular masses separated by constrictions corresponding to the boundaries of the definitive metameres. Typically the somatic and splanchnic layers draw apart a little, while retaining continuity along the longitudinal boundaries and at the segmental constrictions. The series of spaces so formed, a pair in each metamere, are the **coelomic cavities** (Fig. 7.9B). Presently the cavities become connected serially when the mesoderm at the metameric constrictions also draws apart a little. This process may be carried to completion in some parts of the bodies of some embryos, but never throughout all the segments. Either of the major steps mentioned above may end their development in any given segment or region: having formed, the coeloms may not become serially continuous; or the splanchnic and somatic mesodermal layers may not draw apart at all so that no cavity is formed. In this last event the mesodermal metameres may be identified only to the extent that segmental blocks are formed. Mesodermal segmentation, accordingly, can be very difficult to identify, but it ought to be obvious that the failure of a coelomic cavity to appear in an arthropod embryo is no proof that a segment is absent. Alternatively, some investigators have professed to believe that coelomic cavities may appear adventitiously where there is no metamere. However, it seems much more likely that definitive metameres in arthropods, especially in the head region, may fail to form their prototypic coeloms than that coeloms can form without rhyme or reason, unrelated to metamerization.

The somatic mesoderm later forms the muscles of the body wall, the dorsal diaphragm and the pericardium. The splanchnic mesoderm forms the visceral muscles, the genital ridges and much of the fat body. These two mesodermal layers have important contributions to make, but the spaces between them, the cavities, have little value in arthropods. It then should not be surprising to find that coelomic cavities are suppressed; it is much more surprising to discover that they so often persist.

Blocks of coelomic mesoderm form for each definitive metamere, but never form either in the telson or in the acron. Taken along with the paired ventral ganglia and the limb rudiments, the behavior of mesoderm in embryos sheds light on the difficult and highly controversial problem of cephalic segmentation in both insects and arachnoids. In insects there must be *at least* three protocephalic segments. Cephalic coelomic mesoderm is identifiable in insects for the intercalary, the antennal and a preantennal segment, an observation fully in agreement with segmentation of myriapod embryos, in which a preantennal appendage rudiment, in addition to the coeloms, is sometimes present. In arachnoids there is an elongated coelom in front of the coelomic cavity of the cheliceral segment; since this coelom is associated with the four ventral chain ganglia mentioned above, it probably is a fusion of the coeloms of several segments (Fig. 7.10). This situation raises the question of whether the arthropod protocephalon consists of *only* three metameres, or whether there are actually *more* than three.

Like the coeloms, furrows and ganglia, the limb rudiments appear first on anterior segments, then on the successive posterior segments as these become defined. Each rudiment is a bud-like evagination of the ventro-lateral ectoderm (Fig. 7.7) into which some somatic mesoderm is carried. Provided it is to become an adult structure, each rudiment elongates and is divided into sections corresponding to the eventual limb segments. Alternatively the rudiment may regress and disappear or in rare cases fuse with another structure; such is the fate of most rudiments on the abdominal segments of insects. In insects with holometabolous metamorphosis, the ontogeny of the limb rudiments, along with that of most other structures, is arrested during larval life. The mouthparts and thoracic legs of holometabolous larvae generally reach a stage in their development where some but not all of the ultimate limb segments are present. In some cases, for example, in Lepidoptera, the abdominal rudiments are still present on larvae as the prolegs. During pupation, when ontogeny is resumed and completed, the abdominal rudiments, if present in the larva, regress, while the cephalic and thoracic limbs attain the adult forms and the specializations. This process is extremely difficult to follow, however. As a general rule, the resumption of ontogeny is marked by the discarding of the larval structures and the formation of adult structures *from the same anlagen* (rudiments), rather than the literal completion and perfection of the partly developed immature structures.

The process of segmentation in the embryo is one of considerable significance to basic questions of adult homologies. During this period the metameres are indicated by the coeloms, the neural ganglia, the intersegmental furrows and the limb rudiments. The problem is to locate and identify structures at an early stage and to follow their progress to the adult. But it is far easier to state this problem than to solve it and even more difficult to thread the maze of conflicting evidence and interpretation of evidence.

The gnathocephalon of insects and myriapods consists by all criteria of three segments, each with a pair of coeloms and a pair of ganglia, and respectively bearing the rudiments of the mandibles, maxillae and labium. That the gnathochilarium of diplopods must be formed from a fusion of maxillary and labial rudiments seems clear from Pflugfelder's account (1932), since all three gnathocephalic segments are present in the early embryo, as well as the three "thoracic" segments.

The protocephalon is far more difficult to evaluate because coelomic, neural and appendicular structures do not always develop clearly. When they do not, as is true in most insects and some myriapods, their failure to appear undoubtedly represents a form of evolutional advance, rather in the nature of developmental short cut. The facts that arthropods are coelom losers and that the protocephalon is a very ancient tagma support such an interpretation. Coeloms and ganglia account for at least three metameres—aside from the acron which, like the telson, does not develop metameric structures serially with the rest of the body. Roonwal (1939) and others have reported a fourth coelomic formation anterior of the preantennal; this might account for the double nature of the protocerebral ganglion. Of possible procephalic appendages, only the antennae appear quite generally in mandibulates. Appendage rudiments of the intercalary segment appear briefly in many insects and develop into the chelicerae in arachnoids, but are always absent in myriapods. Limb rudiments of the preantennal segment have been found in a few species, notably a chilopod and a phasmid, and in a very few species the labrum arises as a paired structure. For this reason it has been thought by some to be serially homologous with the appendages, but the theory has had little acceptance.

Study of the embryo demonstrates rather conclusively that the protocephalon consists of at least three metameres and the contribution of an evanescent fourth has not been ruled out.

In the arachnoids the rudiments of the five cephalothoracic appendages appear first, the cheliceral and abdominal rudiments appear later. Abdominal appendages contribute to the pectines of scorpions, the spinnerets of spiders, the protective orifices of book lungs in both orders and the genital apertures of most arachnoids. Early regression disposes of the abdominal rudiments having no adult function. In some families of mites some or all rudiments of locomotory appendages regress at once, only to reappear later in embryogenesis. In some cases the reappearance of these legs occurs while the embryo is still within the egg, in others they reappear during larval development—it depends entirely upon how precociously the embryo leaves the egg.

Although the arachnoid cephalothorax is effectively a single region in the adult, it develops as three separate tagmata in the embryo—the cheliceral segment, which divides from the protocephalic macrosomite; the several anterior leg-bearing segments, which appear to be a macrosomite, perhaps equivalent to the gnathocephalon; and the posterior leg-bearing segments, which develop serially with the abdomen. Arachnoids are usually said to lack a true head, but a number of investigators have independently reported precheliceran limb rudiments in certain spider embryos. As Dawydoff (1949) comments, this is perfectly logical and should be more widely investigated. Nearly all arachnoid embryos have one pre-cheliceral coelom (Fig. 7.10), and in some, no less than three have been found. Furthermore, at least three paired ventral ganglia occur and in a few species a fourth (Fig. 7.10C) has been found. Apparently the traditional concept of the arachnoid cephalothorax must be revised. These animals begin with the components of the true head, components which are quite homologous with those of insects and myriapods. The arachnoids carry a little further an evolutional trend already noted in other arthropods—the trend to fuse protocephalic elements.

ECTODERMAL STRUCTURES

The ectoderm, at least, is undisputed material. It comes into definitive existence when the blastoderm gives rise to the inner cell layer (Figs. 7.6 and 7.7) and in general produces the integument with all its invaginations and delaminations, as well as the entire nervous system.

Before either of the gut invaginations begins and as soon as the inner layer appears, a midventral furrow, the neural groove (Figs. 7.7 and 7.9), forms in the ectoderm, keeping pace with or slightly preceding the successively posterior intersegmental furrows. Eventually the neural groove extends from just behind the stomodaeum to just ahead of the proctodaeum. As it forms in each metamere, neuroblasts delaminate on the inner face of the ectoderm between it and the inner cell layer. These neuroblasts, dividing, form the two longitudinal neural ridges. The segmental ganglia immediately form from the ridges. In due course the neuroblasts differentiate into the neurons, the processes of which form the segmental interganglionic connectives (commissures), the definitive ventral cords and the motor elements of the segmental nerves.

Anterior of the stomodaeum the neural ridges continue into the protocephalon only imperfectly and the ganglia are not clearly differentiated except in more primitive forms. The absence of the neural groove in the protocephalic region has led some investigators to believe that the "brain" is not part of the ventral chain, but it appears more probable that the anterior end of the neural groove is limited by the movement of the stomodaeum ventrad and back from the anterior body pole.

In *Scolopendra* (Chilopoda) the location of the paired ventral ganglia of the trunk region is indicated externally by tiny pits in the ectoderm. Similar pits appear under the paired ganglia of the preantennal, antennal and intercalary metameres. Anterior of the preantennal segment, marked in the embryo of this myriapod by the brief presence of limb rudiments, a row of two pits on each side appears and above the apex of each pit a ganglion develops. Before any other procephalic ganglion develops, a

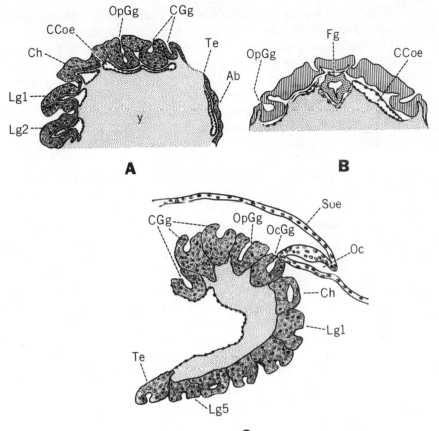

Figure 7.10. Sections through spider embryos. (A) Part of a parasagittal section through the embryo of *Dolomedes fimbriatus* and a cross section (B) through the optic ganglia; (C) sagittal section of the embryo of *Ischnocolus*. *Ab*, abdomen; *CCoe*, cephalic (precheliceral) coelom; *CGg*, cerebral ganglionic invaginations; *Ch*, cheliceral segment; *Fg*, foregut; *Lg1*, first leg (pedipalpal) segment; *Lg2*, *Lg5*, second and fifth leg segments; *Oc*, pocket forming the outer part of the median eye; *OcGg*, ocellar lobe; *OpGg*, optic lobe; *Soe*, somatic ectoderm; *Te*, telson; *y*, yolk. (A and B after Pappenheim, 1903; C redrawn (after Schimkewitsch, 1911) from Dawydoff, 1949, by arrangement with Masson et Cie)

237

median ganglion forms anterior of the four anteriormost pits. This ganglion has been attributed to the acron, and if such is the case, it must be sympathetic rather than truly central. These five anterior ganglia fuse with the preantennal ganglia to form the protocerebrum. The anterior median ganglion contributes the corpora pedunculata, the medio-lateral pair become the dorsal cortex and the lateral pair become the frontal and optic lobes of each side. A somewhat similar though slightly more evolved (less obvious) situation has been observed in the development of the protocerebrum in certain grasshoppers and in some other of the more primitive insects.

The entire visceral sympathetic system—frontal ganglion, recurrent nerve, hypocerebral, esophageal and stomacic ganglia—forms from neuroblasts derived from the dorsal wall of the stomodaeum. The dermal sensory system, including the eyes and ocelli, develops from neuroblasts delaminated from the ectoderm as that layer assumes its position as the hypodermis in the head.

There are two alternatives in interpreting the position of the stomodaeum. One theory assumes that the stomodaeum is in relatively the same position it has always been and that it still marks the anterior axis of the body; accordingly there is no alternative but to interpret as nonsegmental acron all material anterior of the stomodaeum, except the intercalary segment which unquestionably becomes preoral during ontogeny. This was the view first offered by Holmgren and later elaborated by Hanström and received a wide circulation for a time, but it soon became evident that such an interpretation is in direct conflict with the weight of embryological and phylogenetic evidence and today has but few proponents.

The opposite interpretation assumes that the stomodaeal invagination has been rotated ventrad and back from the anterior body axis, passing between (as it were) the ganglia of the protocephalic metameres before they became definitive and ultimately forcing them to a dorsal position when the anteriormost metameres flex upward during cephalization. Evidence of such a movement by the stomodaeum is difficult to obtain, since it happens—if it happens—before the germ disc has any useful topography. The stomodaeum has the same location in all arthropods. If it ever were at the true anterior pole in any ancestral form, that animal probably was prearthropodian—and, it must be added, preannelidian as well. The fact remains that regardless of how it came to pass, the arthropod mouth is morphologically located ventral and posterior of the body pole and is preceded by segmental material in which no element of the enteron forms.

As it grows, the stomodaeal invagination tends to draw in some of the surrounding ventral tissue, thus forming the buccal cavity within which

is the true mouth, the original point of invagination. At first the stomodaeum grows in a dorsal direction (Fig. 7.11), then swings posteriorward
parallel to the ventral body wall. The stomodaeum and proctodaeum grow
toward each other, but do not meet (except in a few highly modified
insects which may lack a true midgut), and the midgut forms between
them; the ends of the two blind hypodermal sacs rupture, forming a continuous alimentary canal. In a great many insects the midgut forms from
cells which lie either near or actually *on* the ends of the proctodaeum,

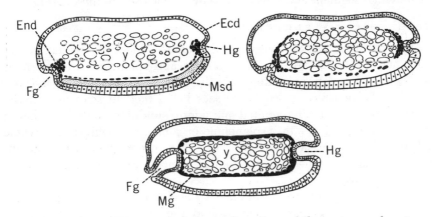

Figure 7.11. Diagrammatic sagittal sections of three stages of an insect embryo showing the development of the enteron. *Ecd,* ectoderm;
End, endoderm; *Fg,* stomodaeal (foregut) invagination; *Hg,* proctodaeal
(hindgut) invagination; *Mg,* midgut; *Msd,* mesoderm; *y,* yolk. (Redrawn
from Snodgrass, 1935, by arrangement with McGraw-Hill Book Co.)

stomodaeum or both. Many embryologists state that the midgut forms
from ectoderm because they see quite clearly that the midgut epithelium
proliferates from cells at the tips of these invaginations. The lineage of
the cells has never been traced carefully in such cases. They may be, as
some have suggested, endodermal in that they could have derived from
the middle strand of the inner layer or from the yolk cells. Or it may be
that cells of whatever lineage, when they lie on the tips of the stomodaeum and proctodaeum, form the midgut epithelium through positional
determination, an interpretation particularly attractive because it fits well
with principles discovered at earlier stages by experimental methods. The
malpighian tubules grow from the material at the tip of the proctodaeum
and are therefore similar in origin to the midgut epithelium, whatever
that origin may be. Dawydoff (1949) states that in arachnoids the malpighian tubules always arise from endoderm but almost all entomologists

state that they arise from ectoderm; it seems probable that their origin is the same in both arachnoids and insects.

The apodemes, including the tentorium, develop from invaginated folds of the hypodermis. The tracheal systems, book lungs, distal genital ducts and the paired glands of the antennal and three gnathocephalic segments all form as hypodermal invaginations. The corpora allata form as shallow invaginations at or just behind the base of the mandibles, then pinch off and become attached to and eventually invested by the coelomic sacs of the antennal segment and thus are ectoderm enclosed in mesoderm.

MESODERMAL STRUCTURES

The mesoderm is laid down when the inner cell layer forms just before segmentation. Differentiation into somatic and splanchnic mesoderm is incomplete (Fig. 7.9), affecting only the lateral parts of the inner layer. Between the two rows of coelomic sacs lies a median strip of material which is largely undifferentiated mesoderm—undifferentiated in that it cannot be assigned as either splanchnic or somatic, though on the whole it behaves like somatic mesoderm. Whether this median strip contains cells that may be called endodermal is a moot question and has been discussed above.

Only two groups of structures clearly develop entirely from splanchnic mesoderm: the muscular system around the alimentary canal and the genital ridges. The genital ridges lie against the dorsal wall of the abdominal hemocoel and at first extend through a series of segments, the exact number varying with the species. The proliferating primordial germ cells migrate to these ridges and presently collect in only one segment, where the gonads form. The central parts of the gonads derive entirely from splanchnic mesoderm of the genital ridges, though they generally are invested with protective layers from other sources. The upper (mesodermal) genital ducts connect with ducts invaginated from the hypodermal ectoderm.

Both splanchnic and somatic mesoderm apparently contribute to the formation of the heart and aorta, the fat body, the head glands of apterygote insects and diplopods, the thoracic coelomic glands of arachnoids, and the investment of the corpora allata of insects. The muscles of the body wall, appendages and dorsal diaphragm derive partly from somatic and partly from undifferentiated mesoderm. Blood cells arise from that part of the median strip of the inner cell layer which sometimes is defined as endoderm, sometimes as meso-endoderm, sometimes as mesoderm; to the extent that this tissue produces the hemocytes it may be regarded as mesodermal.

BLASTOKINESIS

Blastokinesis is now used as a generic term to include all rotations, flexions, displacements and other movements of the embryo within the egg or equivalent membranes. Every species, during its early growth, alters its position in its own characteristic way which, once observed, serves the embryologist well as a kind of time table. How these motions

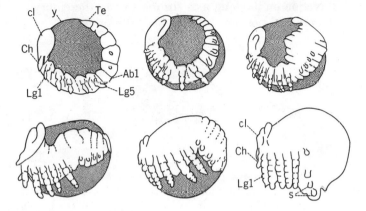

Figure 7.12.   Six stages of blastokenesis of the embryo of the spider *Agelena labyrinthica*. *Ab1*, first abdominal segment; *Ch*, cheliceral rudiment; *cl*, cephalic lobe; *Lg1*, *Lg5*, first and fifth leg-bearing segments; *s*, spinnerets; *Te*, telson; *y*, yolk. (Redrawn (after Wallstabe, 1908) from Dawydoff, 1949, by arrangement with Masson et Cie)

serve the embryo itself is an open question though apparently they are necessary, for their absence seems to lead to death.

The simplest blastokinesis is found in spiders and most other arachnoids, in chilopods and in some insects. The germ band elongates over the surface of the yolk so that eventually the cephalic and caudal ends approach each other or even meet at one pole; the embryo is flexed backward, ventral side out (Fig. 7.12). Meanwhile an additional movement occurs. The right and left halves of the segmented embryo separate along the midline and move apart, being joined only at the anterior and posterior ends. Each half of the embryo thus approaches a U shape and the whole structure traces a pattern on the yolk not dissimilar to the seams of a baseball. Both the dorsal and ventral margins then grow toward each other, eventually meeting and enclosing the yolk.

Collembola and Aptera similarly elongate over the surface of the yolk, but instead of the body being divided in half as in spiders, the middle part of the germ band flexes down into the yolk, bringing the caudal and cephalic ends of the embryo near together, with the ventral surface concave—a jackknifed position (Fig. 7.13). Most insects flex back at each end, the extremities of the growing germ band pushing into the yolk, leaving only the midsection at or near the surface. A little later the embryo moves from the ventral to the dorsal side of the egg, either by sliding caudal end first, or by rotation on the long axis. In most cases the embryo eventually returns to its original position by reversing the process.

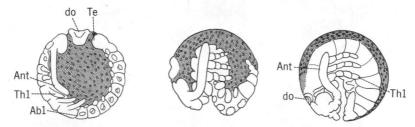

Figure 7.13. Three stages of blastokenesis of the embryo of *Campodea* (Aptera). Extraembryonic area is stippled. *Ab1*, first abdominal segment; *Ant*, antenna; *do*, primary dorsal organ; *Te*, telson; *Th1*, first thoracic segment. (Redrawn from Johannsen and Butt, 1941, by permission of McGraw-Hill Book Co.)

Chilopods flex the posterior end into the yolk so that during the greater part of the early developmental period only the head is seen at the surface.

IRREGULARITIES

Certain deviations from straight-line development may have far-reaching consequences in an animal's life cycle although the departure itself may be only a minor one. The several forms of parthenogenesis, discussed earlier in this chapter, are modifications of the process of gametogenesis and fertilization. **Polyembryony** is a deviation during cleavage. **Neoteny** involves the precocious maturity of the gonads. In **hermaphrodites** both male and female gonads develop in the same individual, an anomaly of the determinant-suppressive system. In **viviparity** the embryo is retained in the maternal reproductive tract and the process may involve complex modifications of the extraembryonic membranes.

The holometabolous life cycle also is a deviation from the norm, the embryo hatching precociously as a larva whose embryogenesis is arrested or slowed, later telescoped to a rapid completion in the pupal instar. Were holometabolism a rare circumstance there would be little difficulty in recognizing it as a deviation. Since it is characteristic of so many large, important insect orders and thus is both common and familiar, it has come to be regarded as normal rather than as a deviation from the normal.

POLYEMBRYONY

The most familiar form of polyembryony is identical twinning, since it occurs in man and other mammals. When the zygote divides, the daughter cells separate and become independent zygotes, each developing into a new individual. Since each of these individuals has the same chromosome and gene sets, they necessarily are of the same sex. Should one or both of the daughter zygotes again divide into additional zygotes, identical triplets or quadruplets would result.

Polyembryony is quite unusual among insects and is unknown among myriapods or arachnoids. In one of the Strepsiptera and in some of the parasitic Hymenoptera, however, it is a regular procedure. Repeated divisions of the zygote lead to the formation of numerous new zygotes before cleavage begins. The polar body nuclei, instead of degenerating, produce an extraembryonic membrane, the **trophamnion,** which encloses the developing embryos and relays nutritive material to them from the host tissues. Where very large broods of parasites are produced or where both sexes appear, more than one egg has been deposited in the host. Little advantage seems to accrue to polyembryonic species, since none is especially common despite the multiplication of zygotes. In general, the females of these species produce relatively fewer eggs and in some cases the polyembryonic larvae cannibalize each other so that the whole elaborate process may result in only a few mature individuals.

Polyembryony has also been observed to occur abnormally in Acrididae (Orthoptera) and in a few species of moths (Lepidoptera).

NEOTENY

Neoteny (pedogenesis) involves the precocious maturity of the ovary so that young are produced by a mother who has not reached the imaginal instar. It is known in both parthenogenetic and nonparthenogenetic species.

In gall midges (Cecidomyiidae: Diptera) and a small family of beetles (Micromalthidae: Coleoptera) the primary reproductive form is a larva. Although adult males and females occur, there is some doubt that they are able to reproduce. In a few of the true midges (Chironomidae: Diptera) larvae are produced viviparously by the pupal instar, but in this case, the insect is an adult by embryogenetic criteria, although final ecdysis has not yet taken place. The ovaries of parthenogenetic aphids (Hemiptera) also mature precociously, embryos being found in immature females.

A striking example of neoteny in a sexually reproductive insect was discovered by Hagan in the rare, very peculiar Polyctenidae (Hemiptera), a family of external parasites infesting tropical bats. Copulation occurs while the female is immature and the young develop by an advanced form of viviparity.

In Strepsiptera the female is often described as "degenerate." In fact, these females never complete embryogenesis, and, although the ovaries mature, many of the other typically adult structures fail to develop beyond rudimentary stages. The same thing occurs in the Psychidae (Lepidoptera) and thrips (Thysanoptera). Reproduction in these groups thus is neotenic. Reproduction by wingless termite (Isoptera) castes of some species probably also is, strictly speaking, neoteny.

HERMAPHRODITISM

Genetic sex determination involves a physiologic catenation leading to the suppression of gonads of one sex and the development of gonads of the other. Without this control, both ovaries and testes, potentially present in all embryos, would develop. Should the catenation break down at some point, suppression would not occur and the individual would then be a hermaphrodite.

Only three cases of hermaphroditism have been confirmed in insects. Males of *Perla marginata* (Plecoptera) have both testes and an ovary. The oögonia have the male chromosome set and fail to complete development; only the testes are functional. In *Icerya purchasi* (Hemiptera), a scale insect with haploid males and viviparously produced young, the genetic females are functional hermaphrodites. Their gonads, really double organs formed during embryogeny by fusion of originally separate rudiments, produce male gametes from the central testicular part and female gametes from peripheral ovarioles. Unfertilized oötids develop into normal haploid males, but much more frequently, the oötids are fertilized and develop into hermaphroditic females. Fertilization may be accomplished either by copulation with one of the rare normal males or by self-fertilization. Unlike the earthworm, these hermaphrodites do not copulate with each other. The third case is found in *Termitostroma* and related phorid flies (Diptera). Each individual has both ovaries and testes; functional gametes of both sexes are produced. Both cross-fertilization and self-fertilization occur.

VIVIPARITY[1]

Instead of laying eggs, some species give birth to their young as larvae or pupae. In the simplest and probably the primitive form of viviparity, the eggs are simply retained in the maternal reproductive tract and the larvae hatch there. In more complex versions the egg chorion is missing and the extraembryonic membranes become highly modified, functioning much like the mammalian placenta. Hagan (1951) classifies the many variations and degrees of viviparity into four categories:

In **ovoviviparity** the egg, normal in all respects except that the chorion is thin and membranous, is retained in the oviduct instead of being deposited. The embryo is nourished by the yolk until hatching. Immediately after hatching, the mother deposits the young larvae in suitable places. This type of reproduction occurs regularly in solpugids, some mites, certain thrips (Thysanoptera), a few cockroaches (Dictyoptera), in various flies (Diptera) and beetles (Coleoptera) and in Coccidae (Hemiptera). It occurs irregularly in some Tineidae and Picridae (Lepidoptera). It has been reported in Corrodentia, Anoplura, Plecoptera and Hymenoptera, but these cases need confirmation.

Adenotrophic viviparity appears to be a refinement of ovoviviparity. The eggs are retained and the embryos are nourished on the yolk until hatching. Hatching occurs at a relatively earlier stage of development. The larvae then pass through several instars in the maternal tract, nourished by a secretion from the uterine glands, and finally are deposited just before pupation. The tsetse flies (Glossinidae) and members of the three families of pupiparial Diptera (Hippoboscidae, Streblidae and Nycteribiidae) all employ this mode of development, and it is also characteristic of the Pseudoscorpionida.

Hemocoelous viviparity is an adaptation associated with neoteny in the Strepsiptera and the two dipterous families Cecidomyiidae and Chironomidae. The reproductive females are larvae in which only the mesodermal parts of the ovaries have developed, the ovaries thus lying free in the hemocoel. Copulation with adult males occurs in Strepsiptera, but in the midges development is parthenogenetic. The eggs completely lack a

---

[1] Hagan (1951) discusses the correct usage of this and related terms, concerning which there has been wide inconsistency in entomological writings. Following Hagan, *viviparity* is used in this book as the generic term for all situations in which a live insect is "born," as contrasted to the process (*ovoparity*) of laying eggs which subsequently hatch. *Ovoviviparity* is used only to designate one of the special cases of viviparity. The term *ovoviviparity* has been used so loosely and in so many different ways that, except as Hagan defines it, it has become almost meaningless.

chorion, become detached from the ovaries and float free in the hemocoel where the embryos develop. Nutrition is supplied by maternal secretions and fluids. Young strepsipteran larvae escape through pores in the mother's ectoderm (brood canals). The midge larvae generally devour the maternal tissues.

The most highly advanced viviparity is the type termed **pseudoplacental.** The egg has almost no yolk, the extraembryonic membranes are highly modified to provide for the transmission of nutriment from the mother, and sometimes maternal tissues also enter into the pseudoplacental formation. Pseudoplacental viviparity is typical of the Scorpionida, two families of Dermaptera, several roaches (Dictyoptera), a psocid (Corrodentia), aphids and related families (Hemiptera) and the Polyctenidae (Hemiptera).

Postovarian Embryogenesis

Consider that the caterpillar
Becomes a horrid dusty miller,
  Which is just what he deserves.
In his depredatious ravages
He destroys whole rows of cabbages
  And eats a rug for hors d'oeuvres.

Hatching serves as a useful marker when the development of a single species is being studied, because in any given species a characteristic ontogenetic pattern and time table are closely followed—though the schedule may be retarded or accelerated by variations in temperature or by other environmental conditions. No two species follow exactly the same pattern and time schedule; no two species reach exactly the same point of development for every system when hatching occurs.

Between the extremes of hatching times there is the greatest divergence. From the grasshopper egg there hatches a perfectly recognizable grasshopper (Fig. 8.2) which, because it has appendages and a body form much like the adult, cannot be mistaken for any other kind of insect; it remains only for it to feed, grow and to perfect the wings and other parts needing completion. From the butterfly egg there hatches a caterpillar (Fig. 8.4) bearing no slightest resemblance to the adult, compared to which it has imperfectly formed cephalic and thoracic appendages and internal structures, some of the abdominal limb rudiments are still present and only the histologist can find the rudiments of the wings and reproductive system. Newly hatched Protura (Fig. 8.1) have but eight abdominal segments, though they otherwise resemble the adult; another segment is added at each molt until there are eleven—embryological segmentation remains unfinished at hatching. The larva hatching from the egg of *Platy-gaster* (Hymenoptera) inside the body of the gall midge larva (Diptera) is little more than a germ band (Fig. 8.6B) with its abdominal segments not yet defined.

It is clear that the time of hatching has no chronological significance in comparative embryology because it is incommensurable from one species to another. When the embryologist confines his studies to the events within the egg, he learns most of the embryogenesis of the grasshopper, some of the embryogenesis of the butterfly and only the earliest stages of the embryogenesis of *Platygaster*.

In general, hatching may be said to occur at the earliest convenient point in ontogeny. The central question is whether or not the embryo will be able to survive after hatching and live long enough to contribute to the continuation of the species. Enough yolk must, of course, be present in the egg to feed the embryo while it is within the egg: once the yolk has been exhausted, the embryo is obliged to find its own food from some other source. The amount of yolk in an egg probably is not the real factor determining the time when the embryo hatches; rather, the amount of yolk present is sufficient for the embryo *until* it hatches, a time that depends on other factors. As Hagan (1951) points out, when a female must provide large quantities of yolk for future eggs as well as provide for her own needs, her vitality is thereby drained; conversely, if the female need provide only a small amount of yolk in each of her eggs, she has a better chance of living longer and of producing more eggs. But a reduction in yolk volume is possible only when hatching occurs at an earlier point, the result of some speeding up or telescoping of development. Quite probably, this is an important selective factor favoring the holometabolous cycle, in that the precociously hatching larvae utilize structures while they are still incompletely developed and need not remain in the egg, and so require a smaller food supply before hatching.

Platygaster illustrates still another method of getting the embryo out of the egg at the earliest possible point. This wasp's egg, containing little yolk, is inserted into the egg of a dipterous host. The parasite larva hatches into the body of the host larva, where adequate food is at once available. It is accordingly convenient and feasible for *Platygaster* larvae to leave the egg exceptionally early. Though this wasp offers an extreme example, the principles involved must be true for all species; other situations may be less obvious and less dramatic, therefore more difficult to evaluate.

LIFE CYCLES

One of the most striking features of the phylum Arthropoda is the diversity of life cycles and of immature forms found among its numerous members. It was recognized more than a century ago that this almost infinite variety is in some way related to the diversity of ecologic niches occupied, that it undoubtedly is adaptation for survival and that the many different forms of immatures all are modifications of a basic pattern in ontogeny. A suitable classification of life cycles must take into account all variations present *in the entire phylum*, not just those in one or two of the classes, and must be based upon embryogenetic considerations.

All arthropod cycles fall into one of two broad categories: **anamorphosis** and **metamorphosis** (**epimorphosis**), depending upon whether or not embryonic segmentation is completed before the immature animal must fend for itself (Vandel, 1949). In **anamorphosis** the animal that hatches from the egg has fewer abdominal segments than characterize the adult; this general type of life cycle occurs in Trilobita, Crustacea, Merostomata, Diplopoda, two families of Chilopoda and, among the insects, the order Protura (Fig. 8.1). In **metamorphosis,** embryonic segmentation is completed before hatching; it is found in the other two families of Chilopoda, all Insecta except Protura, and all Arachnida.

The word *metamorphosis* has not always been used precisely and consistently in zoological literature. In one context it implies only the fact that during the course of its development an immature animal passes through one or more stages during which it bears little superficial resemblance to the adult form. Within this context the frog undergoes metamorphosis *because* the tadpole is such an un-frog-like creature and the butterfly cycle is metamorphosis *because* the caterpillar and pupa stages are so dissimilar to the adult, whereas the silverfish (Thysanura) does not undergo metamorphosis *because* the young looks so unmistakably like the adult. The derivation of the word (from the Greek: *change in form*) supports these implications. On the other hand, if *metamorphosis* is to be used to designate life cycles that are not *anamorphosis* (Greek: *additional form*), the word must apply to some cycles, such as that of the thysanuran, in which there is not necessarily a striking change in form during development. This second context is undoubtedly a more useful one, the derivation notwithstanding. The alternative is to use instead the less familiar *epimorphosis* (Greek: *external change*).

Metamorphic life cycles may in turn be divided into two main categories: **hemimetabolous metamorphosis** (**incomplete, simple** or **direct**) and **holometabolous** (**complete** or **indirect**) **metamorphosis** (Imms,

1957). In **hemimetabolism,** the newly hatched immature bears a recognizable likeness to the adult (Fig. 8.2) and must only perfect its reproductive system, add finishing touches to the integumental structures and, if the species is a winged one, develop wings. In **holometabolism,** the immature bears no similarity to the adult (Fig. 8.4), eats and grows during a

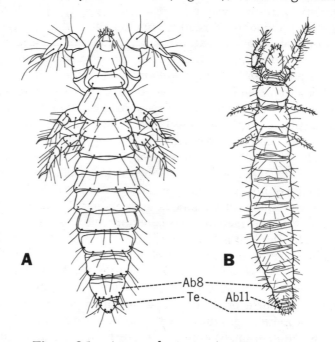

Figure 8.1. Anamorphosis in *Acerentomon microrhinus* (Protura). Dorsal views of (A) newly hatched immature with eight abdominal segments, actual size about 0.576 mm.; (B) adult with eleven abdominal segments, actual size about 2.0 mm. *Ab8, Ab11,* eighth and eleventh abdominal segments, *Te,* telson. (Redrawn from Berlese, 1909b)

series of instars and finally completes embryogenesis very rapidly, becoming adult. In contrast with the grasshopper's gradual growth (hemimetabolism) from a tiny but quite recognizable grasshopper, the development of a beetle from a grub or of a fly from a maggot is especially remarkable in the total dissimilarity between immature and adult forms. Wigglesworth (1959) emphasizes, however, that the process of growth is essentially the same in both hemi- and holometabolous cycles and notes that physiologic changes during the development of hemimetabolous insects are sometimes more extensive than those occurring in most holometabolous insects. The real, basic differences between these two main categories of metamorphosis rest upon the degree of development attained at hatching; it is this and only this that accounts for the obvious structural disparity between immature and adult.

ANAMORPHOSIS

In this kind of development the newly hatched immature looks much like the adult, but has fewer abdominal segments (Fig. 8.1). At each molt an additional segment appears between the telson and what previously had been the last abdominal segment, until the definitive adult number has been reached. It should be noted that abdominal metameres are added in this way by the embryos of metamorphic species while they are still in the egg.

Anamorphosis is found in the more primitive classes of arthropods, including the Trilobita, Crustacea and Merostomata. In Diplopoda, Pauropoda and Symphyla the first instar larva has six legs, a pair on each of the three anteriormost trunk segments; in a few cases one or several partly differentiated abdominal metameres intervene between the telson and the "thoracic" segments; in two of the four families of Chilopoda the larvae hatch with only seven pairs of legs. During larval instars the rest of the segments and legs are added.

The order Protura—essentially a connecting group between myriapods and insects—exhibits anamorphosis. Newly hatched immatures have eight abdominal segments, the second instar has nine, the third ten and the fourth eleven like the adult; in the fifth instar the reproductive system is completed.

While the cycle in Collembola does not overtly fit the definition of anamorphosis, since the first instar immature has the five segments (plus telson) of the adult, it may well be considered as a special case of anamorphosis in which segmentation during immaturity has been suppressed.

Platygaster, with a first instar larva in which the abdomen is not yet segmented (Fig. 8.6B), however, is not a case of anamorphosis but a modification of metamorphosis in which the embryo hatches far more precociously than usual.

HEMIMETABOLOUS METAMORPHOSIS

As previously noted, hemimetabolism involves the completion of the greater part of ontogeny before hatching. There is little difficulty in understanding the evolutional derivation of this kind of cycle from anamorphosis. The newly hatched hemimetabolous immature is closely similar in appearance to the adult, lacking only full size, a mature reproductive system, adult pigmentation and cuticular structures and, in some cases, wings (Fig. 8.2). Body metamerization, segmentation of appendages and formation of compound eyes and of most internal systems have been brought *nearly* to completion—more in some species, less in others.

This kind of cycle is the least complicated of all. Particularly where

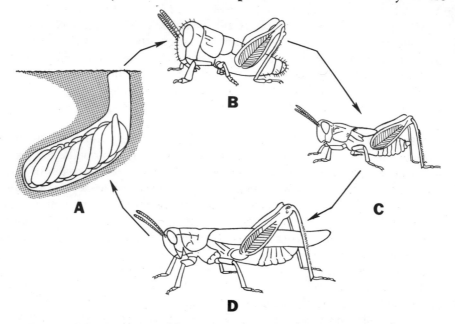

Figure 8.2. Diagram of hemimetabolous (paurometabolous) metamorphosis in a grasshopper, *Melanoplus*. (A) Egg mass in an excavation in the soil; (B) first instar nymph, greatly enlarged; (C) fourth instar nymph with wing pads, somewhat enlarged; (D) adult. (A redrawn from Morse, 1920; B–D redrawn from Packard, 1898)

the animal involved is wingless, development is not metamorphosis in the sense that there are striking changes in form; it *is* metamorphosis in the sense that the cycle is not anamorphosis and it should be noted that internal changes may be much more profound than external changes indicate.

Aside from Insecta, hemimetabolism occurs in a few of the more advanced orders of Crustacea, in all Arachnida except Acarida, and in two families of Chilopoda. The hemimetabolous insect orders are the Aptera, Thysanura, Ephemerida, Odonata, Plecoptera, Dermaptera, Grylloblattodea, Phasmida, Orthoptera, Dictyoptera, Isoptera, Embioptera, Zoraptera, Corrodentia, Mallophaga, Anoplura and nearly all the Hemiptera.

Comstock (1918a) introduced three subdivisions of hemimetabolism, along with a terminology for the immature stages of each: **ametabolous metamorphosis, paurometabolous metamorphosis** and **hemimetabolous** (in a restricted sense) **metamorphosis.**

The animals undergoing **ametabolous metamorphosis** are primitively wingless. The newly hatched immature, called a **nymph,** differs from the adult mainly in size, reproductive capacity and the arrangement of the integumental setae. Molting may continue indefinitely after maturity is reached. Into this category, according to Comstock, fall the insect orders Collembola, Aptera and Thysanura.

In Comstock's scheme the orders Dictyoptera, Isoptera, Zoraptera, Grylloblattodea, Phasmida, Orthoptera, Embioptera, Dermaptera, Corrodentia, Mallophaga, Anoplura and Hemiptera (except a few families) develop by **paurometabolous metamorphosis.** The immatures, also called **nymphs,** live in the same environment and eat the same food as do the adults. This kind of cycle differs from the ametabolous cycle mainly because the insects having it are either winged or secondarily wingless and molting ceases with the winged adult instar. In such secondarily wingless groups as Mallophaga and Anoplura, the influence of wingedness in the ancestry is seen.

To a third subdivision Comstock reserved the term **hemimetabolous metamorphosis** in a limited sense, applying it to the insect orders Ephemerida, Odonata and Plecoptera. The immatures of these three orders are termed **naiads** and they have such true aquatic modifications as gills, while the adults are terrestrial. Because of the striking and sometimes prominent gills, naiads are often externally quite dissimilar to the adults. It was once thought that hemimetabolism (Comstock sense) represents an evolutional stage connecting the paurometabolous with the holometabolous cycle. That such an interpretation is incorrect is suggested by the fact that these three orders are represented by some of the oldest fossil insects known. Their characteristic aquatic modifications were apparently developed a very long time ago and these orders represent "dead ends" of evolution rather than some intermediate stage. It must be noted, too, that while the Ephemerida and Odonata are closely related, the Plecoptera belong to a different infraclass and have little relationship with the other two.

Aside from the unintentional self-contradiction of the term *ametabolous metamorphosis* (from the Greek: *change in form without change in form*), Comstock's alterations of the then time-honored meanings of *hemimetabolism, larva,* and *nymph*—all words having application in branches of zoology other than entomology—have resulted in an international confusion, still unresolved, both in concepts and in terms. Grassé (1949, 9: 444) appended this footnote to his discussion of the life cycle of termites, "The American biologists designate as *nymphs* all the larval stages of these insects. Such a procedure, contrary to all usage, makes it difficult to read scientific works and to compare the results." The usage Grassé defends had been well established long before Comstock introduced his changes, and it is a usage that has been followed by entomologists everywhere except in the United States.

Be that as it may, the Comstock innovations have become accepted in North America, for which reason they will be followed in this book. American students are cautioned, however, that when reading reports by foreign workers, they must exercise care to understand just what the writer intends, for *larva* and *nymph* have meanings different from those to which we are accustomed. To foreign entomologists—and to acarologists everywhere—the first stages are always larval; the immature does not become a nymph until it undergoes certain changes which are not necessarily external or superficial. In this application, the last immature instar of the grasshopper is a nymph and the pupa of a beetle is a nymph, as is the octopod immature of a mite. In American usage, the immature stages of only the holometabolous insects are larvae. Note, too, that foreign authorities use *hemimetabolism* in the broader, generic sense.

Of the insects undergoing ametabolous metamorphosis, Thysanura have been best studied with respect to their life histories. The first instar nymph lacks a functional reproductive system, external genitalia, styli and integumental scales. Scales and styli are present in the third instar and the genitalia develop during the several later instars. In various species there are from six to twelve immature molts. After maturity is reached, ecdysis occurs every twelve or thirteen days at optimal temperature (about 37°C) and continues throughout life.

In paurometabolous development, the adults of all orders either have wings or are secondarily wingless—descended from winged ancestors. Because of this fact, the nymphs are much less similar to the adults than is true in ametabolism. Furthermore, ecdysis does not occur after maturity and wings are acquired. While the wing rudiments begin to develop internally before hatching from the egg, they are not externally evident as projecting wing pads until after several molts. With each successive instar the wing pads become a little bigger, and in the last nymphal instar they grow rapidly and sometimes almost reach adult size. Other changes include alterations in integumental coloring and setae and the gradual development of the external genitalia. In the Orthoptera (as well as in the hemimetabolous Odonata) the nymphal wing pads rotate so that the costal margins become posterior and lie toward the dorsal midline, while the hindwings cover the forewings; in the last immature instar the wing pads turn back to the adult position. In many of these orders the antennae and cerci (when present in the adult) are not fully formed when the young nymph hatches from the egg. In certain orders there is a brief first instar form in which the appendages are not fully developed and which is still enclosed in embryonic cuticle; this evanescent stage is called the **vermiform larva** in Orthoptera, the **primary larva** in Cicadidae (Hemiptera); it also occurs in the hemimetabolous order Odonata (the **pronymph**) (Imms, 1957).

In the social Isoptera, development is complicated by the existence of polymorphic castes, always wingless, in addition to winged males and females. Immatures destined to become normal adults pass through a series of instars during which wings and reproductive systems form as in other paurometabolous orders, and just before final ecdysis pass through a quiescent period lasting from several hours to several days. In some of the primitive species of termites and in most newly established colonies the immatures function as workers. In advanced species and in older colonies there may be a variety of worker and soldier castes and even some intercaste individuals. These castes are suppressed adults which do not pass through as many instars (Fig. 8.3) as do the winged sexual forms (Grassé, 1949), a phenomenon under the control of factors not at present fully understood. The grotesque head shapes or peculiar mandibles characteristic of some of the castes apparently are to be regarded as special structures of immaturity, like the gills of aquatic larvae. Some termite species normally produce "stand-by" reproductive individuals which are neotenic in that they fail to undergo the full number of ecdyses and do not acquire wings.

In the three hemimetabolous (restricted sense) orders, first instar nymphs lack gills and rely on cutaneous respiration; gills begin to appear in the second instar. Wings develop as external pads and gradually increase in size. Where the adult has atrophied mouthparts, as in mayflies (Ephemerida), regression occurs at final ecdysis. All naiads (aquatic nymphs) feed actively. In the Ephemerida immaturity may extend as long as three years and may include a great many ecdyses. The anterior pair of gills appear at the second instar and additional pairs develop with each molt until the full quota for the species is present. The last immature instar moves to the surface of the water and ecdysis leads to the first imaginal instar (Hinton, 1948) (**subimago**), which has translucent wings and an incompletely pigmented body. The subimago lasts from a few hours to a full day and is terminated by a final ecdysis from which emerges the second instar imago, with full body pigmentation, transparent wings and mature gametes. Mayflies are the only living insects that molt following the completion of wing development.

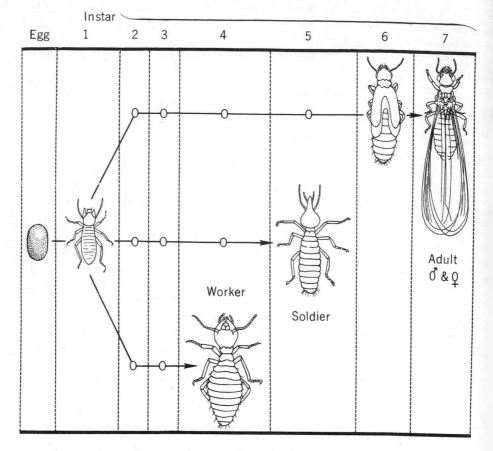

Figure 8.3. Diagram illustrating the development of polymorphic castes in the termite *Nasutitermes matagensis* (Isoptera), one of the less complicated situations. First instar nymphs are undifferentiated, but at the second instar the three castes can be distinguished by head size and shape. Workers "mature" at the fourth instar, soldiers at the fifth, neither undergoing further ecdysis. External wing pads appear in the third instar of males and females and are well developed in the sixth instar. (Redrawn (after J. Bathellier) from Grassé, 1949, by arrangement with Masson et Cie)

HOLOMETABOLOUS METAMORPHOSIS

The holometabolous immature (Fig. 8.4B), universally called the **larva**, is a wingless, more or less worm-like form bearing little resemblance to the adult. Compared to the hemimetabolous immature it is precocious in that it leaves the egg at a less advanced stage of development. Hatching

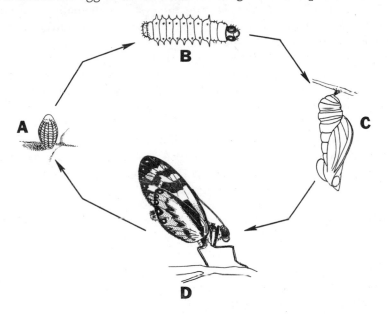

Figure 8.4. Diagram of holometabolous metamorphosis in the butterfly *Mechanitis* (Lepidoptera). (A) Egg glued to a leaf of the food plant; (B) larva; (C) pupa suspended from a twig; (D) adult; figures not to scale. (Drawn from photographs made in Peru, courtesy of Dr. E. S. Ross)

occurs at some stage after metamerization has been completed but before body and appendages have reached adult form. Within these limits there is wide variation. True ocelli are never present. The so-called "lateral ocelli" (**stemmata**) (see Fig. 6.6C, D) are innervated from the optic lobes and occupy the same position as the adult compound eyes; they are, morphologically, the compound eyes in an incomplete stage of formation, having only a few isolated visual units, each with a single external facet. The larvae of most Diptera lack eyes entirely, the result of head development being strongly suppressed. This situation stands in clear contrast with the optic equipment typical of hemimetabolous immatures in which the eyes have reached a many-faceted stage of development within the egg.

During the larval stages embryogenesis is greatly slowed, evidenced only in the slight advances made by internal rudiments of various parts. Once substantial food reserves have been built up and full growth attained, residual embryogenesis is telescoped into a relatively short space of time punctuated by a molt. During the instar immediately preceding this molt, histolysis of larval tissues and histogenesis of imaginal structures from the embryonic rudiments take place at a rapid pace. This instar is the prepupa (**last** or **mature larva; first nymph** in European terminology) and externally resembles the preceding instars. Following this molt is an instar called the pupa (**second nymphal instar** in European usage) in which definitive adult organization, begun in the prepupa, is present. This instar is a pharate adult. Frequently it is a quiescent stage passed in some protected place such as a cocoon or an underground cell. It may include a more or less protracted diapause. In a few cases it is an active, even an aggressive stage. The pupa is terminated by a final ecdysis from which emerges the active, fully functional adult.

All holometabolous groups are highly evolved. The traditionally holometabolous insects are the Neuroptera, Mecoptera, Trichoptera, Lepidoptera, Diptera, Siphonaptera, Hymenoptera, Coleoptera and Strepsiptera. It is now recognized that among otherwise hemimetabolous groups there are a few which have evolved holometabolous cycles: Thysanoptera and certain families of Hemiptera (Aleyrodidae, Phyloxeridae, Coccoidea).

Generations of zoologists have sought to bring order to the chaos of diverse life cycles and even more diverse immature stages in the arthropods. Some of these efforts have been merely listings in which the aim has been to detect and name all discernible variations. While such studies have some value, "the use of special terms is apt to blind us to fundamental relationships" (Hinton, 1948). A central question is the relationship between hemi- and holometabolism in insects. All evidence from phylogeny and embryology shows that holometabolism was derived from hemimetabolism. But how? In terms of the hemimetabolous cycle, what are the holometabolous larva and pupa?

Berlese (1913) applied to insects the theories generated earlier by students of general invertebrate zoology. In the light of more recent information certain of Berlese's specific conclusions must be modified or rejected, but he should be credited with stimulating broad, constructive thinking and experimental study of metamorphosis and pointing out to entomologists the proper path to take.

Among his observations there is one that has survived repeated expert attack: Berlese noticed a certain parallel between the development of appendages by hemimetabolous embryos while still in the egg and the development of appendages by holometabolous larvae after hatching; he defined three stages of embryogenic development applicable to either situation. In the **protopod stage** (Fig. 8.5A) the embryo has limb rudiments on the gnathal and thoracic segments but none on the abdominal

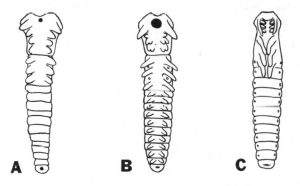

A   **B**   **C**

Figure 8.5. Berlese's stages of development in the embryo. (A) Protopod stage, in which only the rudiments of cephalic appendages are present—the thoracic rudiments have not yet developed and segmentation of thorax and abdomen is at an elementary level; (B) polypod stage, in which all limb rudiments, including those of the abdomen, are present; (C) oligopod stage, in which the abdominal limb rudiments have regressed, while the cephalic and thoracic rudiments approach or reach definitive form. (Redrawn from Berlese, 1913)

segments, which are not yet fully metamerized. In the **polypod stage** (Fig. 8.5B) the gnathal and thoracic appendages are partly segmented and differentiated, while the fully metamerized abdomen bears limb rudiments. In the **oligopod stage** (Fig. 8.5C) the gnathal and thoracic appendages are well developed, while the abdominal rudiments either have regressed or have begun conversion to adult structures. It was Berlese's contention that hemimetabolous (in the broader sense) nymphs hatch during or at the end of the oligopod stage of embryogeny and that holometabolous larvae hatch earlier, typically in the polypod stage.

Such a direct sequence of events does indeed occur during the development of many insects. That all holometabolous larvae do not obviously pass through each stage while living free by no means undermines this aspect of Berlese's theory. The protopod or even the polypod stage may occur in the egg; the polypod stage or the polypod and oligopod stages may be included in the telescoped prepupa-pupal period of drastic reorganization and rapid embryogenetic completion. In the latter situation the facts are difficult to observe and evaluate: histolysis of larval structures gives the impression of destroying all that was started in the egg, while histogenesis simulates a new beginning. During the prepupa-pupal period things happen so rapidly, so directly and at the same time in such a confused way that superficial observation may not show that it is merely a foreshortening of the late stages of embryogenesis. Furthermore, many of the highly evolved insects have been able so to modify the primitive sequence of the events of embryogenesis that the larva may not possess abdominal limbs during the oligopod stage, or during the polypod stage. In such cases it is necessary to re-examine the stages and reconcile the facts in order to avoid the obfuscation which so frequently centers around interpretations of insect life histories when differences are treated as being more important than similarities.

During the years after Berlese, many excellent students tried their hands at explaining the relationship between holometabolous and hemimetabolous cycles, presenting a series of conflicting theories. It remained for Hinton (1948) to find the essence of the problem. His reasoning, in brief, was:

Holometabolous insects must have been derived from some group or groups of hemimetabolous insects now extinct. New developmental stages in animals and plants arise only through modification of previously existing stages. The holometabolous pupa is not a halfway stage between larva and adult, but *is* an adult. The adult stage of hemimetabolous insects must be equated with both pupa and adult stages of holometabolous insects, not just with the imaginal instar alone. The essential distinction between the two kinds of life cycles is that in hemimetabolism the adult typically has a single instar, but in holometabolism there are always two adult instars. Did holometabolous insects, then, add an extra adult instar by dividing the hemimetabolous adult stage with a new molt? No. Imaginal molts are deep-seated in arthropod phylogeny; they occur in many wingless groups such as crustaceans, arachnoids and apterygote insects. The hemimetabolous ancestors of holometabolous insects must have undergone molting after becoming adult and acquiring wings. This supposition is supported both in the fossil record and by the living Ephemerida. The subimago of mayflies is in fact a first imaginal instar, equivalent to the holometabolous pupa. Far from being a recently evolved situation, imaginal molting in Ephemerida is very ancient and fossils of both subimagos and imagos of several species have been recovered from the Lower Permian beds of Kansas. There is no reason to believe that ecdysis in winged adults was the exclusive invention of Ephemerida. Why the holometabolic cycle can be developed only where pupation is included had been explained in 1914 by Poyarkoff, who showed that the adult muscular system —which differs radically from that of the larva—can be correctly formed and attached to the hypodermis only by providing a cuticular mold matching the adult shape. When the subimago thus is utilized as a pupa, the previously existing limits on the degree of structural divergence permissible between larva and adult are removed; the larva can then be modified for life in environments previously denied it because of the need to preserve a body form similar to that of the adult. Hinton concluded that the pupal instar had to appear first in phylogeny and that its appearance made possible the elaboration of holometabolism and the diversity of larval forms. He further deduced that holometabolism appeared before the internalization of wing buds and unqualifiedly accepted the Thysanoptera and certain families of Hemiptera as being holometabolous.

While much remains to be learned before the true nature of holometabolism is understood, at present it appears that the most promising approach must combine Hinton's work on pupae with certain features of Berlese's observations on embryos and larvae. In any event, it is of prime importance that embryogenesis be visualized as a continuous process from zygote to adult.

Of the possible ways to classify the many variations of holometabolous larvae, Berlese's embryological approach seems to be the most useful. Each of his developmental stages represents a major larval category, and with such a confusing variety of forms, finding similarities is much more useful than cataloguing differences.

The **protopod larva** is atypic and unusual. As already emphasized, such a larva is little more than a germ band having only the anterior segments differentiated (compare Fig. 8.5A with Figs. 8.6B and 7.7). It would be utterly impossible for protopod larvae to engage in free-living existence; they occur only in the cycles of a few Hymenoptera and Diptera, hatching as parasites either within a host egg or within the body of the host larva. In either case the protopod is supplied with readily available fluid nutriment. This kind of larva is necessarily succeeded in subsequent instars by larval forms belonging to more advanced types.

The **polypod larva** is the earliest stage able to lead an independent life. It is typically caterpillar-like (**eruciform**) with chewing mouthparts (compare Fig. 8.5B with Figs. 8.4B and 7.7). Eyes, antennae, thoracic

legs and internal systems are at an embryonic level of development and
some of the abdominal limb rudiments (**prolegs**) are present. Such a
larva moves sluggishly and generally is phytophagous, living on or in its
food, and is the usual form in Mecoptera, Trichoptera, Lepidoptera and
the primitive Hymenoptera.

The **oligopod larva** has thoracic legs, embryonic eyes and internal

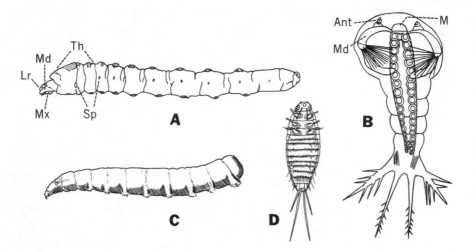

Figure 8.6.   Four types of insect larvae. (A) Scarabaeiform larva of a
cerambycid beetle (Coleoptera), the head to the left; (B) protopod first
instar larva of *Platygaster* (Hymenoptera), the head at top; (C) apodous
larva of *Musca* (Diptera), the head at the right; (D) triungulin first instar
larva of *Eoxenus laboulbeni* (Strepsiptera), the head at top. *Ant*, antenna;
Lr, labrum; *M*, mouth; *Md*, mandible; *Mx*, maxilla; *Sp*, spiracle; *Th*, thorax.
(A from Edwards, 1949, by courtesy of the author; B from Packard, 1898;
C from James, 1947; D from Parker and Smith, 1933)

systems, but no prolegs (compare Fig. 8.5C with Figs. 8.6A and 7.7). It is
better developed than the polypod larva. Two kinds are generally recognized, but there are many intergrades. The **scarabaeiform larva** is less
advanced (Fig. 8.6A), having short, fleshy thoracic legs and a soft body;
on the whole it looks like a caterpillar without prolegs. The onto-
genetically more advanced **campodeiform larva** (Fig. 8.10A) has well-
developed thoracic legs and a more heavily sclerotized body; generally
it is an aggressive predator. Except for the worm-like body form and the
undeveloped compound eyes, it more closely resembles the hemimetabolous larva than any holometabolous type (Imms, 1957). Oligopod larvae

are found in Neuroptera (some of which are aquatic), Coleoptera, Strepsiptera, Thysanoptera and the holometabolous Hemiptera.

Legless (**apodous**) larvae (Fig. 8.6C) are found in all or some stages of Diptera and Siphonaptera, in advanced Hymenoptera and in various groups of Coleoptera, Strepsiptera and Lepidoptera. Such larvae are associated with specialized life histories, undoubtedly are adaptive derivations from either polypod or oligopod types and do not represent a homogenous classification, according to Imms. Each case is a separate phylogenetic problem. In the Diptera the apodous condition is accompanied by marked suppression of head development.

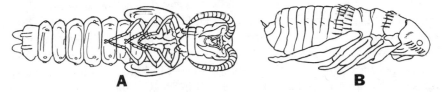

Figure 8.7. Insect pupae. (A) Decticous pupa of *Corydalis* (Neuroptera), ventral view; (B) exarate pupa of *Ctenocephalides canis*, the dog flea (Siphonaptera), lateral view. (A from Packard, 1898; B from Bishopp, 1915)

Based on features thought to have phylogenetic significance, Hinton (1946) recognized three types of pupae. The **decticous** pupa (Fig. 8.7A), typical of Neuroptera, Mecoptera, Trichoptera and the several families of mandibulate Lepidoptera, has functional mandibles and the appendages are movable rather than glued to the body. As soon as the muscular system is sufficiently formed, such a pupa is capable of locomotion; the mandibles are used to cut free from any enclosing cell or cocoon which may be present. The **adecticous** pupa, which does not have articulated mandibles useful for escape at final ecdysis, includes some mandibulate insects as well as those groups having modified, reduced or vestigial mandibles in the adult. When the appendages are free of the body, a pupa is said to be **exarate** (Fig. 8.7B); when the appendages are appressed to the body and glued there by a cuticular secretion, it is said to be **obtect** (Fig. 8.4C). All decticous pupae are exarate. The pupae of Thysanoptera, holometabolous Hemiptera, most Hymenoptera, most Coleoptera, the Strepsiptera, Siphonaptera and the two more advanced suborders of Diptera are adecticous exarate. The adecticous obtect pupa is found in Lepidoptera, some Coleoptera and in the suborder Nematocera and a few other Diptera. Sometimes the puparium of the Cyclorrhapha (Diptera) is called "coarctate" and recognized as a distinct category. Hinton pointed out the fallacy of using "coarctate" as a pupal type, since the puparium is merely the hardened larval cuticle enclosing an adecticous exarate pupa.

The beginning, at least, of the pupal instar is a period of vulnerability. Until the adult musculature is functional, even pupae with free appendages are incapable of locomotion, hence of evasive or protective activity. The obtect pupa is helpless throughout the instar. Accordingly pupation is usually passed in some situation where the insect is protected from predators, as well as from such ecological hazards as unfavorable temperatures or moisture conditions. Sometimes, as in certain Lepidoptera and Coleoptera, the last larval instar burrows into the soil, forming there a chamber for the pupa. More usually the last larval instar constructs a **cocoon** from silk secreted either by the labial glands or by the malpighian organs. Cocoons vary greatly according to the group and the species with respect to color, location and incorporation of foreign material like leaves, pebbles, chips or other debris and in the kind of construction. In most butterflies the pupa (**chrysalis**) (Fig. 8.4C) hangs free by a bit of silk representing the vestigial cocoon, relying upon its protective color and shape and upon its situation for protection. In contrast, the pupae of Culicidae and many Chironomidae (Diptera) and of some of the Neuroptera are quite active through most of the instar.

A separate volume would be required for a full review of the many different kinds of holometabolous cycles; a few examples must serve as illustration.

The most familiar holometabolous cycle is found where the larvae are phytophagous or predatory. In most Lepidoptera the larvae are phytophagous, but the adult feeds little or not at all, primarily utilizing food reserves built up by the immature, supplemented by moisture or fluid food such as flower nectar. As a rule the egg is deposited directly on the food plant, glued to a leaf or twig by a secretion from the female reproductive tract (Fig. 8.4). A tiny polypod larva hatches and shortly begins eating the plant on which it finds itself. During the course of the larval instars—there may be three to nine but most usually four or five— the insect feeds almost constantly and its weight increases enormously. This increase is something like 10,000 times for the silkworm *Bombyx* and 72,000 times for the woodborer *Cossus*, which spends three years accomplishing the feat. Toward the end of the last larval instar steps are taken to provide protection for the pupa—a cocoon is spun, or the larva burrows, or does whatever is normal for the species. At the same time the larva undergoes visible change, mostly with respect to coloring or details of shape while histolysis and histogenesis begin. The pupa is adecticous obtect, but the body assumes definite adult form and the adult appendages and the wings are clearly recognizable. After final ecdysis the emerging (second instar) adult is perfect in all respects except that the wings are small; they are soon expanded to full size by blood pressure exerted from the main hemocoelic cavity. The majority of holometabolous insects have cycles which, while varying greatly in almost every detail, follow the general plan outlined above. Deviations from this typical pattern are mainly associated with such specialized larval situations as internal parasitism.

The term "hypermetamorphosis" has been applied to cycles involving several different larval types in successive instars. For example, in certain Staphylinidae (Coleoptera) the first instar larva is a campodeiform predator which seeks out the puparia of Cyclorrhapha (Diptera). Having gnawed its way into one, the beetle larva molts and subsequent instars are a degenerate eruciform type feeding on the pupa. This type of cycle—an active campodeiform first instar which seeks a host, followed by a series of degenerate parasitic instars—is found in other Coleoptera, notably the families Rhipiphoridae and Meloidae, and in the Strepsiptera.

All Strepsiptera are parasitic on other insects, especially on higher Hemiptera and higher Hymenoptera. The female strepsipteran, a wormlike creature embedded in the host's tissues, retains in her hemocoel the fertilized eggs from which hatch tiny campodeiform first instar larvae (**triungulins**) (Fig. 8.6D). The triungulins find their way out of the maternal hemocoel and leave the host, actively seeking out a new host individual, a process usually so fraught with vicissitudes that many young larvae doubtless are unsuccessful. The successful ones burrow into the new hosts and take up abodes in the hemocoels, displacing the hosts' organs. There ecdysis occurs and subsequent instars are degenerate apodous forms. During the fifth instar the head and thorax become fused into a cephalothorax. During the sixth instar the female larva thrusts her cephalothorax out between the abdominal sclerites of the host; a final ecdysis in this position leads to a larviform, wingless female lacking antennae, eyes or functional appendages. The winged adult male copulates with her in this position—parthenogenesis occurs in some species—and the eggs hatch within her body. The male cycle differs somewhat; there are nine instars instead of the seven found in the female. The cephalothorax forms in the fifth instar and is thrust out of the host during the sixth, as in the female. But the seventh instar is the prepupa, during which the appendages begin to form. The eighth instar, the pupa, takes place within the concentric molted cuticles of the sixth and seventh instars; the winged adult male (see Fig. 13.6G) emerges at final ecdysis.

That the female is neotenic is demonstrated by the fact that there are fewer instars, the last several being omitted. The foregoing account refers to *Xenos,* family Stylopidae.

The parasitic Hymenoptera have a very different but equally modified cycle. The egg of *Platygaster* is inserted into the egg of the dipterous host. When the host larva hatches, the polyembryonic protopod (**cyclopoid**) wasp larvae hatch into the host's hemocoel, generally about eighteen parasite larvae from each egg. The head and first thoracic segment form a kind of cephalothorax equipped with relatively enormous mandibles; three to five abdominal segments are present (Fig. 8.6B). The second instar is apodous, possibly a modification of the oligopod type; if such is the case, the polypod stage must be transient, compressed into the development preceding the first ecdysis. The apodous larva is followed by a rather similar prepupa, an exarate pupa and the adult. In some related genera, the first several instars are protopod; in others, and in some species of *Platygaster*, the first instar is the apodous form and the protopod stage is passed in the egg.

The life cycles of the Thysanoptera and of Coccoidea, Aleyrodidae and Phyloxeridae (Hemiptera) are essentially alike, following a pattern which is approached and foreshadowed in evolution by the related hemipterous families Psyllidae and Adelgidae. The first and second instar larvae of Thysanoptera (Fig. 8.8B) differ from each other mainly in size. They are campodeiform oligopod forms with simple larval eyes and without wing pads. The third instar is the prepupa, during which typical holometabolous structural reorganization begins. In the suborder Terebrantia, wing pads appear externally in the prepupal instar. The adecticous exarate pupa (Fig. 8.8A) has larger wing pads, elongate antennae, compound eyes and adult musculature. Final ecdysis leads to the active, functional adult. In the Tubulifera, the other suborder, internal reorganization of such structures as the alimentary canal begins in the prepupa, but the wing pads do not appear. The pupal instar in this suborder is divided by an ecdysis (Jeannel, 1949). Both first and second pupae have adult structures but differ in size and the degree of developmental advance.

First instar larvae of Coccoidea are oligopod and likewise have larval eyes. The second instar is oligopod in some species, apodous in others. For females the third instar is the last one, since they do not pass through the pupal instar nor metamorphose to adult structures, although the reproductive system matures. The same instar in males is an exarate pupa during which both wing pads and legs grow to adult size. The imagos of most scale insects retain the larval stage of development of the

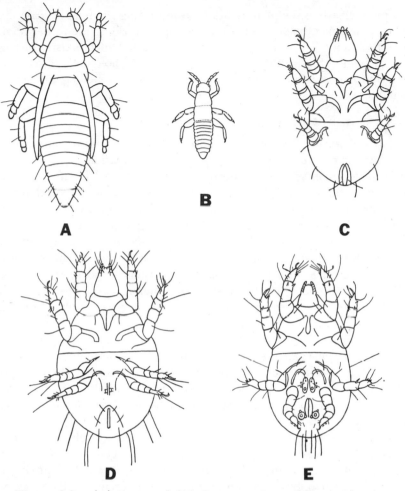

Figure 8.8. (A) Pupa and (B) first instar larva of *Scirtothrips citri* (Thysanoptera); (C) hexapod larva, (D) octopod nymph and (E) adult of *Rhizoglyphus echinopus* (Acarida). (A and B redrawn from Horton, 1918; C–E from Baker and Wharton, 1952, by permission of The Macmillan Company)

compound eyes (stemmata); in the few genera having fully developed compound eyes, they form during the pupal instar.

It is difficult to understand why the cycles of these insects have been regarded as anything other than holometabolous. The larvae have no visible wing pads, they have typically larval eyes and appendages. The prepupal instar is marked by the initiation of histolysis and histogenesis.

The pupa clearly is the pharate adult. Interpreting the female scale insect as being hemimetabolous, as is so often done, overlooks the rather obvious fact of neoteny. The cycle is a special case of holometabolism, just as is that of female Strepsiptera. In the scale insects holometabolism apparently has evolved independently, for they certainly belong in the order Hemiptera.

METAMORPHOSIS IN ARACHNOIDS

Most arachnoids develop by hemimetabolism, but more complex metamorphosis is present in Pseudoscorpionida and Acarida.

Pseudoscorpion eggs are deposited into an external incubation pouch, fastened to the internal ducts by the chorionic membrane, and retained there until hatching. The first instar larvae show no trace of metamerization and possess only a single pair of appendages, the very large first legs (pedipalps). Surrounding the mouth is a specialized sucking apparatus into which the mother injects a special ovarian secretion. This first protopod instar larva leads a kind of parasitic existence and increases greatly in size. The second instar larva loses the sucking apparatus and is sufficiently advanced in development to leave the incubation chamber. Adult structures appear at the fourth instar.

If the first instar is disregarded, pseudoscorpion development does not differ materially from the development of other arachnoids. The only complication is introduced by the precocious eclosion of the embryo as a first instar protopod. Quite possibly this is a primitive feature rather than an evolved one in this order since it is not dissimilar to the cycles of some Crustacea.

The first instar scorpion or the first instar spider closely resembles the adult, but no eyes are present. In view of the generally low level of development of the optic sense in all arachnoids, it is not surprising that the eyes appear only at a point in ontogeny relatively delayed as compared with insects. Internally, the newly hatched young are rather poorly developed. The incomplete alimentary canal is still filled with yolk; the larvae (the Comstock terminology does not extend to arachnoids) do not feed during the first several instars. Characteristic of the class are the high level of maternal care in nearly every group and the special precautions taken by the mother with the helpless first and second instar young. For example, the mother scorpion carries her brood on her back until they can fend for themselves and most spiders provide a cocoon in which the first two instars are spent in passive existence. By the third instar the alimentary system is functional and the eyes have begun to form. During succeeding instars the larvae increase in size and in the preadult instar (**nymph**) develop appropriate adult characteristics such as the reproductive system, integumental pigmentation, spinnerets and tarsal combs. In most newly hatched arachnoids the appendages require only minor development to attain typical adult form, but such is not always the case. The chelicerae of some spiders at first resemble the pedipalps of scorpions and only gradually are altered; in the Galeodidae (Solpugida) all the appendages are of full length in the first instar but are not segmented.

The acariads, on the other hand, closely approach the holometabolism of insects. The fundamental cycle involves the eclosion of a six-legged first instar larva (Fig. 8.8C) in which the posterior pair of appendages either regresses before hatching or fails to develop. In general form the hexapod larva is rather similar to the adult, but always lacks a tracheal system and may even preserve external metamerization which is lost in the adults. After a period of active feeding, the hexapod enters into a transient pupation during which histolysis and histogenesis occur. Ecdysis leads to an octopod nymph (Fig. 8.8D) having the posterior pair of appendages; it differs from the adult principally in the immaturity of the reproductive system, but in one family (Gamasidae) parthenogenetic reproduction may take place at this stage. The next ecdysis results in the normal adult (Fig. 8.8E). There are so many variations of the above "fundamental" cycle that, as Baker and Wharton (1952) observed, it really is the exception rather than the rule. The so-called pupal phase may be omitted, or the hexapod larval stage may be passed within the egg before eclosion, or there may be several larval instars or several nymphal instars. Acariad life cycles—or, for that matter, acariads—are not at present well enough known to permit useful comparison and analysis of these deviations. In general the hexapod stage appears to be a true larva, the "pupa" probably is the prepupa and the octapod seems to be the pharate adult.

LARVAL STRUCTURE

Structures characteristic of and peculiar to immature instars fall into two categories: (1) those common to larva and adult, though differently formed in the immature, and (2) those with no obvious adult counterpart.

Appendages and eyes belong in the first category. One of the clearest contrasts between hemimetabolous and holometabolous immatures is the comparative state of development in these parts. Hemimetabolous immatures, with few exceptions, have appendages and eyes closely similar to those of the adult; holometabolous immatures have appendages and eyes radically different from those of the adult. To the second category belong such structures as gills and respiratory siphons found in species, both hemi- and holometabolous, living in the water or as endoparasites. These special structures, not present in the adult because they are not needed for terrestrial life, are adaptations to the environment rather than results of the state of developmental progress enjoyed by the immature form.

In hemimetabolous immatures the lateral eyes are already compound

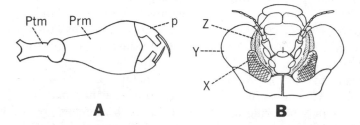

Figure 8.9. Structures of an immature dragonfly (Odonata). (A) Labium or "mask"; (B) dorsal view of head, showing location of areas (X and Z) involved in the ultimate formation of the adult eye after the functional nymphal eye (Y) is histolyzed. p, labial palpus modified as a claw; Prm, prementum; Ptm, postmentum. (A from Essig, 1942, by permission of The Macmillan Company; B redrawn from Lew, 1933)

and do not differ greatly from those of the adult, although the adult eye sometimes has specialized areas not necessarily evident in the young. The ocelli, which in general appear in ontogeny later than the compound eyes, commonly are present in more mature instars in much the same position and stage of development found in the imago. Similarly, the juvenile appendages closely resemble those of the adult, though sometimes spurs or spines typical of the adult are not present in the legs of immatures. A noteworthy exception is the "mask" of the dragonfly larvae (Fig. 8.9A), a spectacular modification of the labium. It consists of two elongated hinged sections (prementum and postmentum) terminating in claw-like palpi. At rest this apparatus folds under the head, from which position it can be suddenly shot out to grasp prey. The "mask" is a modification attendant on the predatory habit of the aquatic larva; it disappears at final ecdysis, to be replaced by a much more reduced labium in the adult. In adult Ephemerida the legs and mouthparts are reduced or atrophied; this is, however, a case of regression during terminal embryogenesis rather than an example of adaptive larval structure. Numerous modifications in hemimetabolous immatures might be mentioned, such as the rows of swimming hairs on the stout legs of Plecoptera immatures, or the immense mandibles of some termite soldiers. The point is that the eyes and appendages of hemimetabolous juveniles differ from the eyes and appendages of their adults chiefly in relatively minor respects having to do with proportion or integumental detail rather than with the basic formation.

By way of contrast, in holometabolous larvae these same structures generally differ profoundly from the adult form—so much so that the continuity and homology between many immature and adult structures frequently are contested in perfectly good faith. The key to understanding the relationship between the stages of the holometabolous species, as well as between hemi- and holometabolous stages, lies in understanding the implications of Berlese's concept of the holometabolous larva as a free-living embryo. Since the holometabolous larva has not reached as advanced a level of embryogenic development as has the hemimetabolous immature, the eyes, appendages, nervous system, alimentary canal and all other parts may be expected to be incompletely formed. But because it is a free-living embryo—because it must use the parts it has, embryonic though they be—one must also expect to find partly developed structures modified so that they are functional. Almost every structure in the holometabolous larva is the result of two separate influences: its basic form is the product of a very ancient, well-established pattern of embryogenesis which has stopped before completion, and many of its details are the product of the need to make partly formed structures work temporarily. Leg rudiments have only simple sets of muscles, for example, and are strengthened by rings of better sclerotized cuticle and the tips of the legs may have little spines or even suction cups. To such an extent there is "sideways" development. Consequently there are present some parts of structures which, while essential to the larva, would hinder the adult and must be done away with before terminal embryogenesis can proceed. This "sideways" development is superimposed on normal ontogeny. The essentially important feature of the holometabolous larva is not such digressive "sideways" formations but the embryogenetic level of the basic framework.

In holometabolous species having ocelli in the adult, these organs first appear on the pupa; they are never present on the larva. The lateral eyes, innervated from the optic lobes, are represented only by a few isolated visual units (stemmata) (see Fig. 6.6D), each terminating in a single-faceted cornea. Each unit is an imperfectly but sufficiently formed ommatidium bearing only the most superficial similarity to a true ocellus.

During larval life the rudiments of the adult compound eye are forming internally from a hypodermal invagination. At pupation the larval stemmata are histolyzed, making room for the compound eye rudiment to develop into the adult structure. That the stemmata and adult eyes are homologous is demonstrated both by position and by the origins of the neural and hypodermal rudiments of each; further, the destruction of the larval eyes and their replacement by adult eyes is not a phenomenon peculiar to holometabolism but a refinement of the process occurring in hemimetabolism. Lew (1933) studied the development of the eyes in dragonflies and showed that surrounding the larval eye there are several areas of tissue which slowly develop during the immature instars (Fig. 8.9B). As part of final ecdysis, the larval eye, though compound, is histolyzed and the eye-potent tissue at its margins develops into the adult compound eye. Bodenstein (1953) pointed out that "The main difference between hemi- and holometabolous insects, as far as the differentiation of functional ommatidia is concerned, is that, in the hemimetabolous, differentiation processes are taking place throughout the entire postembryonic [i.e., immature] period, whereas in the holometabolous, they are mainly limited to the pupal stage."

Of the many normal types of holometabolous larvae, the polypod eruciform of Lepidoptera (Fig. 8.4B) is perhaps the most poorly developed. The antennae are low fleshy lobes weakly divided into the three segments. While the mouthparts are generalized and strong and have most of the standard parts present, they by no means approach the highly modified structures of the adult and will have to be replaced at pupation. The thoracic legs consist of three short sclerotized cylinders—femur, tibia and tarsus—tipped by the post-tarsal claws. Trochanter and coxa are represented by sclerites embedded in the pleural flesh. The abdominal legs (prolegs), in most families present on the third to sixth segments, have but a single segment thought to be the coxa (Snodgrass, 1935), tipped by a retractile lobe (**planta**) on which is a more or less complete ring of curved claw-like setae (**crochets**). These prolegs are equipped with a simple musculature which enables them to grip rough surfaces or to use the plantae as suction cups on smooth surfaces. In comparison with the adult morphology, all these appendages stand at a most incomplete level of development; pupation must involve an almost total reorganization of all of them. The rudiments for the imaginal parts form internally as hypodermal invaginations which are not affected by larval ecdyses.

The oligopod campodeiform larvae of Carabidae (Coleoptera) (Fig. 8.10A) are nearly comparable to the developmental level of the paurometabolous nymphs. The antennae have the three adult segments clearly marked and often are quite long, though not formed in the adult way. The mouthparts are strong, prominent and similar to those of the adult. All six segments of the thoracic legs are present, rather long and slender. No abdominal prolegs are found, but the last segment bears a pair of cerci. At pupation Carabidae must undergo reorganization, though less drastically than in most holometabolous insects, since the larval structures are much more similar to those of the adult.

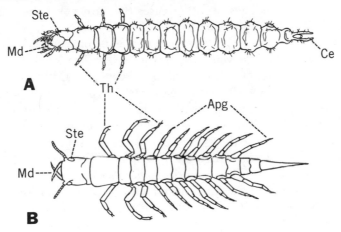

Figure 8.10. (A) Campodeiform larva of *Pterostichus* (Coleoptera); (B) larva of *Sialis* (Neuroptera). *Apg*, gill-bearing abdominal appendages; *Ce*, cerci (urogomphi); *Md*, mandible; *Ste*, stemmata; *Th*, thoracic legs. (A from Edwards, 1949; B redrawn from Snodgrass, 1954)

In both these types of larvae most structures present are continued into the adult organization, but with a greater or less degree of alteration in shape, proportion and integumental detail. Except for prolegs and cerci, none of the structures is uniquely larval.

Since adult insects never have gills, the formation of such organs in some immatures may be said to be true "sideways" development from the main stream of embryogenesis. Aquatic larvae are found in eight insect orders—universally in four and occasionally in four. The principal respiratory mechanisms of these juveniles are of four kinds.

Cutaneous respiration is assumed for all cases where no special structure is present. Even where there are well-developed gills, cutanous respiration is at least a supplementary mechanism and may even be the more important. Blood gills are thin-walled hypodermal areas, often somewhat evaginated, which permit direct exchange between the blood in the hemocoel and the environmental water. In larval Chironomidae (Diptera) it has been shown that the blood gills are involved in obtaining chloride ions from the water. The larval mosquito's respiratory siphons are "snorkel tubes" which, when thrust through the surface film, lead air to the tracheae. Tracheal gills are evaginations, usually finger-like or leaf-like, of the body wall, and are richly supplied with tracheoles. In some cases tracheal gills are developments of or on appendages, including abdominal appendages; in other cases they are not placed in such a way that they can be appendicular modifications.

Each of the first seven abdominal segments of young Ephemerida generally bears a pair of ventro-lateral gills representing the segmental appendages and developed from the limb rudiments. Details of structure and arrangement vary with the species. Mayflies living in clean running water have the gills external, but those inhabiting muddy or sandy bottoms often have the gills concealed in pockets to protect them from abrasion. In young Odonata the gills are located at or near the tip of the abdomen. In damsel flies (suborder Zygoptera) they typically take the form of three caudal processes; in dragonflies (suborder Anisoptera) the gills are on the walls of the hindgut, which is expanded to form a chamber called the **branchial basket.** Water is drawn into and forced out of this chamber, the latter process frequently being used as a form of locomotion by jet propulsion.

One family of Plecoptera has paired abdominal gills on the nymph, but in the rest of the order the gills are filamentous evaginations located on the head, the thorax, the anterior part of the abdomen, the segments or various combinations of these places and are certainly not homologous with appendages. Tufts of filamentous gills are present on the abdomens of larval Trichoptera; in this order also, the gills are not derived from segmental appendages.

Among the Neuroptera, the larvae of the Sialoidea (alder flies) and of some species in the families Sisyridae (spongilla flies) and Osmylidae are aquatic. In the last family no gills are present, but in the other two groups the larval gills are segmented and are apparently modified from appendages (Fig. 8.10B), being provided with coxal muscles. Several genera of Lepidoptera (*Acentropus* and *Nymphula,* family Pyralidae) have aquatic larvae which apparently respire cutaneously, but in several of the species filamentous tracheal gills are present in some instars. Among Coleoptera filamentous or plumose tracheal gills are present on abdominal segments of larval Hygrobiidae, Gyrinidae, Haliplidae and two genera of the Hydrophilidae.

At least twenty families of Diptera have some species with aquatic larvae. A few families—Culicidae and Simulidae are the best known—are entirely aquatic in all larval and pupal stages. A great variety of respiratory structures are found in this order, including blood gills, siphons and tufts of tracheal gills; these last are not appendicular.

TERMINAL EMBRYOGENESIS

In the anamorphic groups embryogenesis is a direct, continuous series of events leading to the fully formed adult. Each structure appears as a rudiment, then proceeds to grow to its ultimate shape and size. As soon as there are enough structures present to enable survival in the environment, the embryo leaves the egg and becomes the first instar larva. Abdominal segments are added without fuss and bother, as the process does not interfere with any of the internal or external structures already present and mainly contributes additional hemocoel and, in myriapods, more locomotory appendages.

Hemimetabolous (in the broad sense) development differs from anamorphosis only in that hatching is delayed until segmentation is complete. Embryogenesis in the hemimetabolous apterygote groups is direct and continuous. The first instar needs only to grow to adult size while the reproductive system matures and the other internal systems, already functional, are improved. The first real complication seems to have been introduced with the wings. When wings are present, postimaginal ecdyses are not practical. The complication of embryogenesis resulting from the winged condition was indirect, as there is little difficulty in wing development per se. The primitive winged insects apparently reached out more and more successfully into new ecological niches; winged adults were no longer restricted to the same life led by immatures. Inevitably, as the distinction between immature and adult ways of life became more marked, certain structures present in the immature would not be utilized by the adult, and vice versa. An obvious situation of this sort is found in Ephemerida, where the aquatic naiads possess modifications of no value to the adult. Gradually embryogenesis becomes less direct, in order to provide the young with necessary adaptations as soon as possible after hatching, a modification which necessitates a reorganization into the adult structures when larval adaptations are no longer advantageous. Even in hemimetabolous development the holometabolous pupa is foreshadowed; some larval tissue is histolyzed and groups of cells held over from prehatching develop into new tissues. As Hinton (1948) pointed out, once pupation was devised—and the process of histolysis-histogenesis is the essential feature of pupation—provisional larval deviations of greater and greater degree became possible. The end result was the holometabolous cycle, but it should now be clear that holometabolism evolved gradually. Furthermore, holometabolism certainly evolved polyphyletically: once in the Hemiptera branch and probably several times on the branch leading to the traditionally holometabolous orders. It is no longer possible to be confident that holometabolous insects are broadly monophyletic.

Terminal embryogenesis in hemimetabolous cycles is something like the remodeling of an old building for a new occupant—a new plank here, some putty there and some paint over the whole. But the demands become more and more complex until, in holometabolism, it is found to be more economical to raze the old building entirely, retaining only the foundations for the new structure. The simile falls short, however, since the insect has anticipated (forgive the teleology) the turn of events—indeed makes them possible—by laying aside the materials for the new construction in the form of **histoblasts** (**imaginal discs** or **buds**). Each reconstructed part is histogenetically descended from the rudiment that first appeared in the embryo. In many cases the original embryonic rudiment has a dual histological history: part of it grows to be a larval structure while the rest of it is held in abeyance; when the larval structure is destroyed, the residual histoblasts develop into the homologous replacement.

Accordingly, terminal embryogenesis is not just the completion of development previously started, though it is mainly that; some preliminary backtracking is necessary. It is not always easy to assess the actual extent of this backtracking. In histological terms it may be profound, but descriptive histology does not take into account the degree to which a cell or group of cells may be *determined*, in the sense used in experimental embryology. In the final analysis the level of development determination is more important than the structural differentiation of a cell, for it is clear that the former must precede the latter. Since histoblasts in the prepupa and pupa proceed quite rapidly to form adult structures, it must be supposed that determination and organization had been previously very well advanced despite the generalized appearance of the cells, a supposition well fortified by experimental evidence. All this places holometabolous terminal development much closer to the main stream of embryogenesis than is sometimes appreciated from superficial appraisals.

HISTOLYSIS AND HISTOGENESIS

Histolysis is the destructive, **histogenesis** the constructive process in terminal embryogenesis, though neither is a phenomenon peculiar only to the embryo. Histolysis involves the death of specific tissue followed by its disintegration. This may be only the chemical breakdown (**autolysis**) of the cells under the influence of enzymes, following which the products of disintegration are dissolved or suspended in the hemocoelic plasma, or it may include the action of phagocytic blood cells that ingest and digest cellular particles, both of which processes enter into the destruction of tissue. In any event, the chemical products of cellular disintegration become available as food material for the constructive process of histogenesis, which involves the mitotic proliferation of cells along with their differentiation and arrangement as new tissue. Although the lineage of the histoblasts has not been traced back to the embryo in every case, it has been accomplished in enough different insects, including some of the higher Diptera where reconstructive processes are especially complicated, to suggest that these groups of cells probably always derive directly from embryonic rudiments.

Not all larval tissues necessarily undergo destruction and replacement. Some are retained as adult tissue, perhaps with modification. How much is destroyed, how much retained and the details of the entire procedure vary widely among different insects and also with respect to different tissues in a given individual.

FORMATION OF ADULT STRUCTURES

Most general accounts of "postembryonic" development give the impression, perhaps in an effort to oversimplify, that imaginal buds are unique to holometabolism. It was noted above that the compound eye of the hemimetabolous dragonfly larva is histolyzed at final ecdysis and that the adult eye itself is formed by the histogenesis of some generalized eye-potent cells located around the periphery of the larval eye. These histoblasts can only be regarded as the imaginal eye buds, even though they are on the external hypodermis during the later larval instars; there is nothing in the definition of an imaginal bud which requires it to be internal. Similarly, the earliest stages of the wings in pauro- and hemimetabolism are imaginal buds.

Another impression gathered from general accounts is that there is a sharp, clear distinction between the way the wing develops in hemimetabolous insects and the way it develops in holometabolous insects. This impression is confirmed by superficial observation, for wings apparently develop externally in the hemimetabolous groups, internally in the holometabolous; closer examination tends to weaken the distinction.

Even in nymphal insects the visible wing pads are preceded by internal buds imaginal wing discs of histoblasts (see also Chapter Four). As these cells proliferate, the discs evaginate; growth is continuous and gradual, so timed that when the larva is mature the wings are ready for use. In holometabolous larvae there is no external sign of the wings until just before pupation, when their position is marked by bulges where the wing buds press out the larval cuticle. When the prepupal cuticle is sloughed, the wings become external for the first time.

In both kinds of development the wings pass through three phases. In the first phase, always internal, the histoblasts are organized, determined and begin proliferation. In the second phase the buds increase in size and assume the definitive shape, venation and coloring of the adult. The final phase occurs immediately after the ecdysis ending pupation: the small but otherwise perfect wings are expanded by blood pressure to their final size, following which some of the hypodermis is destroyed so that they soon are principally cuticular. The first phase ordinarily begins in the egg. In pauro- and hemimetabolous insects the second phase begins late in the first or early in the second instar, progressing slowly to completion during nymphal life; the wing buds are external but enclosed in larval cuticle. The third phase occurs immediately after final ecdysis. In holometabolous insects the first phase is prolonged through larval life. During this period the slow proliferation of the wing histoblasts leads to the formation of an area of tissue that has nowhere to go except to infold beneath the cuticle; apparently it cannot be everted until a certain point in embryogenesis is reached—which occurs relatively later in holometabolous than in hemimetabolous larvae. Consequently the imaginal disc—never large, never histologically differentiated as wing tissues, never definitive in shape or structure—is evaginated in the prepupa and enters the second phase of development. That the second phase is completed so rapidly in holometabolism may be because of a greater advance in physiologic organization and embryogenic determination during larval life.

The shape of the internal wing bud varies among holometabolous insects. In some larvae it is a bud evaginated from the hypodermis exactly as it is in nymphs, but is not enclosed by larval cuticle; instead, the cuticle pushes the bud back toward the body so that it lies in a depression. From this beginning, seen in most Coleoptera, the depression may become deeper and deeper, and the wing bud comes to lie in a rather deep pocket. The pocket may form first. In Diptera the bud evaginates from the bottom of such a pocket, while in Neuroptera and Lepidoptera it evaginates from its anterior wall.

Viewed in such a light, holometabolous internal wing buds do not appear to be such a different development after all; they are, rather, the perfectly logical, inevitable consequence of the earlier embryonic stage of the holometabolous larva and the temporary deferment during the larval instars of further major embryogenesis. Berlese apparently was fundamentally correct in believing that the holometabolous larva is not the equivalent of the hemimetabolous nymph.

The behavior of imaginal buds of the eyes and the appendages in holometabolous larvae is entirely consistent with the way the wings develop—except that generally the adult eyes and appendages replace larval homologues, while the wings are uniquely imaginal. The formation of the entire adult head in many Diptera, however, presents an analogous situation, in that head structures are mostly or entirely missing in the larvae. In *Calliphora* (bluebottle fly) the cephalic somites invaginate into the thorax during or soon after embryonic segmentation. The true head is thus represented through larval life by embryonic tissue situated internally. The imaginal buds of eyes, antennae and mouthparts become deep invaginations which eventually are almost or entirely separated from the hypodermal layer. Like the wings, these structures develop in phases— a preliminary phase of determination and initial proliferation, followed at pupation by a phase of differentiation and rapid growth. In other insects, where adult and larval appendages are similar both in form and position, the imaginal buds often form within the immature structure like a hand within a glove, or they may form in hypodermal pockets at the base of the larval appendage, everting at pupation.

The fate of the larval hypodermis at pupation is exceedingly varied. It is mostly retained in Coleoptera and becomes the imaginal hypodermis. In Diptera the larval hypodermis is histolyzed—not all at once—and replaced from histoblasts arranged in centers of regeneration. These are the extremes between which other insects exhibit various steps and degrees. The fate of the larval fore- and hindguts generally follows that of the integumental hypodermis. They are retained, though often lengthened and otherwise modified, when the general hypodermis is retained; they are destroyed and replaced from histoblasts when such is the case with the integument. The midgut is more usually replaced at the pupal instar and may again be replaced before ecdysis to the imago, regardless of the fate of ectodermal parts of the gut; in general, the malpighian tubules follow the fate of the mesenteron. The dorsal blood vessel, the tracheal system and the central nervous system are normally carried over into the adult with minimal modification. The tracheal system characteristically becomes more complex through the formation of air sacs or of additional ramification and sometimes there is some shifting in the positions of the spiracular openings. The nervous system commonly becomes more centralized at pupation, the ganglia being drawn forward, and some may be fused. Because the adult musculature in holometabolous insects differs sharply from that of the larvae, diverse and radical reorganization is typical. Hinton (1948) thought that the need for a hypodermal matrix to which to affix the new musculature is the real basis for pupation. Richards and Davis (*in* Imms, 1957) list five different possibilities in the metamorphosis of the muscular system: some larval muscles are retained unchanged; some undergo modification without destruction; some are histolyzed and not replaced; some are histolyzed but replaced; some are formed for the first time.

ECDYSIS

Ecdysis is the arthropod solution for the problem of growth despite the restrictive exoskeleton. While the hypodermis itself is perfectly capable of growth and indeed does grow, it is not sufficiently rigid to provide suitable attachment and leverage for the muscles or to afford a stable form and adequate external protection. All these requirements are met by the cuticle, secreted everywhere by hypodermal cells, both externally and within invaginations such as the fore- and hindgut, the tracheal system, the ducts of the reproductive system and the ducts of certain glands. But the hard cuticle, while providing for present needs, establishes a limit to size and volume and thus does not provide for growth. To increase body size or to alter body shape, the cuticle must be discarded and a new one formed.

At the approach of ecdysis, feeding and other activities cease. If the animal has been living in a more or less exposed situation, it may seek a more protected place, for during ecdysis it will be relatively helpless. Internally, the hypodermal cells become larger and mitotic division may occur at various sites. The hypodermis secretes a molting fluid containing enzymes which act on the proteins, chitin and other materials of the cuticle. The inner cuticular layers, digested by the molting fluid, are resorbed. The hypodermis then begins secreting the new cuticle. The more impervious outer layer appears first, followed by the successive inner layers. At first the completed new cuticle is soft, flexible and somewhat wrinkled. The old cuticle, now merely a free shell, is ruptured along abscission lines in the anterior dorsal region when pressure is exerted by a swelling of the body. This pressure is the result of the animal swallowing air or water and is transmitted by way of the blood cavity. The animal then wriggles through the break in the old cuticle and is free of it. Further expansion of the body establishes the size of the new cuticle and smoothes out the wrinkles. Hardening and pigmentation follow as tanning and other agents from the cell layer diffuse through the cuticle, and normal existence is resumed. The sloughed cuticle ordinarily includes not only the external enclosure, but also the linings of the fore- and hindgut, the tracheal system and the invaginated ducts.

Ecdysis involves hypodermal replacement only in some of the most advanced holometabolous groups, and in these cases, only at the ecdysis leading to the pupal instar. It should be noted that where hypodermal histolysis occurs, it occurs *after* ecdysis proper and *after* a firm new cuticle has been laid down for the instar. This replacement hypodermis will not be required to form another cuticle until the end of the pupal period. The formation of the pharate adult involves two distinct but concurrent steps: an ecdysis essentially similar to all the previous ecdyses; the accelerated and telescoped events of terminal embryogenesis.

As has been frequently observed, the sloughing of the old cuticle, the act of molting itself, is not a true point of division between one instar and another. When the old cuticle is sloughed, the new instar has already occupied a new cuticle for a certain length of time. In some cases, as in pupiparial Diptera, the old cuticle is not sloughed until a still later ecdysis, but is utilized as an additional protective shell. The best point of division between one instar and the other is when a new cuticle is laid down. But one cannot escape the fact that development is continuous from one instar to the next, from zygote to adult.

As explained in Chapter Six, control of ecdysis and of metamorphosis rests with the endocrine system and involves the interaction of several hormones. One is **ecdyson (molting** or **growth and differentiation hormone)**, produced periodically by the prothoracic gland in response to a hormone produced by neurosecretory cells in the procephalic ganglia. Various factors may stimulate the secretion of the "brain" hormone. In *Rhodnius* (Hemiptera) Wigglesworth has demonstrated that feeding— this species normally takes a single blood meal at each instar—leads to activity on the part of the procephalic neurosecretory cells, perhaps through the distention of the hypodermis against the cuticle. When ecdyson builds up in the blood, molting occurs. Another hormone, **neotenin (juvenile hormone)**, is continuously produced by the corpora allata during larval life. In its presence embryogenic progress is inhibited or, to put it another way, only larval structures are formed at ecdysis. It may be thought of as a selecting mechanism for immaturity. At the end of larval life the corpora allata cease producing neotenin; there is suggestive evidence (but so far no proof) that at this point the corpora allata may begin to produce some "imaginal-determining" substance. Ecdysis in the absence of neotenin, and possibly also in the presence of a hormone succeeding it (if there is one), results in embryogenic progress and the formation of imaginal structures. This general process has been amply demonstrated by experimental studies and applies both to hemi- and to holometabolous insects.

Wigglesworth (1959) viewed each hypodermal cell has having dual or triple potentialities in that it might become larval, adult or pupal tissue. Which potentiality is realized at molting depends upon the presence or absence of neotenin. Cells form adult tissue in the absence of neotenin and under the influence only of ecdyson; pupal tissue results from ecdyson plus a small amount of neotenin; larval tissue results from ecdyson and a large amount of neotenin. While Wigglesworth seems to believe that adult, pupal and larval tissues are separate formations, each a dead end in itself, his interpretation is not essentially inconsistent with the concept of each instar being a logical continuation of the previous one, and of the holometabolous larva as an embryo in which most externally obvious embryogenic progress is held up until pupation. Thus neotenin during larva life permits growth but prevents terminal embryogenesis; when it tapers off in the prepupa, the pharate adult is formed; when it ceases entirely, the definitive adult results.

Molting is often understood to apply only to "postembryonic" stages, but as a matter of fact it begins in the egg where it has been observed in arachnoids and in many insects. The deutovum and tritovum of arachnoids are delicate cuticles secreted by the embryonic protohypodermis; the former cuticle is produced when limb rudiments appear and the latter a short time afterward. The embryonic cuticles are less persistent in insects but probably are always produced, according to Johannsen and Butt (1938), who believed that these membranes have been often overlooked. First instar orthopteroids are still encased in an embryonic cuticle when they hatch, which leads to the misnomer "vermiform larva" for this stage.

Like hatching, ecdysis occurs without reference to ontogenetic progress but rather in response to the needs of the individual. Accordingly the instars of various species are not necessarily chronologically homologous. While control of ecdysis rests with the endocrine system, extraneous circumstances may upset the hormone balance to the end that extra ecdyses —hence extra instars—are produced, or the reverse may result. Variation in the number of ecdyses has been produced experimentally by upsetting the endocrine system, and to some extent development has even been reversed. Under normal conditions most species follow a set pattern involving a certain number of molts spaced at more or less predictable intervals. Unfavorable ecological conditions, such as insufficient food supply or parasitism, may alter the pattern. Where a species has several generations during a year, larvae developing during colder weather may have one or several more instars than the generation developing during hot weather. In some cases the sexes differ in the number of normal molts. Females of certain Lepidoptera pass through more ecdyses than the males, while neotenic females (Strepsiptera, Coccoidea) undergo fewer ecdyses by omission of the final stages. The number of molts experienced by castes of Isoptera varies both with the caste and with the age and condition of the colony. Primitive insect groups tend to undergo a greater number of molts than the more advanced groups; there appears to be a broad evolutional trend toward economy in this respect.

Classification

Classification is the attempt to impose order on an otherwise confusing diversity of things and to arrange them so they may be found again. Both the purpose and the method are the same regardless of the things being classified—records in a business office, books and journals in a library, organic molecules in a chemical index, animals or plants in a taxonomic system. In this context classification is a clerical task and as such **taxonomy,** the science of classifying plants and animals, had its beginnings. Even today the clerical task remains the obvious and most easily grasped aspect of taxonomy—and the only one imputed to it by most nontaxonomists and even by some taxonomists. Classification is the basic approach to any scientific endeavor. Strip the gimmicks and peculiarities from any body of scientific knowledge—cell physiology, subatomic physics, electronic computation, pharmacology—and what remains is a system of classification, the *sine qua non.*

The process of classification requires that the units be recognized and defined, that they be arranged into a series of groups, that these groups in turn be collected and arranged into groups, and so on, until the classifier is satisfied that he has arrived at a system both logical and useful. The process also requires that every unit and group be given a unique designation which cannot be confused with the designation of any other unit or group. Thus there are two distinct processes involved, in fact: the process of defining the units and groups, along with their arrangement and the correct placing of everything into its category, and the process of applying unique designators to all units and groupings.

Application of these two aspects of the process of classification varies in difficulty with the things being classified. Books and magazines, letters and purchase orders are obvious kinds of units. The fact that they are composed of words and thus of the alphabet provides the office manager or the librarian with a convenient device for establishing categories and arranging them in logical sequence. Animals are something else again.

THE HIERARCHY OF TAXA

The biological unit is the individual organism. The taxonomic system in zoology is therefore the classification of all individual animals. Closely related, similar individuals are grouped into a **species,** the unit category of taxonomy. Species that seem to be closely related are grouped into a **genus.** Genera are grouped into a **family,** families into an **order,** orders into a **class,** classes into a **phylum,** phyla into a **kingdom.** Haekel, in the nineteenth century, first used phylum, but the rest of the hierarchy of categories (**taxa**) is that used by Carl von Linné in the tenth edition of *Systema Naturae,* 1758, in which animal classification was formalized and consistently applied.

Finding the animal kingdom to be much more extensive and vastly more complicated than Linné realized, taxonomists now use a hierarchy with many more levels of taxa. By applying prefixes to the names of traditional taxa, new categories can be designated with relative rank as implied in the prefix. A *sub*family is a division of a family. Related families may be grouped into a *super*family. A third prefix, *infra-,* is sometimes used and ranks next below *sub-.* The **tribe** is often placed between genus and family; still other categorical names—**cohort, phalanx, series, section, division**—have been used by various taxonomists. Use of these prefixes and various of the less traditional categorical levels allows the construction of a hierarchy with as many ranks as anyone might desire. In his classification of mammals, Simpson (1945) used twenty-one levels of categories, as compared to the six found in *Systema Naturae.*

The hierarchy used depends entirely upon the needs and preferences of the taxonomist erecting the system. Almost any combination is permissible provided the basic seven categories are present in the traditional relationship and provided all additional taxa are interpolated logically. There is no need for uniformity between one taxonomist and another, or between one part of a classification and another. For example, it may be desirable to employ the superfamily in classifying the large order Lepidoptera, whereas in a small order like the Thysanura, the superfamily might not be necessary. Students should not allow themselves to be confused by such apparent inconsistencies. A similar situation arises in an office filing system in which correspondence is classified by the initial of the last name of the person signing a letter: there would be little need to subdivide the "Z" or "Q" file, but it might be very convenient to establish *sub-M* categories—"Ma," "Mc," "Me," "Mi," "Mo," "Mu."

An expanded taxonomic hierarchy is given below and a far more complex system using many more ranks could easily be devised. The one given here could be simplified by removal of some of the prefixed categories: by preference, *infra-* categories would be omitted, as being less usual than *sub-* or *super-* categories.

Phylum
Subphylum
Superclass
Class
Subclass
Superorder
Order
Suborder
Infraorder
Superfamily
Family
Subfamily
Tribe
Subtribe
Genus
Subgenus
Species
Subspecies
Infraspecies

NAMES AND NAMING

In the second paragraph of this chapter it was pointed out that there are two separate processes included in the general process of classification. When he defines, arranges and classifies his units and groups, the taxonomist makes purely biological decisions. Once these biological decisions have been made, and not until then, he must apply designators, the scientific names, to the various groupings he has reached. The first process is scientific research, the second is not.

Scientific names are Latin or latinized words derived, applied and used in accordance with regulations set forth in the International Code of Zoological Nomenclature (1961). Like naming molecules in chemistry, naming animals in zoology is routine. Inherently trivial, it is nevertheless absolutely essential to the entire field of zoology. A part of the practice of taxonomy, *naming* is the least important and certainly the least difficult part, but it is important that it be done correctly; otherwise the use of names becomes difficult or impossible for the many zoologists who do not specialize in naming. For example—it is interesting to learn from a physiologist that he has isolated an enzyme from an insect, that the chemical composition of the enzyme is such and such, its function thus and so; it is also essential to know *exactly* which insect has this enzyme. If the scientific name for the insect is used by the physiologist, all is well; if it is not used, he is not only wasting his time, but many of his colleagues will wonder why he thus makes it impossible for them to repeat his experiment.

In principle, scientific names are analogous to common names, expressing a concept of designation inherent in every language. When animal taxonomy was established in the eighteenth century, Latin was used because it was then the *lingua franca* of educated people of all countries. If the scientific name is just the common name of an animal translated from a vernacular into Latin, why not use the vernacular name? There are excellent reasons. Not only does the common name for a given animal differ with each language, but it often varies geographically within a language area. The "red squirrel" of eastern United States is not the same animal called "red squirrel" in California, for example. Furthermore, no common name is found in any language for the vast majority of animals. Common names are available only for the animals ordinarily encountered by the hunter, fisherman or farmer—most mammals, many birds, some amphibians, reptiles and fish, but a very small proportion of invertebrates. The so-called "common names" for birds and butterflies found in popular works are in main artificial contrivances, often the scientific name translated into English, and are known to and used by only a handful of enthusiastic amateur naturalists.

Insofar as true common names existed in European languages, Linné and the early naturalists used the Latin forms of the words. Thus the scientific name for bears became *Ursus*, for horses *Equus*, for frogs *Rana*, for shrews *Sorex*, and so on. But there are different kinds of bears, horses, frogs and shrews, a fact recognized in vernacular tongues as well as in Latin. The common European shrew is a little smoky-colored animal, whence its scientific name, *Sorex fumeus*. The water shrew is *Sorex palustris*, the grey shrew is *Sorex cinareus*, the arctic shrew is *Sorex arcticus*. In scientific nomenclature, as in the vernacular, the name of a specific kind of animal consists of two words (**binomen**) : the name of the genus, a noun always written with a capital initial, and the name of the species, an adjective always written with a lower case initial. The generic name indicates the general kind of animal—bear, horse, frog, shrew. The specific name designates which exact kind is meant—the arctic shrew, for example, rather than the water shrew or any other shrew. Binomens are always italicized in print or underscored when typewritten or handwritten (except sometimes in titles of books or articles).

Whether or not an animal happens to have a common name, the system of binomial scientific names can always be applied; in the absence of a common name to translate into Latin, any noun can be used for its genus, any modifying word for its species, always provided the resultant combination is not identical with some other combination in use. Such a very large percentage of the animal kingdom never had common names that taxonomists long ago gave up thinking in terms of translating a common name into Latin. The fact of the matter is, scientific names of animals are not *really* Latin: they are *latinized* combinations of letters which are made to look like Latin and for tradition's sake are treated according to some of the rules of Latin grammar. Even Latin words lose their Latin meanings when used as scientific names. *Papilio* in Latin means butterfly —any and all butterflies; as a scientific name it means only one particular genus of butterflies. *Papilio brevicauda*, used as a scientific name, does not mean "short-tailed butterfly"; it means only and exactly a certain species of the genus *Papilio*. Suitability has nothing to do with it. If the butterfly in question happened to have very long tails, but was legally named *brevicauda*, that would be its name and no one could properly change its name to, say, *longicauda*.

INTERNATIONAL CODE OF ZOOLOGICAL NOMENCLATURE

The purpose of a scientific name is to provide a designator which will mean the same thing to all people of all nations through all foreseeable time. In short, the names must be defined clearly and they must be stable. "A correct and fixed nomenclature is an imperative antecedent to all truly scientific investigation and discussion" (Holland, 1929).

The early naturalists used scientific names according to their personal preferences. Some made an effort to apply, wherever suitable, the names previously used by others. Some worked without libraries or paid little attention to what others did or were doing. Some accepted the authority of certain naturalists, rejected others and used names accordingly. As a result, many species and genera were given different names by different workers, while some names were applied by different workers to entirely different animals.

In 1842 the British Association for the Advancement of Science adopted a general set of rules to govern procedure in nomenclature. The American Association developed a code of its own in 1871, as did the French in 1881 and the German in 1894. Meanwhile the geologists formulated still another code in 1881 for naming fossils while American ornithologists devised a code in 1885 to apply to bird names. Some lesser groups and many individuals proposed other rules. At least, the zoologists recognized that they had a problem.

The First International Congress of Zoology, meeting in Paris in 1889, considered the possibility of a uniform set of rules, but it was not until 1901 that national and disciplinary differences were sufficiently reconciled that the first version of the Code was adopted by the Fifth Congress at Berlin. Every International Congress since then has contributed amendments or additions. The version currently in force was completely re-written and was approved by the Fifteenth Congress in London in 1958 and published in 1961. The Code has no legal authority, nor can it be enforced except insofar as zoologists themselves believe it desirable to follow it. By adhering to the provisions of the Code, all zoologists who create or use scientific names of animals can help to avoid confusion in nomenclature and to keep names in their proper perspective—as useful tools. Scientific names are unimportant in themselves: they take on importance only as they are useful.

The underlying principle in the Code is **priority.** The name first applied to a taxon—names of genera and species are particularly mentioned—shall be the name of that taxon, provided the author of the name made himself perfectly clear as to what he intended, provided he used Linnean binomial nomenclature and provided he published all this in a scientific book or journal, properly printed and properly circulated. Subsequent names for the same taxon become **synonyms** and are not used.

Another principle is **homonymy,** which seeks to prevent a name from being used in more than one context. Accordingly a generic name can be used only for one genus of animals. Should a name be applied to a second genus, different from its original application, it is automatically a **hom-onym** and must be replaced with a name not already in use. Similarly, every species within a genus must have its own name which cannot be duplicated by the name of any other species in that genus.

Still another principle is that of the **type**. When a species is described, the author must, among other things, select one specimen as the **holotype**. All other specimens of his species before him at the time of his original publication of the name become **paratypes**. The holotype is the key to the name of the species and settles questions in connection with the name itself. It is *not* the type of the species, or even necessarily a typical individual of the species; it is the type of the *name*. Paratypes have little importance to nomenclature, except that they may help to illustrate what the original author had in mind, but they can be of great value in the scientific aspect of taxonomy, as distinct from naming.

The type principle is also applied to genera and families. Each genus name must have a **type-species,** which stands in the same relationship to the generic name as the holotype does to the species name. What other species properly belong in the genus with the type-species is a biological decision. Each family must have a **type-genus,** which fixes the application of the family name.

Family names of animals are formed by adding the ending *-idae* to the grammatical stem of the name of the type-genus. Names of tribes, subfamilies or superfamilies are respectively formed by using the ending *-ini, -inae, -oidea*. Names for subgenera are similar to names of genera and cannot be duplicated in the animal kingdom by the name of any other genus or subgenus; they are always written in parentheses between the genus name and the species name.

The full name of a certain mosquito found on the Canary Islands is *Aedes (Stegomyia) aegypti canariensis* Pittaluga. The first word is the name of the genus. The second, written in parentheses, is the subgenus; *Aedes* has been divided into several subgenera. The species *aegypti* is found in most tropical and subtropical regions of the world, not just in Egypt as the name seems to imply. The fourth word is the subspecies, one of a series of slightly different geographic populations. Another subspecies is *Aedes (Stegomyia) aegypti aegypti* (Linné), found on mainland Africa. The four words written in italics make up the scientific name in its most complete form; the second and fourth, designating *sub-* categories, are appendages, and the name is still technically binomial. The fifth word, Pittaluga, not in italics, is the name of the scientist who first described and named that particular subspecies of *Aedes aegypti*. It is customary (but optional) to cite the name of the original author, and sometimes also the date when the name first was published, along with the scientific name, as an aid to future bibliographic work.

NAMES OF HIGHER CATEGORIES

The International Code does not deal with names of taxa above the rank of superfamily because, as Bradley wrote in his preface to the Code, "the practice of zoologists in regard to them is not sufficiently uniform to permit the formulation of rules covering them at this time." Probably it was wise not to weaken the moral force of the Code by trying to legislate on a topic about which there is no general agreement.

The names of higher categories—orders, classes, phyla—remain therefore a matter of personal preference, influenced by usage which sometimes is traditional in the best sense, sometimes is not, and frequently is inconsistent. In main, the names of these categories are supposed to be more or less descriptive of the animals included, though some, like Arachnida, are allusions to mythology. The ordinal name for flies is Diptera (*two wings*, in translation) and for thousand-leggers is Myriapoda (*very numerous feet*). Few of these names are really suitable for and descriptive of *all* members of the taxon. Their ordinal name notwithstanding, the only flies to have two wings in fact are the so-called "wingless" forms like the family Nycteribiidae, in which the front pair is missing; most flies have four wings, since the halteres are actually wings, though vestigial and highly modified.

In a later chapter, when insect orders are listed, we cite some of the alternative names for them. Each of these alternative names has had some, or even wide, currency. Certain of the ordinal names are used by everybody everywhere and give no difficulty. Certain other orders are called by one name in the United States, another in Great Britain, another in France and another in Germany, or the selection may be based upon whether the selector happens to be deeply interested in fossil insects, or happens to be interested only in insects of America north of the Rio Grande, or happens to have become accustomed to one or another name. Surely it would seem just as desirable to stabilize the names of higher categories as it is to stabilize the names of species, genera and families.

In preparing the list of names for orders, we consulted many references and many colleagues and found as many differences of opinion on just which names should be used. Accordingly we have followed the lead of Essig (1942), Moore (1955), Chamberlin (1958) and others by using objective procedures in selecting names for higher categories, procedures which are not authorized by the Code but which are not forbidden by it.

Some such set of rules must eventually be incorporated into a future version of the Code. We have been guided by the following considerations:

1. Where a Linnean name is available, it must be used. An eminent colleague who read an early version of this book chided us for using Insecta and stated that "Hexapoda is to be preferred." We prefer Insecta, as do a little more than sixty per cent of the entomologists writing books in recent years, because it was used by Linné in 1758, whereas the dubiously more descriptive word, Hexapoda, was proposed by Latreille in 1825 and is therefore a synonym.

2. Every name used by Linné for a higher category must be used, though not necessarily for all the same animals he included. However, at least one such animal must still be a member of the group. Subsequent revisers cannot properly remove from a class or order *all* animals included by Linné, thus leaving the name denuded, as had been done in the case of the insect order Aptera. Following Essig (1942), we restore Aptera for the order sometimes designated Diplura, a junior name devised by Borner in 1904.

3. Where a Linnean name is not available for a class or order, priority should be applied and the oldest name used, *unless* by so doing the nearly unanimous usage of all entomologists everywhere is upset. If a prior name has had a certain currency in recent years, it should be used in preference to other current names.

4. Whether or not the name used for a category is descriptively apt in translation has no bearing on its selection; it is no more than a combination of letters used to designate a taxon.

THE BIOLOGICAL PROBLEM

Taxonomy was never just a matter of giving names to animals and groups of animals: the biological process has always been the fundamental one. Historically, the concept of the biological process has undergone an evolution of its own, an evolution closely related to and forming an essential aspect of the evolution of modern scientific thought.

To Linné the biological problem was relatively simple. "There are just as many species as the Infinite Being created in the beginning," he wrote in *Systema Naturae*. It was therefore the job of taxonomists to find samples of all these species and put them into some logical classification. Eventually all species would be located and classified and the job would be done. When that time arrived, the biologist and the theologian could collaborate to elucidate the Divine Plan. Even the mechanics of Creation seemed clear. It was believed that the Creator used an **archetype,** something like a mold, to turn out a male and female. They, their progeny and all their descendants right up to the present make up a species. With some minor adjustments, the mold was then used to create another species. This would account for the fact that all the individuals in a species are structurally similar, and for the fact that certain species have many structures in common and form a "natural" genus.

Modern biology has provided taxonomists with new sets of criteria and a completely different approach to classification. There is, as a result, no longer any reason to believe that the task of classifying the animal kingdom can ever be completed. It is not possible to imagine a time when taxonomists can present the scientific world with a set of books and say, "Here are all animals correctly arranged into categories for your reference," because he would have to add, "Every category fully and accurately reflects all the information you and your colleagues have amassed, and you have all certified this information to be accurate and not subject to revision, because it is perfect."

The point is that taxonomy has become fully as interdisciplinary as has every other branch of biology. No longer is it a self-sufficient naming service. In its best practice, taxonomy is a wonderfully promising area of synthesis for all biological knowledge.

THE SPECIES

The nature of species is a central problem in biology and of the utmost concern to taxonomists, who must deal with species constantly. To say that a species is the sum of all the individuals belonging to it does not say what a species *is*. Although every working zoologist *knows* what a species is, none has ever seen or touched one. *Species* is not a thing; it is a concept, though no less real for that. The mental image of *species* is not and probably never will be standardized: no one has yet formulated a clear, inclusive, accurate definition.

The Linnean concept of species was exclusively morphologic: all individuals of a species are very much alike in structure; every species differs from all other species in structure to a greater or less degree. Because this morphologic concept is based on observable fact, the morphologic criterion for species continues to serve as an indispensable tool in taxonomy.

In recent years zoologists have repeatedly reassessed the species concept. Dobzhansky (1937) stated that a species is an array of forms which, during the evolutionary process, became physiologically and genetically incapable of interbreeding with other arrays. Mayr (1947) expressed it another way: "A species is a group of actually or potentially interbreeding natural populations which are reproductively isolated from other such groups." Simpson (1961) thought these statements were biased too much by genetics and suggested that, from the evolutionary view, a "species is a lineage evolving separately from others and with its own unitary evolutionary role and tendencies." None of these is a full definition and none can stand on its own feet without help. But a workable concept emerges when they are taken together and added to the older but still valid morphologic view. A species has morphologic, physiologic, genetic, ecologic and evolutional integrity. But this, too, needs help. Certainly, to use it the taxonomist needs to have a comprehensive knowledge of most if not all branches of biology.

In its original form, the morphologic concept assumed that there is a kind of structural gap between species, a discontinuity of structural modifications which would be easily recognized by any competent morphologist. Although a survey of individuals of a species might demonstrate that a considerable latitude of structural variation occurs, the limits or boundaries of these variations would be defined by discontinuity, and the variation among the individuals properly assigned to the species could be arranged in a graduated series. Thus within a species, a certain set of markings on the wing could vary from many to few, if all other species have entirely different markings. In a general way, this idea is acceptable to contemporary zoologists, provided it is understood that the "gap" between species need not be large and need not be superficially evident. The famous fruit fly species, *Drosophila pseudobscura* and *D. persimilis* can be distinguished morphologically only with extreme difficulty, unless the chromosomes are studied. The morphologist will not correctly distinguish true species if he does not look at the right structures; the study of chromosomes, for example, has not yet become a standard taxonomic technique. Situations of this kind, which are exceptions rather than rule, occur frequently enough that *cursory* examination of morphology cannot be regarded as definitive. The existence of separate species among groups of individuals which appear at first to be one species has often been discovered by nonmorphologic methods; but it should not be overlooked that morphologic differences between species always confirm the findings of other methods.

The physiologic integrity of species has not been tested extensively except in relation to man; comparative physiology is in its infancy, but should prove to be a more and more useful tool as it comes of age. In passing, it might be noted that the failure to recognize physiologic integrity as a characteristic of species has led to some fallacies which would be amusing were they not taken so seriously. An example is the assumption that the dermis of a rat and the alveolar tissue of human lung should react similarly to tars, or that DDT affects man in the same way it affects insects. However, some use has been already made of superficial aspects of species physiology—differences in food habits, in temperature, humidity or light requirements, for example—and some of this has led to interesting work in biochemical physiology.

Genetic integrity includes not only the familiar idea of "breeding true," or "like begets like," but includes also all morphologic, physiologic and behavioral variations present. Insofar as variation has a genetic basis, it may continue to appear in the population and must be taken into account in the definition of a particular species. Thus, each of the many different-looking females of the African swallowtail butterfly *Papilio dardanus* is a normal part of the species—a biological decision identifying this variation as infraspecific—and therefore the different kinds of females are not separately nameable according to correct practice. The species is not a fixed phenotype; it is the sum of all its variations: the species is not a fixed set of genes; it is all the genes of all the interbreeding individuals (**gene pool**). This viewpoint lies behind Dobzhansky's and Mayr's definitions of species cited above. So long as nothing prevents random mating within a population and between adjacent populations, the species maintains genetic integrity. Should a barrier to the free interchange of genes occur—an intersterility mutation is only one of many possibilities—the original species would become two or more species, each with its own, separate genetic integrity.

Mutations are of normal occurrence in all species—rather frequently in some, quite rarely in others. As time passes, the gene pool of a species gradually is altered as certain genetic factors, arising as mutations, become established: the result is evolution. Genetics and evolution are inseparable in the long view, collectively representing a four-dimensional concept of living things. The large body of information available on the composition, nature and behavior of genes and on the genetics of individuals and of populations has direct relevance to the species concept. As the basis for genetic study broadens—for example, in population genetics—ecology, physiology and morphology are correlated and the work becomes a study in evolution. In this way an approach is made to questions of *how, why* and *under what circumstances* can a species (or other taxon) evolve.

In the classic concept a species comprised all individuals having morphologic identity and a genus was a cluster of species having a large degree of morphologic similarity. The classic taxonomist was largely concerned with defining the nature and degree of differences "permissible" within a species, and tended to speak of this feature as being a "species difference" or of that feature as being a "generic character"—thinking, no doubt, of the original molds used in Creation.

Today the approach must be dynamic rather than static; the taxonomist must think in terms of evolution, not just of morphology. It is not important whether there is wide structural difference or only a very little; it is no longer a question of whether a group of individuals is different enough from another group of individuals to justify putting the groups into two species. Analysis of the evolution and phylogeny of a species, however, is often difficult even when the taxonomist has the benefit of a series of pertinent fossil forms representing most of the steps of change through time leading to living species. The insect taxonomist seldom has a good series of pertinent fossils. In such a situation, conclusions are necessarily based upon speculation concerning the *probable* phylogeny. It can only be assumed that the basic principles developed from study of groups like the mammals, with many good fossil forms to support phylogenetic analysis, probably hold true also in insect phylogeny.

The brief discussion presented in this chapter may suffice to indicate that the biological decision involved in classifying animals is a complex one. Indeed, taxonomy properly based in animal biology is one of the most complex problems in the entire field of the natural sciences. The references cited in the bibliography are commended to the attention of students interested in further pursuit of information on the biological basis of taxonomy.

CHAPTER TEN

The Phylum Arthropoda

Somewhere, behind Space and Time,
Is wetter water, slimier slime!

RUPERT BROOKE

From almost any point of view, the arthropods are the most important phylum in the animal kingdom. In terms of numbers, something like eighty-five per cent of all known animals, from *Amoeba* to man, belong to this group, whereas fewer than five per cent are vertebrates. In terms of evolution, the arthropods include a far greater diversity of morphologic modifications and ecological adaptations than any other phylum. If one considers all animals, including mankind, objectively as animals, it becomes evident that the Arthropoda as a whole are the most successful and best adjusted for survival. Were all arthropods to disappear suddenly, human survival would become difficult, even though so many troublesome and dangerous pests would be removed (see Chapter One).

To afford a general overview of the arthropods, the major classification is summarized below. The principal terrestrial classes—the insects, the arachnoids and the myriapods—will be presented in more detail in the next three chapters. Various classifications of this phylum have been and are advocated by the numerous zoologists who have given attention to the problem. Conservative thinking on arthropod phylogeny and classification is well reflected in the general discussion by Vandel (1949), from which the presentation below has drawn heavily.

Phylum Arthropoda Siebold and Stannius, 1845

Metazoan animals with bilateral symmetry; metamerization; sclerotized exoskeletal cuticle articulate between the segments and molted periodically; coelomic cavities metamerized in the embryo but strongly reduced in adults, the general body cavity being a hemocoel; central nervous system consisting of a double chain of ventral segmental ganglia connected to each other and to supraesophageal ganglia by a pair of solid nerve cords; essentially with eyes and ocelli; articulated appendages.

Subphylum 1. Trilobitomorpha Störmer, 1944
(Fig. 10.1A, B)

Primitive aquatic arthropods with body divided into head and trunk; head consisting of 4 postoral somites, each bearing a pair of generalized appendages, and of at least 2 preoral somites, the posterior of which bears uniramous multiarticulate antennae; trunk with from 2 to 44 somites, usually 8 to 13, terminating in a telson; appendages, except antennae, typically similar, consisting of a coxopodite bearing a multiarticulate epipodite usually branchial, an endite lobe and a 6-segmented telopodite rarely lobed or branched; anterior and posterior appendages sometimes somewhat modified in advanced species.

The more than 4000 species are known only as fossils (Fig. 10.1A, B) and flourished in very ancient times. They were already fully differentiated and richly represented in the oldest fossiliferous beds known, those of the Cambrian; they disappeared during the Permian. Störmer (1959) grouped them into five classes, the largest being that of typical trilobites. Three other classes appear to trend toward modern mandibulates, especially the Crustacea, and the fifth class more resembles the chelicerates.

Subphylum 2. Chelicerata Heymons, 1901

Evolved arthropods with body divided into cephalothorax and abdomen; cephalothorax consisting of 5 postoral somites (exceptionally more), each bearing a pair of appendages, and of at least 1 preoral somite which bears the chelicerae, a pair of appendages with a basically prehensile function; median ocelli present, compound eyes tending to degenerate and simplify; abdomen consisting of 12 or 13 somites terminating in a telson, but telson and some terminal somites absent in advanced groups; genital opening on second abdominal segment, covered by an operculum modified from a pair of appendages.

Class 1. Merostomata Woodward, 1866   (Fig. 10.1C)

Aquatic chelicerates with compound eyes well developed or only slightly degenerated; abdomen divided into 7-segmented mesosoma and 5-seg-

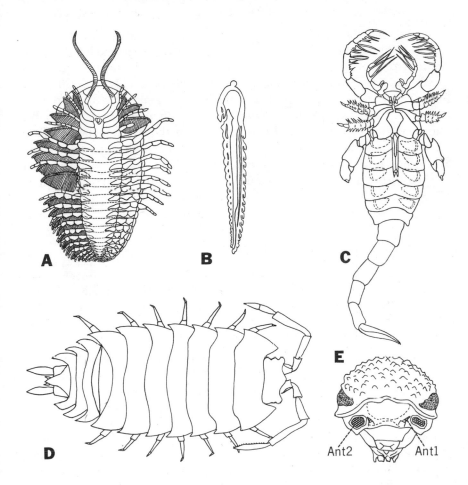

Figure 10.1. (A) Ventral view and (B) sagittal section of *Triathrus becki* (Green), a trilobite from the Carboniferous shales of New York; (C) ventral view of *Mixopterus kiaeri*, a merostomacean from the Silurian of Norway; (D) dorsal view and (E) detail of head of *Porcellio scaber* Latreille, an isopod common in Europe and North America. *Ant1*, first antenna; *Ant2*, socket of second antenna. (A and B redrawn from Raymond, 1920; C from Störmer, 1933; D and E redrawn from Van Name, 1936)

mented tail-like metasoma, the telson well developed; 4 or 5 mesosomal appendages, frequently locomotory, bearing branchiae; tracheae absent.

Of the two subclasses, the king crabs (Xiphosuridea) are the more primitive, clearly derived from primitive trilobites on the one hand, clearly leading to living arachnoids on the other. The early species, found in Cambrian strata, can be separated from the trilobites only with difficulty. Remarkably enough, five species survive today almost unchanged from Devonian time. One of them, *Xiphosura polyphemus* (Linné), inhabits coastal waters of eastern North America from the Yucatan peninsula to the Saint Lawrence River; the genus has been found in Jurassic slates. The other four living species inhabit coastal waters of Indonesia and southeastern Asia. The second subclass comprises the giant sea scorpions (Eurypteridea) (Fig. 10.1C). They flourished during Ordovician and Silurian time and died out during the Carboniferous.

Class 2. Arachnida Cuvier, 1812

Principally terrestrial chelicerates with compound eyes strongly degenerate, median ocelli frequently displaced; abdomen basically 13-segmented, but terminal somites and telson vestigial or absent in many groups; abdominal appendages never locomotory, never bearing branchial rami; respiration tracheal or, in tiny species, cutaneous.

The oldest known arachnoids were scorpions of the Upper Silurian, a time when the Eurypteridea were at their height. While obviously scorpions and not eurypterids, they were much more primitive than living species and may have been aquatic. By the Carboniferous, scorpions were more advanced, differing very little from modern species, and were clearly terrestrial. In these horizons numerous arachnoid fossils have been found; the major lines of arachnoid evolution were already differentiated and the major modern groups already established. Eleven orders are represented, some in great abundance: Scorpionida, Phryneida, Solpugida, Liphisthomorpha and Araneomorpha (spiders), Phalangiida, Ricinuleida and four extinct orders. Mesozoic strata have yielded no fossils which can be assigned definitely to the arachnoids, but Tertiary strata and the ambers contain a very large representation. Amber preservations are especially fine, rather resembling whole mounts made in the laboratory, and from these it has been found that not only were most living groups present (only Palpigradida have not been found as fossils), but that most Oligocene species are still living. According to Waterlot (1949), all the present families of spiders have been found in Tertiary deposits.

The living arachnoids are discussed in Chapter Eleven.

Class 3. Pycnogonida Latreille, 1810
= Podosomata Leach, 1815
Pantopoda Gerstaecker, 1863

Highly modified marine chelicerates with cephalothorax prolonged as a head-like beak which bears chelicerae, palpi and the ovigerous legs; posterior part of cephalothorax bearing 4 to 6 locomotory appendages; abdomen vestigial; compound eyes degenerate; genital openings at base of legs.

The phylogeny of the sea spiders is entirely speculative. The only pertinent fossils are a few specimens from Lower Devonian strata and they are very similar to living species. The structure of sea spiders is so peculiar that some zoologists think they do not belong with the chelicerates.

Preying on coelenterates and other small-sized plankton fauna, most species inhabit the open sea and deep water, some at considerable depths. A few frequent the shores and sometimes may be found at low tide. Geographically they occur in all seas, cold or warm, from pole to pole, and are one of the few arthropods found in both Arctic and Antarctic waters.

Subphylum 3. Mandibulata Heymons, 1901

Arthropods with body divided into head and trunk, the latter sometimes further divided into thorax and abdomen; head consisting of 3 postoral segments, each of which bears a pair of gnathal appendages, and of at least 3 preoral somites closely fused, on which are typically found compound eyes, ocelli and 1 or 2 pairs of antennae; respiration branchial, cutaneous or tracheal.

Class 1. Crustacea Pennant, 1777   (Fig. 10.1D, E)

Primarily aquatic mandibulates with body divided into head, thorax and abdomen, the head and thorax sometimes fused as a cephalothorax; 2 pairs of antennae, the first uniramous, the second biramous and placed on the intercalary somite; locomotory appendages typically many, though reduced along with body segments in specialized groups, biramous and generally bearing branchial rami; genital ducts opening on fifth leg-bearing segment; many highly modified groups.

This exceedingly large, extremely variable class is almost entirely aquatic, inhabiting nearly all marine and fresh-water situations. A number of groups are aberrant, modified and adapted for specialized lives—for example, the sessile barnacles and the parasitic copepods. Only a few live in terrestrial situations, principally near water. Of these, only the "pill bugs" or "sow bugs" (order Isopoda) (Fig. 10.1D, E) are commonly encountered. They are found under stones or debris in damp situations and sometimes are pests in greenhouses. Respiration is partly tracheal. They have elongate-oval bodies, well segmented and flattened dorso-ventrally. Their numerous legs give them the appearance of tubby little myriapods, but the presence of two pairs of antennae is diagnostic.

Some of the trilobites were crustacean-like, strongly suggesting the origin of the Crustacea. True Crustacea have been found in Cambrian strata, with three or four lines of crustacean evolution (subclasses) represented, and it is indicative that these fossils have been regarded by some paleontologists as being trilobites. More specialized forms occur in Silurian horizons, and by the Carboniferous, which has yielded a rich crustacean fauna, all living orders had differentiated.

Class 2. Myriapoda Latreille, 1802

Terrestrial mandibulates with body divided into head and trunk, a thoracic region sometimes indicated but never clearly differentiated; 1 pair of uniramous antennae, no appendages on the intercalary somite; ocelli absent; locomotory appendages on most trunk somites, uniramous, never with branchial rami; genital ducts on trunk, either posterior or anterior.

Fossil diplopods have been found in Upper Silurian strata and both diplopods and chilopods in Carboniferous beds. Known fossils do not connect this class with other fossil groups and the origin of diplopods cannot be directly demonstrated. It is suggestive that the giant diplopods of the Carboniferous had well-developed compound eyes and apparently biramous appendages. Compared to their ancestors, living myriapods have undergone morphologically retrogressive evolution in that many structures—the eyes, for example—have degenerated.

Living myriapods are discussed in more detail in Chapter Twelve.

Class 3. Insecta Linné, 1758
= Hexapoda Latreille, 1825

Terrestrial mandibulates with body divided into head, 3-segmented thorax, and abdomen; 1 pair of uniramous antennae, no appendages on intercalary somite; locomotory appendages uniramous, never branchial in adult, a pair present on each of the thoracic somites; genital ducts on abdomen, posterior; mostly with wings.

Further discussion of the insects is deferred to Chapter Thirteen.

PROBLEMATIC CLASSES

Three major classes must be considered in connection with the Arthropoda, classes with structures which either have led some taxonomists to have doubts on their correct placement in the phylum or have made doubtful their proper position and affinities.

Class Onychophora Grube, 1853

Worm-like terrestrial creatures with body divided into head and metamerized trunk; antennae, oral papillae, appendicular jaws and single-faceted eyes present on head; most trunk segments not externally marked but bearing a pair each of fleshy locomotory appendages; respiration tracheal, reproductive organs ciliated, paired segmentally arranged nephridia, hemocoelic body cavity.

About sixty-five species and ten genera are known, of which the most famous is *Peripatus,* discontinuously distributed in tropical America, Australia, Tasmania, New Zealand, New Britain, New Guinea, Sumatra, Malay Peninsula, Tibet, Congo and South Africa.

Class Tardigrada Spallanzani, 1777

Minute aquatic or semiaquatic arthropods with distinct head and a trunk composed of 4 coalesced segments bearing fleshy locomotory appendages; no special respiratory or excretory structures; nervous system well developed, eyes present.

The "water bears" live in damp moss, wet sand, fresh or salt water; about 280 species are known.

Class Linguatulida Frölich, 1789
= Pentastomida Rudolphi, 1819

About sixty species, all internal parasites of vertebrates, are known. The adults are highly degenerated and worm-like, but the larvae are mite-like and indicate that this group belongs with the arthropods.

ORIGIN OF ARTHROPODA

The fossil record provides no solution to the question of the phylogenetic origin of the arthropods. The few specimens—actually only bits and pieces—from Proterozoic strata cannot be identified with certainty in most cases. By the Cambrian period, which provides good specimens, all fossil arthropods were definitely arthropods. The phylum must have differentiated at some earlier time.

The only recourse is to speculation, the process of "educated guesses" known as deductive logic—a fascinating game that anyone is eligible to play.

A comparison between living arthropods and living annelids demonstrates a number of very important similarities in fundamental organization, similarities which must be more than mere coincidence. In both phyla the body is made up of a series of basically identical metameres closed off at each end by nonmetameric "lids," the anterior acron and the posterior telson. Each fundamental metamere contains a unit of each of the internal systems, a condition modified in both phyla by the formation of regions—obvious and external in the case of the arthropods, but on the level of internal regions not externally obvious in the annelids. The metameric coelomic cavities tend to be reduced in all the arthropods, but only in some of the annelids. Coelomoducts are present in both phyla, functioning as excretory structures in all annelids but only in some of the arthropods (primitive arachnoids). The ventral chain of ganglia making up the central nervous system is found only in these two phyla. The differences separating annelids from arthropods seem to be of a less fundamental nature, representing arthropod additions to the basic body plan: articulating appendages and the sclerotized cuticle are the most important. Vandel (1949) thought that the comparison "bristles with evidence" that the Arthropoda and Annelida are closely related and that these two phyla had a common origin. No other viewpoint is so substantially supported by the evidence.

Variations of interpretation center around the nature of the hypothetical common ancestral group. Should that group be regarded as primitive annelids, or should it be regarded as a third phylum, neither annelid nor arthropod? Did the ancestral group, by evolving into annelids and arthropods and possibly other groups as well, thereby become two or more new phyla and completely lose its old identity? Or was that original phylum a group of annelids from which arose modern annelids as well as modern arthropods? It is the old dilemma of Sir John's stockings in another form.[1] It does not matter which of the two possible conclusions is selected. Each is equally correct and the facts remain unchanged. From a very ancient

---

[1] Sir John wore holes in his stockings, which his wife then darned. Through the years, the process continued until the stockings Sir John wore consisted of nothing but darns. Were these the original stockings or not? If not, at what point did they become different?

ancestral group, the annelids evolved in one direction, the arthropods in another (Fig. 10.2). The living forms of both phyla are equally far removed, both in time and in structural modification, from the ancestral stock. It is accordingly fallacious to expect to find in the structures of living members of one phylum any real clue to the evolution of structures

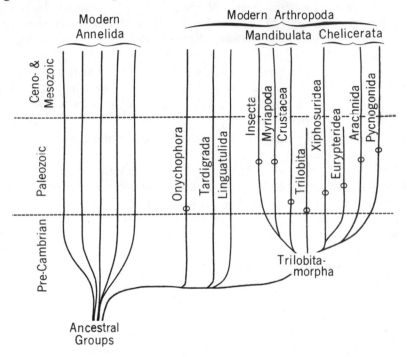

Figure 10.2. Phylogenetic diagram to illustrate the probable relationship between Annelida and Arthropoda and the probable relationships among the arthropod classes. The time scale at the left is not proportional. Circles indicate the approximate age of the earliest fossil record for various classes.

in the other: the fundamental error of the Holmgren-Hanström-Snodgrass theory, for example, is that the nature of the arthropod protocephalon was deduced from analysis of the head and brain of living annelids.

RELATIONSHIP AMONG ARTHROPOD CLASSES

The Onychophora have been a source of delight, chagrin and puzzlement to zoologists. These animals delight some of us because they so neatly combine features of the phylum Arthropoda with some of the features of the phylum Annelida, in effect standing as "missing links." Others seem to be chagrined to find it so. All are puzzled as to how best to classify the Onychophora: As very primitive arthropods? As highly aberrant annelids? Or as a completely separate phylum?

The Onychophora share certain features with the Annelida: (1) a pair of nephridia on each segment of the trunk; (2) ciliated ducts of the reproductive system; (3) the arrangement of the organ systems within the body. Features of the Arthropoda found in Onychophora include: (1) a hemocoel; (2) tracheal respiration; (3) appendicular jaws. But some of the structures in the Onychophora seem to be neither annelid nor arthropod: (1) the tracheae are numerous and the openings are scattered over the body in a way quite dissimilar to the arthropod arrangement; (2) the reproductive organs lie in true coelomic cavities; (3) the appendages are fleshy, not segmented like those of arthropods, and the arrangement of appendicular muscles is different.

Taxonomists who are delighted to find animals that represent connecting links between several groups, and who do not insist on rigidly narrow morphological specifications for taxa, tend to place the Onychophora as the most primitive subphylum of the Arthropoda. Those whose sense of the proprieties is upset by the inconsiderate combination of structures exhibited by *Peripatus* argue that since the Onychophora do not fall within a strict concept of either phylum, they must be placed in a phylum of their own.

The oldest fossil species, found in Middle Cambrian marine deposits, already was a true onychophoran and gives no slightest clue to the origin of the class, except to suggest that the oldest members might have been aquatic. That the Onychophora derived from the same ancestral stock as both annelids and arthropods, there can be little serious doubt. The insoluble problem is whether all three derived separately from the hypothetical ancestral group, or whether the annelids and arthropod evolutional lines branched off first, followed by an early branching by Onychophora from the arthropod line. Today, the usual policy is to put Onychophora into a separate little phylum. It is equally logical to make them a primitive subphylum of Arthropoda and to stretch the definition of the phylum to accommodate them. It is entirely a matter of taste, for there are no facts whatsoever to support either decision.

There is available much more concrete evidence to support theories on the evolution of the two major groups of arthropods proper, the mandibulates and the chelicerates, though on this question also there is wide diversity of interpretation. The Trilobitomorpha—trilobites in the broad sense—furnish the key. These primitive arthropods flourished during Cambrian, Ordovician, Silurian and Devonian times, began to die out during the Carboniferous and became extinct in the early Permian. The oldest records of definitely mandibulate arthropods are fossil Crustacea, and of definitely chelicerate arthropods are fossil Xiphosura; both sets of earliest fossils are Cambrian. Even though no fossils are known from pre-Cambrian times, all three groups must have existed before the Cambrian.

There are several schools of thought on the origins of mandibulates and chelicerates: (a) some see in the trilobites a close affinity with crustaceans and would classify the two groups together, (b) some think the trilobites belong with the chelicerates, (c) some throw in the towel and claim that the three groups have no special connection with each other. The many arguments put forward in support of these views need not be reviewed here. Evidence points best to a fourth interpretation: (d) the pre-Cambrian trilobites were the ancestral stock from which the mandibulates, the chelicerates and the more advanced trilobites all developed. A number of intermediate forms exist. For example, *Emeraldella* and *Sidneya*, found by the American paleontologist Walcott in Middle Cambrian strata of British Columbia, have merostome (chelicerate) bodies, crustacean (mandibulate) antennae and trilobite appendages.

It is easy enough to follow the general evolutional path from trilobites to Xiphosurea and Eurypteridea, thence to scorpions and other modern arachnoids. While the fossil record does not demonstrate exactly how each arachnoid order developed and from what source, the very numerous similarities among them preclude polyphyletic origins.

Of the mandibulates, only the origin of the Crustacea from trilobites can be supported by fossils. The earliest known insect fossils were Upper Devonian Collembola, followed by a rich Carboniferous fauna of true insects. In every case these fossils are already insects and give no clue to their origin. Similarly, the oldest myriapod fossils were already myriapods. One can only suppose that the myriapods and insects must have evolved either from very primitive, generalized crustaceans or from crustacean-like trilobites. There is no way of knowing whether the myriapods and insects represent a common line of descent, or two different but related lines.

A fossilized myriapod or insect is the result of an incredible series of improbable circumstances, whereas the fossilization of aquatic forms is merely unlikely. A properly documented solution to the origin of insects and myriapods is not to be expected, therefore, and the game of "educated guessing" will continue to be played (as it should).

As to the two problematic classes not mentioned in the foregoing discussion, both have been reviewed in some detail by Cuénot (1949). He regards the Tardigrada as being related to the Onychophora, but separate from them and a little more typically arthropod-like. The Linguatulida are also considered to be subarthropodian, but somewhat more advanced than the tartigrades; Cuénot supposes that they were an aquatic group which became parasitic in reptiles during the Paleozoic Era.

The Class Arachnida

I pluck you out of the crannies.

TENNYSON

The deepest loathing to the stomach brings.

SHAKESPEARE

Linné placed the arachnoids known to him into four genera of his catchall order Aptera. The separate class Arachnida was established by Lamarck. The number and composition of the arachnoid orders, the correct name to apply to each and the best sequence in which to present them have varied greatly through the years, and even today specialists in the class do not agree on these matters. The classification adopted here is that of Petrunkevitch (1955), who took into account both the phylogeny of the arachnoids and the need for stability of names for the major categories. The orders recognized in this system are also those used by Millot (1949) and his associates in Grassé's *Traité*.

The oldest arachnoid fossils are scorpions from the late Silurian and acarids from the Devonian. Ten other orders appeared abruptly in the Carboniferous. In every case, the oldest preservations of each phylogenetic line represent animals already definitively differentiated so that the fossil record gives little useful information on the relationship of the orders with each other. It can only be inferred that their development must have taken place very much earlier, during periods of time when conditions were not favorable for their fossilization. Ten orders are represented by living forms, five orders are extinct. Of the living orders, most seem to be curious relics of bygone times—living museum pieces. Only the Acarida, the Arancida and perhaps the Phalangiida appear to be thriving under contemporary conditions.

In the following outline of classification, orders including only extinct arachnoids are placed in parentheses and are not numbered.

CLASS ARACHNIDA LAMARCK, 1801

Order 1. Scorpionida Latreille, 1817
Order 2. Pseudoscorpionida Latreille, 1817
    = Chernetes Simon, 1879; Chelonethi Thorell, 1882
Order 3. Phalangiida Perty, 1833
    = Opiliona Sundeval, 1833
(Order Phalangiotarbi Haase, 1890
    = Architarbida Petrunkevitch, 1945—Carboniferous only)
Order 4. Acarida Nitzsch, 1818
(Order Haptopodida Pocock, 1911—Carboniferous only)
(Order Anthracomartida Karsch, 1882—Carboniferous only)
(Order Trigonotarbi Petrunkevitch, 1949—Carboniferous only)
Order 5. Palpigradida Thorell, 1888
    = Microthelyphonida Grassi and Calandruccio, 1885 (seldom used)
Order 6. Thelyphonida Latreille, 1804
    = Tartarides Cambridge, 1872; Uropygi Thorell, 1882; Colopyga
        Cook, 1899; Schizopeltidia Börner, 1904; Schizomida Petrunke-
        vitch, 1945
(Order Kustarachnida Scudder, 1890—Carboniferous only)
Order 7. Phryneida Gervais, 1844
    = Amblypygi Thorell, 1883; Phrynichida Petrunkevitch, 1945
Order 8. Araneida Latreille, 1801
Order 9. Solpugida Leach, 1817
    = Solifuga Sundeval, 1833
Order 10. Ricinuleida Thorell, 1892
    = Podogonata Cook, 1899; Rhinogastra Cook, 1899

Order 1. Scorpionida Latreille, 1810
(From the common name for these animals in Latin)
Scorpions
(Figs. 2.12, 3.2F, 3.9, 3.22A, 5.6, 7.8)

Relatively large arachnoids with a tough integument; anterior 7 abdominal segments (**mesosoma**) as wide as the cephalothorax and broadly
attached to it; posterior 5 segments tail-like (**opisthosoma**); telson modified as a hook-like sting and containing poison glands. 2 to 5 pairs of lateral
(degenerate compound) eye facets and a pair of dorso-median ocelli. Chelicerae pincer-like, with 3 evident segments. First legs (pedipalps) with
6 evident segments, the last 2 forming a prominent pincer; second, third,
fourth and fifth legs all with 7 evident segments, including 2 trochanters,
and none bearing pincers. Genital operculum immediately behind cephalothoracic sternum; appendages of the segment next posterior modified as
pectines; paired book lungs opening ventrad present on next 4 segments.
Viviparous; hemimetabolous metamorphosis.

Eggs are retained in the female reproductive system until hatching. The tiny, pale-colored young are carried on the mother's back until shortly after the end of the first instar. Maturity is reached in twelve to eighteen months and there are eight larval instars.

Scorpions prey on any live animal small enough for them to kill—insects, myriapods, other arachnoids, worms and even small mice—but they feed only occasionally and can survive in captivity for almost a year without food. Scorpions are generally found in colony-like groups, not because of any social instinct, but rather because they are essentially sluggish and remain near their birthplace. They are largely nocturnal, seeking sheltered hiding places during the day under rocks, beneath tree bark, in holes and, at times, in human habitations. Some species construct burrows for themselves. Despite their formidable armament of claws and sting, scorpions tend to be retiring and unaggressive.

The effects and effectiveness of the scorpion's sting vary greatly with the species. In all cases the poison quickly kills the small invertebrates which are the normal prey, while a mammal as large as a guinea pig will die within two hours after being stung by some species. Only a few scorpions are dangerous to man: *Androctonus* of North Africa and *Centruroides* of Mexico and Arizona are the worst. More than 1700 deaths from the sting of *Centruroides* were recorded between 1890 and 1931 in the State of Durango, Mexico. The toxicity of the venom of *Androctonus australis* (Linné) of the Atlas Mountains and northern oases of the Sahara is said to be equivalent to that of the cobra, killing a dog within seven seconds. The sting of a few other species in various parts of the world causes local paralysis, tumefaction and a fever which may last for several days, but does not kill a healthy person. The vast majority of scorpion species are not dangerous, though the sting can be painful.

The order includes about 615 species grouped into eighty-one genera and six families. They are widely distributed throughout the world between 50° north and 50° south latitudes, but rarely at altitudes. Exceptions include *Scorpio maurus* (Linné), found in the Atlas Mountains up to 9000 feet above sea level, a species inhabiting the Tyrolean Alps as high as 5000 feet and one found in Sequoia National Park, California, at similar altitudes. The humid tropical forests are richest in variety and numbers and may be regarded as the primary habitat, although there are many desert species and some are distributed in the temperate zones.

The oldest fossil scorpion known was found in an upper Silurian deposit; a number of specimens, representing five extinct families, have been recorded from the Carboniferous. The several Tertiary species were Miocene and Oligocene and are difficult to distinguish from living forms.

Snodgrass has quite correctly objected to the frequently expressed view that the scorpions are primitive. No group of living arachnoids is truly primitive. On the whole, the scorpions are the most generalized, since they have retained such features as clear body segmentation and the unspecialized uses of the cephalothoracic legs; they most resemble, in general form, the extinct euryptids.

Order 2. Pseudoscorpionida Latreille, 1817
(From the Latin: *false* and *scorpion*)
Pseudoscorpions

Tiny arachnoids, never larger than 7 or 8 mm., elongate oval and flattened dorso-ventrally; cephalothorax covered by a carapace and broadly connected to the clearly segmented abdomen, which consists of 11 segments and a reduced telson; posterior abdominal segments not tail-like. 2 to 4 pairs of lateral (degenerate compound) eye facets; ocelli absent. Chelicerae pincer-like, containing the silk glands, 2 evident segments, including the articulated post-tarsal "thumb." First legs (pedipalps) with 6 evident segments, the last 2 forming relatively large pincers similar to those of scorpions and containing poison glands; posterior 4 pairs of legs ambulatory, basically with 7 segments, the small post-tarsus bearing claws, but trochanter 2 sometimes fused with femur, tarsus sometimes divided into 2 subsegments. Genital opening on second abdominal segment between posterior coxae. Respiration tracheal, a pair of spiracles each on the third and fourth abdominal sternites. Hemimetabolous metamorphosis; eggs developed in an external incubation chamber.

The remarkable early development of pseudoscorpions has been detailed for *Chelifer* by Vachon (1938). The male produces a gelatinous spermatophore and induces the female to take it into her genital tract. The female then constructs a silken nest; maturation is completed about a month after fecundation. Fertilized eggs are not deposited externally, but are retained in an external diverticulum of the reproductive duct, the incubation pouch, which forms ventrad and at first looks like a hernia. The embryo (first larva) is attached by its buccal region to the wall of this pouch. The ovaries become distended with a yolk-like secretion of the epithelium and fill the whole abdomen. This vitelline secretion is pumped into and nourishes the embryos. After molting an embryonic cuticle, the second instar larva (protonymph) leaves the mother and the tissue of the incubation chamber is sloughed as a kind of afterbirth. The successive instars are the deutonymph, the tritonymph and the adult.

Ecdysis always occurs within a protective silken nest or cocoon and requires about a week. Maturity is reached in a year and the life span is
two to three years.

Pseudoscorpions prey actively on minute insects and arachnoids, including each other, killing the victims with the poison secreted by the
glands in the pincers of the pedipalps. They frequent moss, dead leaves,
loose tree bark and the substrate under stones; a few species may be
found in low vegetation and others sometimes are found in human habitations. A great many pseudoscorpions are especially adapted for cave
dwelling. About twenty-five species generally hitchhike on other animals
—Orthoptera, Hemiptera, Coleoptera, Hymenoptera, Phalangiida and even
birds; a few of these approach the status of ectoparasitism. Although not
rare, pseudoscorpions are generally overlooked because of their small size.

There are about 1000 species known, grouped into 200 genera and
nineteen families, the vast majority of which are tropical or subtropical;
a few species are temperate. No fossil pseudoscorpions are known, but
the order nevertheless is undoubtedly ancient.

Order 3. Phalangiida Perty, 1833
(From the Greek: *fingers*)
Daddy longlegs, Harvestmen
(Fig. 3.2B, D)

Small to medium (1–22 mm. long) arachnoids with oval bodies, the
abdomen and cephalothorax not clearly separate, typically with very long,
slender legs. Abdomen with 10 segments, not always distinct; telson vestigial. Cephalothoracic skeleton fused, generally covered by a carapace.
Lateral (compound) eyes absent; 1 pair of median ocelli, usually well
developed, rarely absent; ventral ganglia drawn into a cephalothoracic
mass. Chelicerae pincer-like, 3-segmented. Legs with trochanter 2 fused
with femur; first pair (pedipalps) sensory, sometimes also prehensile; tarsi
of walking legs either with numerous subsegments or very flexible. No
venom glands; 1 or 2 pairs of repugnatorial glands opening near margin
of carapace above third or third and fifth coxae. Well-developed tracheal
system, a single pair of spiracles located on second abdominal sternite.
Males with copulatory organ, females with ovipositor. Hemimetabolous
metamorphosis.

The female deposits her eggs in some protected situation—under a
stone, in a crevice or in a depression in damp soil—but exhibits no maternal solicitude. Early larvae differ from the adults mainly in the spines
and ornamentation of the cuticle and in the shape of the anterior margin

of the carapace. There are eight immature instars; the entire life cycle takes a year or less.

Phalangids are always associated with damp situations and mostly live near water. Only a few are active in direct sunlight. Several genera are cave dwellers. Members of the order are found almost everywhere except in very dry or very cold climates and the vast majority are tropical, but some live above timberline in the mountains of western United States. Like all arachnoids, the phalangids are essentially carnivorous, but unlike other arachnoids they are scavengers, feeding typically on dead insects, including bits and pieces they find in debris. Some species also include plant material in their diet. The active hunters of living prey are exceptional: *Scotolemon,* a cave genus, particularly attacks small beetles; *Ischyropsalis,* with enormously elongated chelicerae, feeds on small gastropods.

About 2400 living species are known, grouped into a dozen families and three suborders. The earliest known representatives lived in Carboniferous time. The numerous Tertiary fossils represent a few extinct and many living genera.

Order 4. Acarida Nitzsch, 1818 [1]
(From the Greek: a *mite*)
Mites, Ticks
(Figs. 3.2C, 3.10B, 8.8C, D, E)

Small to microscopic arachnoids; abdomen usually united with cephalothorax; the anteriormost segments, including cheliceral and pedipalpal, distinctly set off from rest of body as a false head (**capitulum** or **gnathosoma**); segmentation mostly obscured. Ocelli and eyes present or absent. Chelicerae pincer-, fang- or lance-like; with 6 or fewer segments, usually 2 or 3. First legs (pedipalps) on gnathosoma, basically with 6 segments, trochanter 2 fused with femur; variously developed as sensory, prehensile or feeding structures, rarely vestigial. Walking legs (pairs 2–5) usually with 6 segments, sometimes 7 when trochanter 2 is distinct; fifth pair generally absent in larvae; some adults with 1 or more pairs absent. Respiration tracheal or cutaneous; spiracles, if present, variously placed. Holometabolous metamorphosis.

[1] The ordinal name, spelled with a *d* rather than with an *n,* adopted here is that used by Petrunkevitch (1955) in accordance with a policy of standardizing certain ordinal names by use of the ending *-ida,* reserving the ending *-ina* to suborders (Moore, 1953–1960). The name itself is based on the genus *Acarus,* from which have also been formed subfamily, family and superfamily names, each identifiable by its distinctive standardized ending. It is believed that the custom of designating this order as Acar*ina,* while quite general, is inconsistent and that it would be profitable to follow the lead of Moore and Petrunkevitch by designating them hereafter as Acar*ida.*

This large, diversified and very important order is not at all well understood. Baker and Wharton (1952) divided it into five suborders, listed
325 families and nearly 1600 genera, but did not venture an estimate of
the number of species recorded. The minute size of most acarids and the
tediousness involved in collecting them and preparing satisfactory reference collections have made them relatively unattractive study material to
most biologists, so that for many years they have been neglected, perhaps
more than any other major group of arthropods. During the past several
decades the increasing appreciation of the part played by mites and ticks
as vectors of diseases of man, his domestic animals and his crops has
stimulated the study of identification, life history and control of certain
groups. Aside from the practical agricultural and paramedical research
now being conducted to an ever-increasing degree, the acarids stand in
sore need of broad, basic biological analysis with a view to understanding
the morphology, physiology and embryology of the order and eventually
arriving at an explanation of their phylogeny. Many acarologists regard
the Acarida as a heterogeneous, polyphyletic grouping of convenience;
some have questioned its relationship with other arachnoids, preferring
to establish a separate class. Certainly the members of this order exhibit
a very remarkable range of structure, habit and habitat; whether this
diversity truly indicates polyphyletic origins remains to be seen.

Mites are found in nearly every imaginable situation in every part of
the world. Free-living mites include both terrestrial and aquatic groups.
They may be predators, scavengers or plant feeders. Most terrestrial forms
are found on or under the surface of the soil, on low vegetation or in
caves; almost all prefer humid situations, though certain species are found
among dry debris in deserts and semideserts. Some of the free-living
predaceous species are beneficial to man in that they make an important
contribution to the control of insect pests. Several species are cultivated
and used in the control of plant lice, for example. A species of *Laelaps*
(suborder Mesostigmata) is well regarded in Italy for its assistance in
controlling insect pests of buckwheat, though when the adults accidentally get on the skin of a field worker, a troublesome rash results.

Among aquatic mites, some are active swimmers while others merely
crawl about on submerged vegetation. The marine species, largely confined to shallow seas, feed on the juices of green algae, of dead annelids
or of living sponges. Fresh-water species are found in every sort of pond,
stream, lake or river—cold or warm or even in hot springs.

Other acarids exhibit various kinds and degrees of parasitism, utilizing
as hosts nearly every kind of animal or plant. Sometimes the damage to
the host results from the sheer weight of numbers alone, sometimes from

the presence of the parasite in some vital internal situation such as the air sac system of birds, the urogenital system of man or the tracheal system of insects. Those with sucking mouthparts feed on animal blood or plant sap and may enter into the cycles of various pathogenic micro-organisms. A few of the important diseases transmitted to man are relapsing fever, Rocky Mountain spotted fever, Colorado tick fever and Q fever carried by various ticks (suborder Ixoidides), and scrub typhus carried by harvest mites (chiggers, suborder Trombidiformes). Texas fever and piroplasmosis of cattle and spirachaetosis of fowl are transmitted by ticks. Mange, scabies, rash and other dermatoses of man, dog, horse, poultry and a great many other animals are spread by several groups of mites or result from their presence on the skin.

Two major superfamilies of mites, the Tarsonemoidea (suborder Trombidiformes) and the Eriophyoidea (suborder Sarcoptiformes) cause galls and other malformations in their host plants, which include, in one part of the world or another, nearly every crop, ornamental shrub and shade tree. Some of the Tarsonemoidea are known to carry fungus spores from plant to plant, disseminating disease in such crops as oats, sugar cane, rice and tea. Widespread use of the insecticide DDT, ineffective against most acarids, has so reduced the insect predators in some areas that the role of mites in plant pathology has become increasingly important.

The life history of acarids, outlined in Chapter Eight, though not *identical* with holometabolism as evolved by insects, in the "typical" form is undoubtedly similar in principle. Much remains to be done before a general interpretation of the embryogenesis and phylogeny of the acarids can be attempted.

The oldest known fossil acarid was a member of the family Eupodidae, some of the living members of which are serious pests on certain crops. Petrunkevitch (1955) says that the fossil species was fairly common in Devonian time. Numerous preservations have been found in the ambers and other Tertiary strata and represent a great many living families and genera.

Order 5. Palpigradida Thorell, 1888
(From the Greek: *palpi* and *to walk*)
No common name

Tiny arachnoids, 0.5–3 mm. long, white or translucent; body elongated, first abdominal segment constricted and forming the pedicel; abdomen with 11 distinct segments plus a flagellate, multiarticulate telson sometimes longer than the whole body. Compound eyes and ocelli lacking. Chelicerae with 3 segments, pincer-like. Legs similar, second pair sensory and carried like antennae; trochanters and femur fused on all legs; patella fused with tibia on first legs but separate on the other 4 pairs; tarsi subdivided into 2–5 segments; post-tarsi with claws. Cephalothorax with 5 distinct sternites. Cutaneous respiration. Malpighian tubules absent; coxal glands developed, functioning in excretion. Hemimetabolous metamorphosis.

Very little is known of the life cycle of these microscopic arachnoids. Apparently the eggs are laid in pairs at any time of the year. The larval instars lack the genital structures and have fewer setae, fewer cheliceral teeth and fewer segments in the telson than adults. Only twenty-one species are known, forming a single family. They have been recorded from most tropical and warmer temperate areas. They require ample moisture, desiccate rapidly without it, and are strongly photophobic. The only known fossil species is Jurassic.

Order 6. Thelyphonida Latreille, 1804
(From the Greek: a *strong poison*)
Whip scorpions, Vinegarones

Small to rather large (2–65 mm. long) arachnoids, drably colored; abdomen with 12 segments and a usually multiarticulate tail-like telson; juncture of cephalothorax and abdomen constricted. 3 pairs of lateral (degenerate compound) eye facets, sometimes absent; 1 pair of dorso-median ocelli, sometimes absent. Chelicerae with 2 evident segments, the "fixed finger" reduced. First legs (pedipalps) short and stout, trochanters fused, patella fused with femur; second legs antenniform, greatly elongated and slender, tarsus subdivided, no post-tarsal claws; third, fourth and fifth legs ambulatory, with only 1 evident trochanter, tarsus usually subdivided, post-tarsus usually bearing claws. Book lungs present on the second and third abdominal segments. Hemimetabolous metamorphosis.

The eggs of *Thelyphonus caudatus* (Linné) are described as being about three millimeters in diameter and yellowish in color. Twenty-five to thirty-five are deposited in the female's burrow, which she does not leave until the larvae hatch. The pale yellow young have adhesive organs on the tarsi, with which they cling to the mother's back during the first instar. Second instar larvae begin finding their own food. Molts are well spaced, sometimes a year apart, and maturity is reached in three years.

Whip scorpions are predaceous on small insects, other arachnoids, myriapods, worms, slugs, small lizards and amphibians. They are entirely nocturnal and most are found only in humid situations; during the day they seek shelter in burrows, in cracks or under stones. A few species dwell in deserts. Their only defense is their powerful pedipalps, which are beset with sharp spines, and their anal glands, which emit an unpleasant odor. There is no venom.

The ninety-eight known species are divided into two families, sometimes recognized as separate orders. They are exclusively tropical and subtropical. Fossil species are known from the Carboniferous and the Tertiary.

Order 7. Phryneida Gervais, 1844
(From the Greek: Phryne was a notorious Athenian woman)
No common name for these unusual creatures
(Fig. 3.2G)

Small to medium-sized (4–45 mm. long) arachnoids, somberly colored, dorso-ventrally flattened; abdomen with 11 segments and a reduced segment-like telson, the anterior and posterior segments small. 3 pairs of lateral (degenerate compound) eye facets and a pair of medio-dorsal ocelli, reduced or absent in cave-dwelling species. Chelicerae with 2 evident segments, hook-like. Powerful first legs (pedipalps) with 7 evident segments, including a single trochanter and a spine-like post-tarsus, used for capturing prey; second legs antenniform, very long and slender, the tarsus divided into more than 40 subsegments; third to fifth legs ambulatory, with only 1 trochanter but tibia and tarsus subdivided. 2 pairs of book lungs opening on the second and third abdominal sternites. Hemimetabolous metamorphosis.

The eggs are relatively large, two to three millimeters in diameter and the mother carries them until they hatch in a parchment-like sac formed from secretions of the lower oviduct and glued to the ventral side of her abdomen. The first instar larvae cling to the mother's body and are relatively helpless; second instar larvae disperse and fend for themselves. Development is slow, maturity being reached in the third year.

The various insects and other small animals on which the phrynids feed are captured and held between the pedipalps and cut to pieces by the scissors-like action of the chelicerae. Phrynids are nocturnal, resting during the day in protected situations. Upon being exposed they feign death, but flee with agility when touched. Despite their very formidable appearance, they are quite harmless.

There are about sixty species, forming two families, distributed exclusively in the humid tropics. Many species are cave dwellers; one species inhabits termite hills. The four known Carboniferous species are quite similar to living forms.

Order 8. Araneida Latreille, 1801
(From the Greek: *spider*)
Spiders
(Figs. 2.13, 3.10A, 3.22B, C, 5.1B, 5.5, 5.7E–H, 6.8C–H, 7.10, 7.12)

Mostly moderate-sized arachnoids, but some microscopic, some gigantic; abdomen connected to cephalothorax by a narrow pedicel, segmentation usually obscured. Eyes variable in position and number, sometimes absent; 3 or fewer pairs of lateral (degenerate compound) eye facets; 2 or fewer pairs of ocelli. Chelicerae 2-segmented, the terminal segment fang-like; poison glands present. Legs with 1 trochanter; first legs (pedipalps) sensory, always short with 6 evident segments, the post-tarsus with a tiny claw or absent, tarsus bearing copulatory structures in male; second to fifth legs ambulatory, the tarsi 2-segmented, the post-tarsi bearing claws. Ventral surface of abdomen with genital orifice anterior, flanked by a pair of spiracles opening into book lungs or tracheae; second pair of spiracles further posterior, sometimes fused on median line, opening into tracheae or book lungs; 2–4 ventral pairs of spinnerets generally posterior. Hemimetabolous metamorphosis.

The modification of the pedipalps of the male as a copulatory organ is a feature unique to spiders. The inner face of the tarsus bears a syringe-like structure which is filled with spermatic fluid from the genital orifice. Copulation, which consists of inserting the pedipalps into the female genital orifice, is a hazardous and frequently fatal undertaking for the male. The female's predatory instincts are inhibited but briefly during copulation; most males are devoured immediately afterward by their mates. Cytological fertilization occurs when the eggs are laid several weeks or even many months after copulation. Sperms of spiders, as of many arthropods, remain viable in the female genital tract for long periods. The eggs are always relatively large; their size has no relationship to the size of the adult. Adult size seems to determine the *number* of eggs produced: some of the very large spiders may produce several thousand eggs at a time, while small ones rarely lay more than a dozen. The females exhibit a high degree of maternal instinct. All but a few species place the eggs in a silken cocoon until they hatch, and the young are guarded and fed by the mother. The longevity of spiders varies widely. In some species there are several generations a year, but others have but one. A few kinds are known to live for as long as twenty years.

Spiders are carnivores, feeding on live prey of convenient size. It has been estimated that spiders in England annually destroy something like 220 trillions of insects! The gigantic species may attack amphibians, reptiles, birds or small mammals. South American mygalomorphic spiders, of the genus *Grammostola*, feed on the venomous snakes of the genus *Crotalus* (rattlesnakes).

Most spiders obtain their prey by actively hunting from ambush or by trapping. Hunting species range over the ground or vegetation, stalking their victims until they have an opportunity to spring on them. Sites of ambush vary: ground-dwelling species may conceal themselves in cracks or crannies; several groups of spiders are so colored that they advantageously lie in wait for unwary insects visiting the heads of flowers. Once captured, the prey is immobilized with a mesh of silken threads and killed by the venom injected by the chelicerae.

The large body of folklore centering around the danger of spider bites is largely without foundation. The vast majority of spiders are totally inoffensive, either because the chelicerae cannot penetrate human skin or because their venom is not toxic to man. The bite of a certain number of the larger spiders produces momentary pain something like a wasp's sting, but is otherwise without ill effects. Of the thousands of species known, fewer than a score, most of which inhabit the American tropics, can be considered dangerous to man. Of these, *Phormictopus*, *Ctenus* and several species of *Lycosa*—all tropical—are large enough and have sufficiently toxic venom to kill a man within a few hours after biting him. More famous is the genus *Latrodectus*, with species in both subtropical and temperate regions, of which the notorious "black widow" is one. Although she should be treated with respect, the danger of the "black widow" is generally overestimated. She is not aggressive and is so small that it is doubtful that enough venom could be injected with a bite to kill a healthy adult person. Reported cases of death from her bite are either dubious or concern small children or unwell people.

The venom of these dangerous spiders is of two kinds. That of *Lycosa* causes local skin lesions and a creeping necrosis, difficult to heal, in the region of the bite. The venom of the others mentioned, including *Latrodectus*, is essentially neurotoxic, causing a general discomfort, sometimes violent pains or cramps of the abdominal and diaphragm muscles, a lowering of body temperature and hyperexcitation of the nervous system.

Spiders are found in every terrestrial situation from pole to pole; in the forests, the savannahs, the tundras, the deserts, the steppes and in milady's boudoir. Climbers in the Himalayas found spiders living at 21,000 feet. Most species are limited in distribution by climatic factors, though there are a few that live nearly everywhere in the world. Dispersal is primarily by one of two methods. Like most other animals, spiders may be carried across seas on floating objects or they may ride trains, ships, automobiles or planes and sometimes hitchhike on birds or mammals.

The more important method of dispersal is unique to spiders: that of passive flight or "parachuting." Small or young individuals may travel great distances and at considerable heights, aided by their negligible weight and a strand of silk that acts as a sail in the air currents. Spiders in transit have been collected from airplanes flying as high as 4500 feet above ground level and from ships as far as 200 miles from the nearest land.

More than 25,000 species of spiders have been described and it has been estimated that the actual number of living species may be as high as 100,000. The approximately sixty families are grouped into three sub-orders. Of these the Lipistiomorpha is the most primitive. It is well represented by Carboniferous fossils from the United States and Europe, but only nine species now exist, all native to the Far East. The abdomen is distinctly segmented and has separate tergites; the ganglia of the central nervous system remain associated with their metameres. These archaic features, not found in other spiders, are of great value in establishing structural homologies, particularly in the abdomen. The second suborder, Mygalomorpha, has lost the clear segmentation of the abdomen and nervous system, but has retained the horizontal action of the chelicerae. Some 1500 species are known, including some from Eocene and Oligocene horizons.

The majority of living spiders are assigned to the suborder Araneomorpha. There is no visible abdominal segmentation, the ganglia of the central nervous system are drawn up into a mass in the cephalothorax and the cheliceral action is vertical. These structural modifications had already occurred by Carboniferous time and many fossil species of that age have been found. Tertiary fossils of this suborder almost invariably represent genera and even species still living.

Order 9. Solpugida Leach, 1817
(From the Latin: *sun-avoiders*)
Solpugids, Wind scorpions, Vinegarones
(Figs. 3.2A, E, 5.8C, 6.8A, B)

Medium or large (1–7 cm. long), hirsute arachnoids; oval abdomen constricted at attachment to cephalothorax and consisting of 10 segments plus a reduced telson. 1 or 2 pairs of small lateral (degenerate compound) eye facets; 1 pair of well-developed dorso-median ocelli. Chelicerae large, prominent, pincer-like, with 2 evident segments. Legs similar, none bearing pincers; first pair with trochanters fused, patella and femur fused, the tarsus 2-segmented, the post-tarsus bearing an adhesive organ; second and third legs with femur and patella distinct, the second pair essentially sensory, carried antenna-like; fourth and fifth legs with patella and both trochanters distinct; tarsus of posterior 3 pairs subdivided into more than 2 segments. Genital orifice on second abdominal sternite. Tracheal system well developed, with a pair of cephalothoracic spiracles behind the third coxae, 2 abdominal pairs in the membranes between the third and fourth and the fourth and fifth sternites, respectively; a median ventral spiracle between the fifth and sixth sternites in 2 families. Hemimetabolous metamorphosis; marked maternal solicitude for young larvae.

The fertilized female digs a tunnel in the soil about twenty centimeters long and sets up housekeeping at its end. She deposits from fifty to two hundred eggs in a mass and guards them until they hatch. The larvae spend the first few instars in the burrow, the mother foraging for their food. The number of larval instars and the life span are unknown.

The order includes both nocturnal and diurnal species. They are exceedingly voracious predators on any animal small enough for them to attack; the larger species do not hesitate to tackle small lizards or young birds and mammals. They move with great agility and are difficult to capture. Despite their formidable and quite repulsive appearance they are not poisonous because there is no venom, though the bite can draw blood and may be irritated by the animal's secretions.

Solpugida includes ten families and approximately 600 species typically inhabiting tropical and subtropical deserts. Only a few species are found in humid situations or in temperate zones. One fossil species is known, found in a Carboniferous stratum.

Order 10. Ricinuleida Thorell, 1892
(From the Latin: *like a tick*)

Small (5–10 mm. long) arachnoids with granular integument; abdomen with first segment absent, the second to seventh well developed and oval, eighth to eleventh segments reduced and annular, forming with the telson a short "tail." Cephalothorax covered by a carapace and an anterior hoodlike cucullus. Eyes lacking. Chelicerae 2-segmented, pincer-like. First legs (pedipalps) with 5 evident segments tipped with pincers (tarsus and post-tarsus?); second legs with 7 evident segments and post-tarsal claw; third and fifth legs with 5 tarsal subsegments, fourth legs with 4; trochanters of last 2 pairs of legs apparently subdivided. Spiracles dorsolateral, near posterior end of cephalothorax, opening into respiratory chamber (atrium) from which numerous unbranched tracheae originate. Development unknown.

This smallest, rarest and least familiar order consists only of six species in West Africa, nine in America distributed from Texas to the Amazon and nine fossil species from Carboniferous horizons. Little is known of their habits except that they prefer humid situations and that several Mexican species are cave dwellers. A few larvae have been found, apparently first instar since the last pair of legs is undeveloped, suggesting that metamorphosis may be similar to that of the acarids. The tarsi of the fourth legs of males bear peculiar structures thought to be used in copulation, analogous to the specialization of the pedipalpi of male spiders.

The Class Myriapoda

The centipede was happy quite
  Until a toad in fun
Said, "Pray, which leg goes after which?"
That worked her mind to such a pitch
She lay distracted in a ditch
  Considering how to run.

MRS. EDWARD CRASTER

        Linné placed myriapods, along with arachnoids and a variety of other and unrelated wingless forms, in the order Aptera. The name Myriapoda was coined by Latreille in 1802 and applied to a "legion" which Leach elevated in 1814 to the rank of a class. Pocock (1887) recognized the many basic differences between the Chilopoda and Diploda and made classes of them, and created two superclasses, the Progoneata and Opisthogoneata: into the former he put the classes with the genital openings anterior—Diplopoda, Pauropoda and Symphyla; into the latter the classes with genital openings posterior—Chilopoda and Insecta. Pocock's views deeply influenced the systems of classification adopted for these animals in the first half of this century, but during the past decade most major monographs—*Traité de Zoologie* (Grassé, 1949), *Treatise on Invertebrate Paleontology* (Moore, 1953–1960), for example—have restored the Myriapoda as a class with four subclasses.

    The basic reasons for Pocock's classification were sound: there can be no doubt that the four major myriapod groups are quite distinct from each other, or that the chilopods stand apart from the diplopods and probably are closely related to the insects. It should be noted that two of the orders generally assigned to Insecta might just as logically be placed in Myriapoda, probably near the chilopods, provided the classic definition of Insecta as having six legs were recognized as an arbitrary one. Aside from the number of legs, both the Collembola and the Protura are rather more myriapod-like than insect-like in many aspects of structure and, in Collembola, of embryogeny.

Whether to use four classes or only one depends upon the approach. Specialists who describe species and progress toward the major categories of myriapods are prone to recognize four classes; specialists whose first concern is with similarities are more likely to use only one class for the same animals. The distinction between the posterior reproductive ducts of chilopods and the anterior ducts of the other groups now appears to be less fundamental than Pocock thought, however.

The classification used in this chapter was recommended to us by the elder statesman of the myriapods, Dr. R. V. Chamberlin. We have modified his system only by demoting his four classes to subclasses of the Myriapoda—a procedure of which he does not approve—and by interspersing the fossil orders.

So many monographers of the myriapods have seen fit to discard existing names for higher categories and to invent substitutes that the result has been unbelievable confusion only partly reflected by the synonyms listed below. This situation most aptly illustrates the need for regulation of names of higher categories in the interest of stability and common sense. Chamberlin and Hoffman (1958) made a strong plea for the use of priority in these situations; one can only echo a hearty "Amen!"

In the following outline of classification, orders including only extinct myriapods are placed in parentheses and are not numbered.

CLASS MYRIAPODA LATREILLE, 1802

SUBCLASS CHILOPODA LEACH, 1814

Superorder Anamorpha Haase, 1880

Order 1. Lithobiida Newport, 1844
Order 2. Scutigerida Gervais, 1837
    = Notostigmorpha Verhoeff, 1901

Superorder Epimorpha Haase, 1880

Order 3. Geophilida Haase, 1880
    = Pantastigmata Silvestri, 1895
Order 4. Scolopendrida Newport, 1844
    = Oligostigmata Silvestri, 1895

SUBCLASS SYMPHYLA RYDER, 1880

Order 1. Symphyla Ryder, 1880

SUBCLASS DIPLOPODA GERVAIS, 1844

Infraclass Pselaphognatha Latzel, 1884
= Podochila Bollman, 1893

Order 1. Polyxenida Gray, 1842
= Penicillata Latreille, 1829 (rarely used); Ancyrotricha Cook, 1895;
Schizocephala Verhoeff, 1926
(Order Arachipolypoda Scudder, 1881
= Macrosterni Fritsch, 1902; Palaeocoxopleura Verhoeff, 1928—Permian only)
(Order Eurysterna Verhoeff, 1926—Carboniferous and Permian)
(Order Paleomorpha Verhoeff, 1928—Lower Permian only)

Infraclass Chilognatha Latreille, 1802

Superorder Pentazonia Brandt, 1833
= Oniscomorpha Pocock, 1887; Opisthandria Verhoeff, 1894

Order 2. Glomerida Brandt, 1833
= Armadillomorpha Verhoeff, 1887; Plesiocerata Verhoeff, 1910
Order 3. Glomeridesmida Latzel, 1884
= Limacomorpha Pocock, 1894

Superorder Helminthomorpha Pocock, 1887
= Eugnatha Attems, 1899

Order 4. Polydesmida Leach, 1815
= Merocheta Cook, 1895; Proterospermorpha Verhoeff, 1900
Order 5. Chordeumida Koch, 1847
= Craspedesmidae Saussure and Humbert, 1872; Coelocheta Cook,
1896; Merocheta Cook, 1896; Nematophora Verhoeff, 1913
Order 6. Julida Brandt, 1833
= Diplocheta Cook, 1895; Zygocheta Cook, 1896; Symphognatha Verhoeff, 1909
Order 7. Spirobolida Bollman, 1893
= Anocheta Cook, 1895
Order 8. Spirostreptida Brandt, 1833
Order 9. Cambalida Bollman, 1893

Superorder Colobognatha Brandt, 1834
= Siphonizantia Brandt, 1837; Sugentia Wood, 1869

Order 10. Platydesmida Sausure, 1860
= Andrognathinae Bollman, 1893
Order 11. Polyzoniida Gervais, 1844
= Ommatophora Brandt, 1841

SUBCLASS PAUROPODA LUBBOCK, 1866

Order 1. Pauropoda Lubbock, 1866

Subclass Chilopoda Leach, 1814
(From the Greek: *lip* plus *foot*, referring to the poison claws)
Centipedes
(Figs. 2.7A, B, 3.11, 5.2C, 5.4D)

Myriapoda with reproductive ducts opening at posterior end of trunk; mouthparts generalized, consisting of mandibles with independently muscled gnathal lobes, maxillae and paired labia; first pair of trunk legs held under head, provided with poison glands; compound eyes present, well developed, reduced to a few facets or absent; 17 or more trunk segments, not fused in pairs, most bearing legs; legs with 2 trochanters. Development by anamorphosis or hemimetabolous metamorphosis.

The two kinds of development found in centipedes form the basis for dividing them into two groups, Anamorpha and Epimorpha. In the anamorphic orders Lithobiida and Scutigerida the newly hatched larva has only ten trunk segments, seven pairs of legs, relatively few antennal segments and eye facets. At the sixth instar the full adult number of seventeen segments and fifteen legs is attained. During the next five or six stages additional antennal segments and eye facets are developed and sexual maturity is reached. This anamorphic development, undoubtedly the primitive process in myriapods, is similar to that found in the other three subclasses and in the insect order Protura.

The many-faceted eyes of the Scutigerida are quite typically "compound" and are so designated even by morphologists who confuse the lateral and dorso-median eyes of arthropods, since they are entirely similar to those of insects. Among the Lithobiida may be found a fairly complete series of steps illustrating the degeneration of the compound eye from well developed through successive stages of fewer and fewer facets to a single facet; there are some blind species. Surprisingly, the Scutigerida, primitive in so many respects, have the spiracles fused on the dorsal midline. In the Lithobiida and in the other two orders the spiracles are still in their basic position—lateral and paired.

Development in the orders Scolopendrida and Geophilida is hemimetabolous. Segmentation is completed before hatching and the first instar larva has the adult number of segments and legs, though the latter are not fully formed. Between hatching and maturity additional antennal segments and eye facets develop, the size is increased, the legs and reproductive system are completed. These two orders are distinguished from each other mainly by the number of trunk segments: in the Scolopendrida there are from twenty-one to twenty-three, in the Geophilida there are from thirty-one to as many as one hundred ninety.

Centipedes are predaceous on other small animals—insects, worms and the like—which they seize and stun or kill with the poison claws. Because of the small size of all but a few species, they are harmless to man and may even be regarded as beneficial because they destroy pest insects. Some of the tropical Scolopendrida, however, may reach as much as a foot in length. One such specimen was found by a Carnegie Museum expedition near Mazatlan, Mexico, and the collector said that as it walked across the road "it looked like a toy train." Such a centipede could inflict an extremely painful bite, possibly fatal to a small child or a person in ill health.

Chilopods are found on every continent and most islands between the Arctic and Antarctic Circles. The richest faunae are in tropical and subtropical climates. Although the greater number of species prefer humid situations, many are found in deserts, dry rocky slopes or sand dunes near beaches. A few are cave dwellers and some live above timberline. Several species frequently are found in the cellars of homes, where they tend to terrify the housewife but contribute usefully to the destruction of such pests as flies. The harmless little *Scutigera coleoptrata* Linné is one of these and is found in western Europe, in eastern North America and in South Africa. Most of the Scutigerida are diurnal, but the other groups are nocturnal. No centipede is aquatic; yet they have found their way to remote island groups, probably distributed by "rafting"—either as hitchhikers or on literal rafts. Such modes of travel probably account also for the presence of certain species on both South America and Africa, and on both Europe and North America. In historic times many centipedes have found new homelands by way of man's transportation.

Fossil Chilopoda have been found in Carboniferous strata and in many Tertiary deposits.

Subclass Symphyla Ryder, 1880
(From the Greek: *same* and *tribe*)
No common name
(Figs. 2.7E, 3.3B, 3.12C)

Myriapoda with anterior reproductive ducts opening on third evident trunk segment; mandibles with articulated, separately muscled endite lobes; maxillae and labium distinct; eyes and optic nerves wanting; antennae unbranched; 17–24 trunk segments, not fused in pairs; 12 pairs of ambulatory legs, the first reduced; styli generally present on legs 3–12;

cerci present, penetrated by ducts of silk glands. Development by anamorphosis.

Fewer than seventy species of these fascinating creatures are known,
belonging to eleven genera in two families and forming a single order.
Great interest is attached to them because many authorities have thought
them to be very closely related to insects. While this interpretation of
their phylogeny is undoubtedly correct, they are no more so than are the
anamorphic chilopods, from which they doubtless branched. The anterior
position of the genital ducts probably is secondary and is of little fundamental significance in phylogeny, since the gonads themselves are located
posterior in the abdomen.

The symphylids, in their behavior, resemble little centipedes. They are
found in similar situations—damp places under stones, logs and rubble.
Their main diet is decaying plant material, but some species eat dead
insects and others attack living plant tissues and may become pests on
such crops as celery, asparagus or beets.

The first instar larvae have only three legs, segments and legs being
added during larval development. No fossils of this group are known.

Subclass Diplopoda Gervais, 1844
(From the Greek: *double* and *foot*)
Millipedes
(Figs. 2.7C, D, 3.12A, B)

Myriapoda with anterior reproductive ducts opening between second
and third legs; mouthparts specialized, mandibles with independently
muscled gnathal lobes, gnathochilarium (fused first and second maxillae)
usually chewing, sometimes sucking; compound eyes present with many
or few facets, sometimes absent; first 3 or 4 and last 1 or 2 trunk segments
normal, all others fused in pairs, each diplosegment with 2 pairs of legs;
legs with 2 trochanters, trochanter 2 generally larger than femur. Development by anamorphosis.

The numerous species of millipedes are here grouped, following Chamberlin and Hoffman (1958), into fourteen orders, of which three are
extinct. Laurentiaux (1953) used nine orders and an entirely different set
of names, generally showing preference for junior synonyms. The major,
more inclusive groupings, appear to us to be more closely equivalent to
the ordinal categories commonly used for insects and arachnoids.

The most primitive infraclass is the Pselapognatha, comprising the
living Polyxenida and three extinct orders. The integument bears numerous bundles of peculiarly formed setae and in living species is soft and

poorly sclerotized. In the males none of the legs is modified in connection with reproduction. The superorder Pentazonia has a well-sclerotized integument and the gonopods of males are modified from the last two pairs of legs. In the superorder Helminthomorpha the male gonopods are modified from the first legs of the seventh evident segment. The superorder Colobognatha is probably the most evolved. In one of its two orders (Polyzoniida) the mouthparts are modified into a kind of beak used for sucking, while in both orders the male gonopods are formed from the second pair of legs on the seventh evident segment.

Development is always by anamorphosis. The first instar larva has the first four trunk segments clearly marked and followed by one or several undeveloped segments plus the telson. On each of the last three of the first four segments there is one pair of legs. During the larval instars trunk segmentation progresses and all the added segments are fused into pairs, each pair with a single tergite but with two legs and ordinarily with two sterna. The full number of segments and legs is attained with the seventh or eighth instar, at which point the reproductive system matures.

A few species exhibit marked maternal care (as in *Archispirostreptus*), depositing the eggs in a subterranean nest, brooding over the eggs until hatched and guarding the larvae until they can fend for themselves. Several other genera prepare underground cells for the eggs, but after laying, the chambers are sealed shut and forgotten. Some other groups enclose their eggs in protective silken cocoons. Most millipedes merely drop the eggs on the ground.

In a number of families the young larvae spin a cocoon in which to pass the critical, relatively helpless periods of ecdyses. The life span extends from one to seven years, depending on the species. Most are small, not exceeding two inches in length, but several species may become a foot long.

Millipedes live in damp protected places—under stones or rubble, under or in rotten logs, under loose bark. They are mainly phytophagous and generally feed on dead and decaying plant material. The few species that attack living plant tissue sometimes become pests. Many (but not all) diplopods have stink glands which emit vapor with an offensive odor said to be not unlike cyanide and which can kill small insects. This, their secretiveness and the ability of many to coil themselves into balls or spirals are their only means of defense.

Like the centipedes, the Diplopoda are found on all continents and most islands. The numerous Tertiary fossils are assignable to contemporary families and usually to living genera. Paleozoic preservations from

Carboniferous and Permian strata are mostly poor specimens and have been the centers of a certain controversy, but they are now considered to be undoubted diplopods.

Subclass Pauropoda Lubbock, 1866
(From the Greek: *little* and *feet*)
No common name
(Figs. 2.7F, 3.3A)

Myriapods with anterior reproductive ducts opening on third evident trunk segment; endite lobe of mandibles lacking articulation or musculature, gnathochilarium reduced; eyes and optic centers lacking; antennae with 4 short segments terminating in a pair of 1-jointed branches bearing long sensory flagella; 11 or 12 trunk segments fused in pairs, covered by 6 tergites; first legs strongly reduced, second to ninth pairs fully developed, only 1 trochanter. Development by anamorphosis.

This small group of tiny myriapods (up to 1.5 mm. long) includes fewer than two dozen species forming a single family and a single order. Very little is known about their biology and most interpretations of their structure and development require verification.

They are phytophagous and live in damp places under stones, fallen branches and in rubble. Although the reproductive ducts are anterior, the gonads are posterior. The male gonads are formed by the complete fusion of two pairs of embryonic rudiments and the system terminates in a double copulatory organ. The first instar larvae have only the first four trunk segments, with a pair of legs on each of the last three, and the telson. The full number of segments and legs is attained at the fourth molt, the fifth instar being the adult.

Geographically, pauropods are known in Eurasia from Scandinavia, England and Italy eastward to Japan, Java and the islands in the Gulf of Siam, in the United States, Canada, Chile, Argentina and Paraguay. No fossils have been found.

The phylogeny of the pauropods is a controversial question. Formerly they were thought to be primitive, but the highly modified nervous system, mouthparts and trunk segmentation seem to belie such a view. Many specialists place them as a group only distantly related to other myriapods, a position defended by Pocock and others, but they probably should be regarded as aberrant diplopods.

CHAPTER THIRTEEN

The Class Insecta

And we carry home as prizes
Funny bugs, of handy sizes,
Just to give the day a scientific tone.

C. E. CARRYL

The class Insecta was so named by Linné in 1758. Latreille substituted the name Hexapoda (Greek: *six* and *foot*) in 1825. Through the years the Linnean name has been the more frequently used for the class, although Hexapoda also has had some currency, largely on the ground—no longer regarded as important—that it is more accurately descriptive. Among contemporary general references and texts, Insecta is preferred by about seventy per cent. The name Hexapoda, a junior synonym, should be dropped.

The Insecta is the largest class of the Arthropoda—just how large is difficult to say. There can be no accurate figure quoted for the total number of animal species described to date, for the roster is constantly increasing as new research is published. It is estimated that about 2 million different species of animals have so far been named; of these more than 1.5 million are insects. Species new to science are being discovered at the rate of some 6000 a year. When all are known the number may reach 3 million different kinds of insects.

Because they are small enough to be stepped on or swatted, man readily assumes his "lord of creation" attitude toward insects, a bias which might be weakened were he to recall that *Homo sapiens* is but one recently evolved species in the very small, Johnny-come-lately order Mammalia.

It is difficult to imagine the study of entomology without a good microscope, yet in Linné's day only the crudest of instruments was available. One which was little more than a good magnifying glass had been developed by Leeuwenhoek, and though it astounded the Royal Society in 1677, it was regarded by many as an interesting toy rather than as a scientific instrument. Linné must be remembered as one of those who found Leeuwenhoek's toy useful. With such crude equipment he studied insect morphology and devised his system of classification. In the tenth edition of *Systemae Naturae* (1758) he used only seven orders: Coleoptera, Hemiptera, Lepidoptera, Neuroptera, Hymenoptera, Diptera and Aptera. The complicated systems in use today are the products of vastly expanded knowledge, to which two factors have made major contributions: one was the development of better microscopes and the techniques associated with their use; the other was the intellectual climate of the nineteenth century, immensely stimulated by the wealth of biological material provided to the museums by the great explorations of the era. The entire approach to science was directed into new channels which led directly to the fantastic achievements of the twentieth century. One can now add that it is difficult to imagine the study of entomology without a knowledge of the entire animal kingdom, of botany, of paleontology, evolution, genetics, ecology, physiology and biochemistry.

The history of insect classification has reflected the history of science. The system of Brauer (1885) was based on a comprehensive survey of the morphology of living insects. Handlirsch (1908) related living with fossil forms, adding the dimension of geologic time, and his revision of 1939 profoundly influenced the work of later students. For a review of the older systems of classification, see Wilson and Doner (1937). More recent significant contributions have been made by Martynov (1938), Essig (1942), Jeannel (1949), Brues, Melander and Carpenter (1954) and Carpenter (1961).

On the principle that classification should illustrate phylogeny, reflecting both differences and similarities, Insecta is divided into four subclasses:

1. **Oligoentomata** includes only the order Collembola. Adults are primitively wingless, the abdomen consists of five segments plus telson and bears three pairs of modified appendages, none of which is used in copulation or oviposition. Cleavage of the zygote is combination type and postovarian development is apparently ametabolous metamorphosis, though it may really be modified anamorphosis.

Carpenter (1961), observing that all six-legged arthropods are not necessarily insects, removed Collembola from this class. It is true that Collembola are properly regarded as aberrant myriapods apparently related to the chilopods, but since their deviations are obviously in the insect direction it becomes a matter of taste as to which class to place them. Since they have traditionally been regarded as insects we retain them as a subclass, an action which may help to emphasize the close relationship between insects and myriapods. To place them in their own little separate class would serve only to obscure phylogeny.

2. **Myrientomata** includes only the order Protura, originally placed with the myriapods, from which they were undoubtedly derived. Adults are primitively wingless and have only vestigial antennae. The abdomen consists of eleven segments plus telson and bears no locomotory appendages. Cleavage is peripheral (superficial) and development is by anamorphosis.

If Collembola are to be included in Insecta, so must the Protura, for they are far more insect-like.

3. **Apterygota** includes the orders Thysanura and Aptera, true insects which are primitively wingless. The abdomen has eleven segments plus telson and may bear vestigial appendages. Cleavage is peripheral (superficial) and development is by ametabolous metamorphosis.

That these insects are monophyletic with the pterygotes appears doubtful, though it may be true in a remote sense. They seem to be archaic survivors of ancient lines of evolution leading toward the pterygotes, preserving morphologic developments which necessarily preceded the winged condition.

4. **Pterygota** comprises all other insects and are either winged or have lost the wings secondarily. The abdomen basically has eleven segments plus telson, though the terminal segments may be vestigial or absent. Cleavage is peripheral (superficial) and development is by pauro-, hemi- or holometabolous metamorphosis.

Brauer in 1885 separated the pterygote orders into two series, those with hemimetabolous (including paurometabolous) and those with holometabolous metamorphosis, to which he applied respectively the names Homomorpha and Heteromorpha. His plan has been followed for many years, but the nomenclature has been irregular. Sharp (1898) devised the names Exopterygota and Endopterygota for the two series, having reference to the manner of wing development; Börner (1904) substituted Hemimetabola and Holometabola, which he thought were more suitable than Sharp's or Brauer's names.

The understanding that Thysanoptera and certain Hemiptera have true holometabolous cycles (Hinton, 1948) has undermined the probability that holometabolism signalizes a monophyletic line—for so many years an article of faith—and Brauer's two series are not necessarily sound. Thanks primarily to the work of Handlirsch, Martynov, Jeannel and Carpenter, an appreciation of the broad phylogency of insects is emerging.

The most primitive surviving orders are the Ephemerida and the Odonata. Martynov placed them, along with five extinct orders, in an infraclass, the **Paleoptera,** characterized by their inability to fold the wings back over the abdomen, the wings lacking a jugal area. In living examples there are eight or more malpighian tubules. Metamorphosis is hemimetabolous and Hinton has shown that holometabolous metamorphosis probably was derived from a cycle much like that found in Ephemerida.

The orthopteroid orders were grouped together by Martynov as the **Polyneoptera.** Like the Paleoptera, these insects have numerous malpighian tubules, but unlike them, the wings have very well-developed jugal areas with many longitudinal veins and they are folded back over the abdomen at rest. Postovarian development is by paurometabolous metamorphosis.

The hemipteroids, including the orders Corrodentia, Mallophaga, Anoplura, Hemiptera and Thysanoptera, can fold the wings back over the abdomen, but the jugal area is reduced and has only one vein, or is secondarily lost. The malpighian tubules are reduced to four or fewer. Postovarian development is generally paurometabolous, but in the Hemiptera the evolution of the holometabolous cycle may be seen in several families, while the Thysanoptera are entirely holometabolous. These orders were grouped as the **Paraneoptera** by Martynov.

Martynov's fourth series, **Oligoneoptera,** is one of convenience. All members are holometabolous and have four or fewer malpighian tubules (though each may be greatly ramified) and the wings have reduced jugal areas. None of these general characteristics connects these orders as a monophyletic line. Each structural feature simply represents a logical continuation of evolutional trends already established in other series. That Coleoptera and Strepsiptera, which are sometimes included in a single order, probably developed directly from primitive orthopteroids is suggested by the wings, appendages, body skeleton and other structures. The Neuroptera, Mecoptera, Trichoptera, Lepidoptera, Diptera and Siphonaptera are known as the "panorpoid complex" and regarded as a phylogenetic entity. There is no real reason to doubt that Siphonaptera derived from primitive Diptera, but the distinct possibility that these two orders are more closely related to the hemipteroids, as is suggested by the head and mouthparts and is not refuted by the wings, has not been objectively investigated. The derivation of the Hymenoptera is exceedingly problematic and the order is usually attached to the "panorpoids" for want of a better arrangement.

As was emphasized in Chapter Nine, classification involves two different steps: (1) a biological decision as to what constitutes a given taxon and (2) the clerical task of selecting a name for a taxon.

With respect to the orders of Insecta discussed on the following pages, the *biological decisions* all were made by the leading contemporary students of broad insect classification and by the recognized authorities on the various major groups. Thus, the old, broad, familiar order Orthoptera has been divided into a series of orders: Dictyoptera, Grylloblattodea, Phasmida, Dermaptera and Orthoptera (now comprising only the grasshoppers, katydids and crickets). Essig (1942) went a step further by dividing Dictyoptera into *two* orders (Blatteria and Mantodea), but Richards and Davies (*in* Imms, 1957) employ the arrangement used in this book, an arrangement based on the researches of Handlirsch (1908, 1939) and Martynov (1938). The present authors have sought to follow in all cases the work of the leading, widely accepted modern authorities and have not ventured to make biological decisions as to what does or does not constitute an order of insects; it seems best to present current information. On the other hand, there are a few orders about which the leading authorities are in disagreement and we, of necessity, have been forced to choose among several conflicting biological decisions. Whether to accept the Hemiptera as a single order or to recognize it as two different orders is a case at point: a single order is herein recognized, following the lead of Richards and Davies and a number of other authorities. A few less important questions are discussed below under the orders respectively concerned.

As to the clerical task of selecting names, in this book certain procedures designed to further stability of nomenclature have been outlined in Chapter Nine. The biological problems involved in broad insect classification, difficult enough of themselves, have been seriously complicated by the almost whimsical application of names to orders. Other than six of the seven ordinal names by Linné, there has been but little consistency through the years. The mayflies, for example, have been known under more than *forty* different names! The knot must be cut sooner or later, and when it is cut personal preferences will have to be sacrificed. In selecting among possible names those to be in this book, *priority* has been the overriding principle, but a few concessions have been made (reluctantly) to usage. *Usage*, however, establishes a name only if the usage is *consistent* and *universal* and of *many years standing;* a usage of only ten or twenty years in only a part of the world cannot fix a name. The resultant ordinal names, as listed in this chapter, are in no case new, unused or rarely used today; but to any entomologists a few of them are certain to be "not preferred"—which is regrettable but inevitable. If the "preferences" of the present authors had been the guiding motive in selecting the names, the list would have been different, but it is believed that stability is more important.

The ordinal synonymy given in the following list is not complete; a large number of unfamiliar, rarely used names have been omitted. The synonymy is intended only to aid the student in reconciling the names likely to be encountered in various references. Orders comprising extinct insects exclusively are placed in parentheses and are not numbered.

CLASS INSECTA LINNÉ, 1758
= Hexapoda Latreille, 1825

SUBCLASS OLIGOENTOMATA BERLESE, 1909

Order 1. Collembola Lubbock, 1862

SUBCLASS MYRIENTOMATA BERLESE, 1909

Order 2. Protura Silvestri, 1907

SUBCLASS APTERYGOTA LANG, 1889
= Apterygogenea Brauer, 1885 (seldom used)

Order 3. Thysanura Latreille, 1796
Order 4. Aptera Linné, 1758
    = Rhabdura Cook, 1896; Diplura Börner, 1904; Dicellura Haliday, 1904

SUBCLASS PTERYGOTA LANG, 1889
= Pterygogenea Brauer, 1885 (seldom used)

Infraclass Paleoptera Martynov, 1923

(Order Paleodictyoptera Goldenberg, 1854—Lower Carboniferous to Upper Permian)
(Order Protohemiptera Handlirsch, 1903—Permian and Triassic)
(Order Megasecoptera Broigniart, 1893—Upper Carboniferous to Upper Permian)
(Order Protephemeroidea Handlirsch, 1908—Upper Carboniferous)
Order 5. Ephemerida Leach, 1817
        = Anisoptera Leach, 1835; Agnatha Meinert, 1883; Plectoptera Packard, 1886; Ephemeroptera Haeckel, 1896; Archipterygota Börner, 1909
(Order Meganisoptera Martynov, 1932—Carboniferous to Jurassic)
Order 6. Odonata Fabricius, 1792

Infraclass Polyneoptera Martynov, 1938

Order 7. Dictyoptera Leach, 1818
     = Blattaeformia Werner, 1906; Oothecaria Karny, 1915
   Suborder Blatteria Latreille, 1810
     = Cursoria Westwood, 1839; Neoblattariae Scudder, 1895
   Suborder Mantodea Burmeister, 1838
       = Dertoptera Clairville, 1798 (rarely used); Elythroptera Latreille,
         1806 (rarely used); Dacnostomata Westwood, 1839; Phyllop-
         tera Packard, 1883; Pandictyoptera Crampton, 1917; Panisop-
         tera Crampton, 1919
(Order Protoblattoidea Handlirsch, 1908—Carboniferous and Permian)
Order 8. Isoptera Brullé, 1832
Order 9. Zoraptera Silvestri, 1913
(Order Protorthoptera Handlirsch, 1908—Carboniferous)
Order 10. Plecoptera Burmeister, 1839
       = Perlariae Latreille, 1802 (less familiar)
Order 11. Grylloblattodea Brues and Melander, 1932
       = Notoptera Crampton, 1915 (used previously in Pisces)
Order 12. Phasmida Leach, 1815
       = Ambulatoria Westwood, 1859; Gressoria Börner, 1904; Cheleutop-
         tera Crampton, 1915
Order 13. Orthoptera Olivier, 1789
       = Salatoria Latreille, 1817
Order 14. Embioptera Hagan, 1861 (altered from Embidina by Shipley, 1904)
       = Adenopoda Verhoeff, 1904; Aetioptera Enderlein, 1912
(Order Protocoleoptera Tillyard, 1924 = Protelytroptera Tillyard, 1931—Per-
mian)
Order 15. Dermaptera De Geer, 1773
       = Diploglossata Saussure, 1879

Infraclass Paraneoptera Martynov, 1923

Order 16. Corrodentia Burmeister, 1839
       = Psoquille Latreille, 1810 (rarely used); Copeognatha Enderlein,
         1903; Psocoptera Shipley, 1904
Order 17. Mallophaga Nitzsch, 1818
       = Lipoptera Shipley, 1904
Order 18. Anoplura Leach, 1815
       = Parasita Latreille, 1802 (rarely used); Siphunculata Latreille,
         1825; Pediculina Burmeister, 1825; Polyptera Banks, 1892
Order 19. Hemiptera Linné, 1758
       = Rhynchota Burmeister, 1835
   Suborder Homoptera Latreille, 1810
   Suborder Heteroptera Latreille, 1810
Order 20. Thysanoptera Haliday, 1836
       = Physapoda Burmeister, 1838

Infraclass Oligoneoptera Martynov, 1923

Order 21. Coleoptera Linné, 1758
Order 22. Strepsiptera Kirby, 1813
  = Rhipidoptera Lamarck, 1816; Stylopites Newman, 1834
Order 23. Neuroptera Linné, 1758
  = Megaloptera Latreille, 1802; Raphidida Leach, 1815; Plannipenna
    Heymons, 1915
Order 24. Mecoptera Packard, 1886
  = Panorpatae Latreille, 1802 (rarely used)
Order 25. Trichoptera Kirby, 1813
  = Pharyganides Latreille, 1805 (rarely used); Placipennes Latreille,
    1825
Order 26. Lepidoptera Linné, 1758
Order 27. Diptera Linné, 1758
Order 28. Siphonaptera Latreille, 1798
  = Suctoria De Geer, 1778 (rarely used); Aphiniptera Kirby, 1826;
    Pulicina Burmeister, 1829
Order 29. Hymenoptera Linné, 1758

The discussions of the various orders of insects are not concerned with
classification, except in a very general way. Commonly used suborders
are listed and discussed, particularly for the larger orders, but the names
of superfamilies and families are used only for convenience in presenting
some of the varied and interesting aspects of the insects; in most cases,
the family names and family concepts used in Essig (1942), Borrer and
De Long (1954) or Imms (1957) are employed. Where these sources
disagree, family or superfamily names are used in the broadest sense.
It is not possible to present current opinion on the classification of the
insects within each order without either making this book much too
long or scanting the presentation of information considered more essential to an introductory course.

Order 1. Collembola Lubbock, 1870
(From the Greek: *glue* and *peg*)
Springtails, Snowfleas
(Figs. 3.19E, F, G, 13.1A)

Minute with soft bodies either flat or globose. Head prognathous. Compound eyes with at most 8 facets, often absent; ocelli absent. Antennae
4- to 6-segmented, frequently annular. Mouthparts endognathous with
maxilla and labium reduced. Primitively wingless. 1-segmented tarsus
fused on tibia; 2 post-tarsal claws. Abdomen with 5 segments plus telson;
cerci never present. Malpighian tubules absent. 3 abdominal appendages

distinctively modified as collophore, tenaculum and furcula, the last 2 sometimes absent. Tracheae rarely present, respiration usually cuticular. Oviparous; cleavage combination type; development ametabolous (anamorphic ?) with postadult ecdyses.

The mechanism, lacking in some families, from which the name "springtail" derives consists of a forked spring, the furcula, held in place by the clasp-like tenaculum. These structures are modified appendages of the second and third abdominal segments. The abrupt release of the furcula enables these tiny creatures to jump as far as three inches. If human athletes could perform proportional feats, the Olympic broad jump record would be about 120 feet! The collophore, a tube-like structure with eversible sacs at its tip, located on the first abdominal segment, exudes a sticky fluid that enables the animal to adhere to smooth surfaces and also to absorb moisture.

The female may deposit as many as 120 eggs in a group on the ground, covering them with excrement. The young hatch in a little over three weeks but require six to eight molts to reach maturity about a month and a half later. Two weeks is the average adult life; under optimal ecologic conditions there are as many as five generations a year.

Collembola may be found everywhere, including along the seashore and even on snow fields. For most species the main food is decaying vegetable matter in damp soil. Though a few species attack living plants, in Australia a collembolan is a serious pest of alfalfa while in the United States there are several troublesome springtails infesting greenhouses or mushroom cellars. Over 1000 species have been described and the order has world-wide distribution.

An obvious relative has been found as a Devonian fossil, but typical modern collembolans probably first developed during the Cretaceous.

Order 2. Protura Silvestri, 1907
(From the Greek: *first* and *tail*)
Telson-tails
(Figs. 8.1, 13.1B)

Minute insects with somewhat depressed, soft, white bodies and prognathous, conical heads. Eyes and antennae absent. Endognathous, piercing mouthparts. Primitively wingless. 1-segmented tarsus with a single post-tarsal claw and bristle-like terminal pad. Prothoracic legs with sensory function; reduced prothorax. Adult abdomen with 11 segments and telson but no cerci. First 3 abdominal segments with styli terminating in eversible sacs. Respiration cuticular or tracheal. Malpighian tubules elementary. Oviparous and anamorphic.

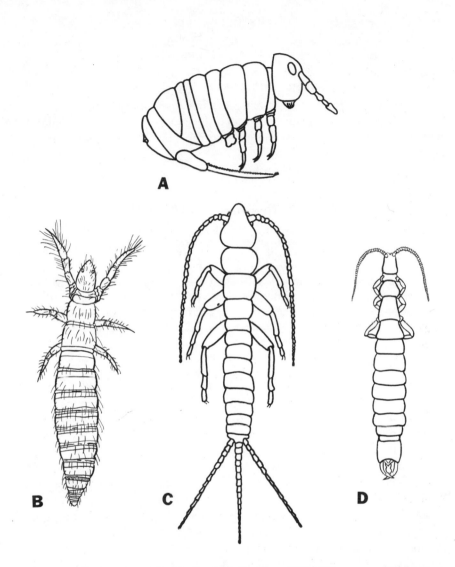

Figure 13.1. (A) Collembola; (B) Protura; (C) Thysanura; (D) Aptera, *Japyx* species. (A after Scott, 1959; B after Ewing, 1940; C after Ewing, 1942; D from specimen in Carnegie Museum)

These insects hatch with eight abdominal segments and pass through three molts, adding an additional segment with each molt. Lacking antennae, they carry the first pair of legs elevated and presumably utilize them for sensory functions somewhat as the spiders use their pedipalps.

Little is known about their life history. They are found in dark, damp situations associated with decaying organic matter and humus.

About ninety species have been recorded, most of which are Holarctic, with a few others scattered in the Neotropical, Oriental and Australian regions.

No fossil of Protura has been found.

Order 3. Thysanura Latreille, 1796
(From the Greek: *tassel* and *tail*)
Silverfish, Bristletails, Firebrats, Slickers
(Figs. 3.19D, 3.20A, B, 6.6B, 13.1C)

Small to moderate size with soft, elongated, somewhat flattened bodies, smooth or covered with scales. Prognathous head with compound eyes; ocelli present or absent. Antennae long, filiform, multisegmented. Ectognathous biting mouthparts. Primitively wingless. Tarsi with 2–4 segments and paired post-tarsal claws. 11 abdominal segments, last sternite often reduced and the tergite greatly elongated into a median caudal filament. Styliform appendages on some abdominal sternites. Cerci long and multisegmented. Oviparous; ametabolous with postimaginal ecdyses.

Some tropical species pass through six or more instars, becoming adult in a year. In the temperate zones two years or more may be required. Molting continues after the reproductive capacity and all adult structures are attained. The male of a species of firebrat is known to molt as often as forty-one times and thirty-eight molts were observed in a female of the same species. The same female laid twelve batches of eggs between her thirteenth and thirty-fifth instars. Some species may pass through as many as sixty instars and live for seven years.

Among indications that they are primitive is the fact that there is no pleural suture, furcae or phragmata. While some species have well-developed compound eyes, in others the number of facets is drastically reduced or the eyes may be lacking. The ocelli are absent in the Lepismatidae.

Thysanura collectively have a wide range of habitats. Various species may be either nocturnal or diurnal, may require dark, damp situations or may prefer hot, dry and exposed places. They are omnivorous in food habits. Domestic forms like the silverfish especially attack starchy materials and are known to be fond of paste, glue and even rayon.

Distribution of the order is world-wide. Some 350 species are known. The earliest fossil specimens date only from the Tertiary, but this fact cannot be taken as an indication of their geologic history.

Order 4. Aptera[1] Linné, 1758
(From the Greek: *without* and *wing*)
Campodeids, Japygids
(Figs. 3.19A–C, 5.8A, B, 7.13, 13.1D)

Small, fragile insects with long, soft, flattened, usually unpigmented bodies. Prognathous head with compound eyes but no ocelli. Long, moniliform antennae with segmental muscles. Endognathous, chewing mouthparts with maxillary and labial palpi reduced or atrophied. Primitively wingless. Tarsi 2-segmented and 2 post-tarsal claws. 11 abdominal segments with the last sternite reduced and the tergite forming a supra-anal plate; sternites 1–7 or 2–7 with styli and sometimes protrusible vesicles. Cerci varied, long, short or pincer-like. Malpighian tubules vestigial or lacking. External genitalia slight or absent. Oviparous; ametabolous.

A small number of eggs, up to twenty, are laid in a shallow cavity in the ground and the female guards them for some time after hatching. The campodeids molt every three weeks, requiring about two years to attain definitive chaetotaxy and fully segmented cerci; in the japygids the cerci are converted to forceps in the second instar.

Aptera are widely distributed in temperate and tropical zones and are particularly abundant in damp, dark places around dead leaves, logs and debris on the ground. Campodeids feed on fungus and japygids are predaceous or herbivorous. About 400 species have been described.

One species of Campodea has been found in the Baltic amber, but there is no fossil record on the projapids. Many entomologists consider this group, of all the living orders, to be most like the ancestral form from which all insects developed.

Order 5. Ephemerida Leach, 1817
(From the Greek: *to live but a day*)
Mayflies, Dayflies, Shadflies
(Figs. 6.7B, 13.2A)

Small to medium size (less than 1 cm.) with long, soft, inconspicuously colored, delicate bodies. Prognathous head. Compound eyes well developed; 3 ocelli present. Setiform antennae short and bristle-like. Ectogna-

[1] See pages 292 and 336–337.

thous vestigial chewing mouthparts. Transparent wings delicate with numerous intercalary veins, held vertically at rest; hindwing sometimes reduced or absent. Weak, clinging legs with 1- to 5-jointed tarsi terminating in 2 claws. Abdomen with 10 well-defined segments, eleventh tergite reduced or elongated as median caudal filament. Large number of malpighian tubules; adult midgut only an air sac. Primitive bilateral external genitalia. Oviparous; hemimetabolous. Aquatic naiads essentially similar in structure to adult; long antennae, well-developed mouthparts and abdominal gills.

A female lays as many as 4000 eggs directly on the water surface. These eggs have little protrusions which, coming into contact with plant stems or leaves, provide anchorage. Hatching occurs within a week to several months, varying with the species. The naiads (larvae) develop leaf-like abdominal gills and have strong chewing mouthparts. Three prominent caudal appendages are typical. Most immatures are herbivorous and their feeding helps to control aquatic flora; a few are carnivorous and attack small animal life. As many as twenty-four molts may be passed during a period of one to three years before maturity is reached. At this point the insect leaves the water and becomes winged, the final ecdysis leading to the subimaginal instar, a stage compared by Hinton (1948) with the holometabolous pupa. The wings are dull, opaque and usually fringed; neither cerci nor legs are fully developed. The subimago is a resting period of relatively short duration—a few hours to a few days. Another ecdysis produces the typical adult with fully formed genitalia, cerci, legs and transparent wings. This ecdysis has often been held to be the only known case of the wing cuticle being molted, but the pupal ecdysis of holometabolous insects also involves shedding the wing cuticle. Adults live but a few days, at most a week, remaining near fresh water and not feeding. Usually mayflies are noticed during the mating flights when they appear in swarms over streams and ponds.

The Ephemerida play an important role in maintaining biotic balance in fresh water, serving both as a minor control of the plants and as a major item in the diet of other insects and of many fish. Both naiads and adults are harmless to man.

The 1500 known species are distributed throughout the world, with the greatest number found in North America. Carboniferous fossils, in which most stages of the life history have been found, indicate that the ancestral mayflies did not show as great a reduction of the hindwings. Typical species of this order have been found in the Lower Permian beds of Kansas and Russia.

Order 6. Odonata Fabricius, 1793
(From the Greek: *toothed,* probably referring to the
prominently toothed mouthparts)
Damselflies, Dragonflies, Snake doctors, Darning needles
(Figs. 3.8A, 8.9, 13.2B, C)

Medium to large size, with slender, well-sclerotized bodies either cylindrical or flattened, frequently of bright metallic hues. Very mobile hypognathous head with large compound eyes and 3 ocelli. Short awl-shaped antennae 3- to 7-segmented. Ectognathous biting mouthparts with strongly toothed mandibles; maxillary palpi 1-segmented, labial palpi 2-segmented. Thorax relatively short and compact. Long, transparent net-veined wings with pterostigmata; forewings larger, wings horizontal at rest, or wings equal and held perpendicular at rest. Legs short and spiny with 3-segmented tarsi, 2 post-tarsal claws and rudimentary empodium. Abdomen elongate with 10 full segments and with a supra-anal plate in the male only formed from the vestigial eleventh. Cerci short, unsegmented. Male copulatory organs on second and third abdominal sternites. Numerous malpighian tubules. Oviparous; hemimetabolous with naiads (aquatic larvae).

The majority of Odonata belong to two suborders, the Anisoptera (dragonflies) and Zygoptera (damselflies), easily distinguished in either the larval or the adult stages:

Anisoptera	Zygoptera
1. Hindwings broader at base, held horizontally at rest. Strong fliers.	1. Wings of equal size narrow at base and held vertically at rest. Weak fliers.
2. Eyes not projecting from side of head.	2. Eyes bulbous, projecting prominently and constricted at base.
3. Most families with reduced or vestigial ovipositors.	3. Females with well-developed ovipositor.
4. Supra-anal plate in male.	4. Male supra-anal plate vestigial.
5. Naiads large with rectal gills.	5. Naiads slender with paddle-like caudal gills.
6. Large and robust at all stages.	6. Small, slender and delicate at all stages.
7. Eggs usually laid on water or surfaces of aquatic plants.	7. Eggs inserted into stems of aquatic plants.

Further distinctions are present in nearly every structure, but especially in details of the complex wing venation. A third suborder, Anisozygoptera, is represented only by a few oriental species, and combines the characteristics of the other two suborders.

All damselflies use their well-developed ovipositors to insert their eggs singly into plant stems just beneath the water surface. The relatively few dragonflies having adequate ovipositors do the same, but most merely scatter their eggs over the water or attach them to a water plant in a gelatinous mass which may contain as many as 800 eggs.

A somber, ugly naiad hatches, well prepared for predaceous life with its grotesque, extensible labium (mask) (see Fig. 8.9A) which can be shot out to seize its unwary prey. The gills of the dragonfly larva are concealed in the branchial basket, a modification of the rectal chamber. Water drawn into the rectal chamber can be suddenly and forcibly expelled to provide the creature with jet propulsion. The gills of the damselfly larvae are easily seen as three paddle-like caudal appendages. The young of a few species burrow into the mud. Development usually takes about a year and in temperate zones the larva is the overwintering stage. Some species, however, pass through as many as ten or fifteen instars before becoming adult, which requires from one to five years.

All Odonata are found close to fresh water, though adult dragonflies often cruise for some distance overland foraging for food. Both young and adults are voracious predators on suitable stages of midges, mosquitoes, flies, gnats and similar pests and make an important contribution to biological control. The aerial artistry of dragonflies is proverbial: they dart, change direction, fly backward or hover and have complete control of their movements. Using the forelegs as a kind of basket, they catch their prey on the wing. Many species are brilliantly colored.

About 5000 species are included in the order, distributed throughout the world, with a majority found in the tropics. Fossils discovered in the French Commentary beds place ancestral Odonata in the Carboniferous period. These insects were less specialized than living forms, but were spectacular in size—including one with a wingspread of more than two feet. Typical Odonata appear as fossils in Kansas Permian strata.

Order 7. Dictyoptera Leach, 1818
(From the Greek: *net* and *wing*)
Cockroaches, Croton bugs, Praying mantids
(Figs. 3.6G, 4.1B, 5.2A, B, 7.7, 13.2D, E)

Medium to large insects with varied coloring. Hypognathous head. Compound eyes well developed, sometimes reduced or absent; ocelli 3, 2 or absent. Antennae filiform, multisegmented. Ectognathous chewing mouthparts. Forewing, when present, a thickened tegmen; hindwing membranous with a large anal lobe, folded under tegmina at rest; some brachypterous or apterous species. Legs similar or with raptorial forelegs;

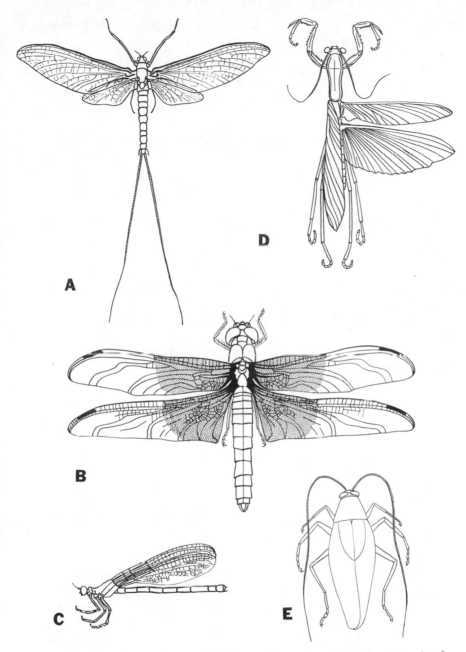

Figure 13.2. (A) Ephemerida, *Hexagenia* species; (B) Odonata, suborder Anisoptera, *Libellula* species; (C) Odonata, suborder Zygoptera; (D) Dictyoptera, suborder Mantodea; (E) Dictyoptera, suborder Blattaria, *Blattus* species. (Drawn from specimens in Carnegie Museum)

coxae enlarged; 5-segmented tarsi with paired post-tarsal claws. 10 evident abdominal segments with a reduced eleventh. Segmented cerci long or short. Ovipositor reduced, concealed by seventh segment; male genitalia complex, partly concealed by ninth sternum, which bears a pair of styli. Oviparous; paurometabolous with terrestrial nymphs.

The cockroaches and mantids are much more closely related than their superficial differences in appearance suggest and represent an ancient offshoot from the orthopteran stem. The older references treat them as two families of a comprehensive order Orthoptera. They differ from the true orthopterans in some major respects: the eggs are laid in an oötheca; stridulating and auditory organs are absent; the ovipositor is reduced and not exserted.

The two suborders are distinguished as follows:

BLATTARIA	MANTODEA
1. Only the pronotum prolonged as a broad hood concealing the head.	1. Entire prothorax elongated, often the longest body segment; small triangular head quite evident, mobile with definite neck.
2. Ocelli: 2, represented by pale spots (fenestrae), or absent.	2. Ocelli: 3 or absent.
3. Antennae extremely long, up to 100 segments.	3. Antennae not especially long in proportion to the long body.
4. Dark or drably colored, except a few tropical species.	4. Usually leaf green, some tropical species with vivid colors.
5. Body oval, dorso-ventrally flattened.	5. Body elongate, cylindrical.
6. Legs similar with large broad coxae; swift runners.	6. Forelegs modified for predation having spined femora and tarsi; other legs weak; walkers.
7. Scavengers; odiferous.	7. Carnivorous; not odiferous.

BLATTARIA

Cockroaches lay from sixteen to forty eggs in a horny oötheca which is usually forced into a crack or crevice though in some species it is retained in the genital tract until the nymphs hatch. Hatching occurs in about a month; the nymphs pass through five to eight instars. It may take as long as five years to reach maturity, as in *Blatta orientalis* (Linné), but the common domestic *Blattella germanica* (Linné) needs only a year. They frequently are gregarious, but have no social organization.

These insects are basically nocturnal and tropical, but they naturalize easily and have become world-wide tourists. Any warm, damp place becomes home to them. They thrive on a varied diet—pantry items (which they seem to prefer), castoff skin, crippled relatives, paper, clothing or shoes. Where there is severe infestation they may even gnaw the foot calluses of sleeping persons. Cockroaches are among the most repulsive of domestic pests and add to their destructiveness by soiling with disgorged food, feces and naseous secretions everything with which they come into contact. Certain studies have suggested that they prey on bedbugs, a mark in their favor entirely outweighed by the fact they are intermediate hosts for parasitic worms infecting birds, rodents and other mammals including man. *Staphylococcus* and cholera bacteria may be carried on their legs and bodies. Despite their well-earned notoriety as unwelcome household guests, most species are "wild," living as scavengers in refuse piles, under stones and logs, among dead leaves and moss, or in decaying wood.

About 2300 species have been recorded from all parts of the world except the extreme Arctic and Antarctic.

MANTODEA

The female mantis lays from sixteen to four hundred eggs in an oötheca attached to a twig or some similar object. At first the oötheca is frothy, but it soons harden into a firm spongy case that protects the contents from the elements and from most predators—though not from parasitic wasps. Females usually mate more than once and deposit several egg cases. The first instar young closely resemble adults in structure and proportion. There are from three to thirteen instars before maturity is attained. At most there is one generation a year. Some species are parthenogenetic.

Mantids are mainly arboreal, exhibiting superb protective mimicry by shape and color, frequently being almost impossible to distinguish from the background vegetation until they move. They can remain immobile for long periods of time, waiting for unwary prey to venture near. The carriage of the forelegs in what seems to be a worshipful attitude has led to many ancient superstitions, as well as the common name "praying mantis": "preying mantis" would be more accurate. They are among the most vicious of carnivores. To watch one consume a live grasshopper as though it were an ear of corn is a gruesome sight. The female has the macabre habit of eating the male during copulation. Since she starts with his head, whereas his procreative impulses are safely controlled by ganglia in one of the last abdominal segments, there is no interference with the production of future generations!

Because so much of their diet includes pest insects, mantids are popularly regarded as exceedingly beneficial: their effectiveness in biological control is greatly overrated. Some of the larger species are known to attack tiny birds and amphibians.

Approximately 1600 species are known from the temperate and tropical parts of the world. Tropical Africa has the greatest concentration of species. In North America there are about twenty species, only one of which is native.

FOSSIL RECORD

The fossil record shows the cockroaches to be among the most ancient of insect groups, apparently reaching their zenith during late Carboniferous (see Fig. 4.1B) and early Permian times. In these strata they account for thirty-four per cent of the known insect population. In the oldest levels of the Carboniferous the cockroaches were already fully specialized and essentially similar to living representatives. The mantids certainly derived from the same ancestry as did the cockroaches, but their fossil record is quite fragmentary until the Tertiary, probably because their arboreal habits made them less likely to be fossilized. Carboniferous forms sometimes referred to the mantids are thought by some paleontologists to be offshoots of the cockroach line rather than mantids in the strict sense. Specimens from Oligocene ambers represent living species.

Order 8. Isoptera Brullé, 1832
(From the Greek: *equal* and *wing*)
Termites, White ants
(Figs. 8.3, 13.3A, B)

Small to medium-sized social insects with highly developed caste system resulting in polymorphic variety in most species. Photophobic, except during mating flight, thinly sclerotized with color ranging from pale to dark tan. Prognathous head. Moniliform antennae with 10 to 30 segments. Compound eyes well developed, sometimes vestigial; ocelli 2 or absent. Ectognathous mouthparts. Prothorax often with distinctive tergal development; thorax broadly joined to abdomen. Alate forms with long membranous similar wings with heavy anterior longitudinal veins and no cross veins, carried flat over back at rest; a basal suture present to facilitate shedding; most castes wingless. Legs short, similar; coxae well developed; tarsi 4- or 5-segmented; paired post-tarsal claws. Abdomen 11-segmented; first sternum atrophied, eleventh represented by paraprocts. Cerci short or with 6–8 segments. In some families frontal gland of head emits repellent secretion through fontanel or elongated rostrum of nasute forms. Oviparous; paurometabolous with terrestrial nymphs.

These insects are sometimes called "white ants" because of their superficial similarity in appearance and social habits to the true ants (Hymenoptera) but in fact the two orders are only remotely related and
are easily distinguished. Termites are soft-bodied and look fat because
the separation between the thorax and abdomen is not constricted and in
winged forms the fore- and hindwings are similar in both size and venation and at rest are folded over the back; ants, on the other hand, are
hard-bodied with a slender waist-like constriction (petiole) separating
the thorax and abdomen and in winged forms the forewings are larger,
have more veins than the hindwings and are held vertically at rest.

The life histories of termites are of the greatest biological interest, involving the production of polymorphic castes, complex social organizations and wonderfully engineered nests. The development and evolution
of these features can, in a general way, be traced within the order itself.
The most primitive of living termites is *Mastotermes darwiniensis* Frog-
gart of the Australian tropics, the sole remaining species of a family which
includes a number of Tertiary fossils. Structural details connect *Mastotermes* with the cockroaches; their nests, habits, social organization and
caste system are simple and primitive. For example, *Mastotermes* deposits
its eggs in an oötheca-like mass, retains a distinct and well-developed
anal lobe on the wings and five tarsal segments. The forms to be found in
a colony consist of the reproductive females and males, a soldier caste
and immatures which function as workers. In the more advanced families
the social organization becomes exceedingly complex and may include a
bewildering variety of polymorphic forms varying both with the species
and with the age of the colony. The principal castes to be found are as
follows:

A. REPRODUCTIVE CASTES. **Primary reproductives** are slender with
normal heads, long membranous wings and darkly pigmented integument;
the compound eyes are well developed and ocelli are usually present.
These are the only true imagos produced. In many species they appear
periodically in large numbers, emerging from the mother nest to migrate
in pairs and found new colonies. Fortunately they do not fly strongly
and the rate of destruction from predators—birds, mammals and other
insects—is very high; only a few reach their objective. The successful
pairs shed their wings, excavate a small chamber in the ground or in
wood (as suitable for the species), mate and become the king and queen
of a new colony. They are monogamous, an unusual trait among insects;
the same male and female live together throughout their lives.

Secondary reproductives are pale-covered with vestigial wings, reduced
eyes and heavier bodies; usually more males than females are produced

and, unlike most primaries, they are polygamous. In some species these supplementary reproductives mature only as replacements when mischance removes the king, queen or both, while in others such as *Reticulotermes* they are regularly functional and may surpass the reproductivity of the primary king and queen. They are neotenic in that they acquire the reproductive capacity, although they pass through fewer instars than the true imagos and do not attain full development of wings, pigmentation and other morphologic details.

Tertiary reproductives are produced by a few species. They are wingless, unpigmented and have only vestigial eyes; obviously they are neotenic. Secondary and tertiary reproductives disappear from the nest at swarming time. Either they are destroyed by the workers, or they migrate by subterranean routes with a few workers and soldiers to form new subcolonies.

B. Soldiers.   The **soldier caste** is made up of males and females that never reach the imaginal instar, but instead acquire specialized structures. They are wingless and only the heavily sclerotized, enlarged, often weirdly shaped, head is pigmented (Fig. 13.8B). Visual organs are frequently lacking. In the order as a whole the two distinct types are recognizable: (a) **manibulate soldiers** with powerful pincer-like jaws and (b) **nasute soldiers** with vestigial jaws and an elongated, pointed frontal rostrum which serves as a nozzle for squirting a sticky, latex-like secretion at enemies. The mouthparts are generally so specialized that soldiers cannot eat normally but must be fed predigested material by workers. In *Anoplotermes fumosus* (Hagan) there are no true soldiers.

C. Workers.   Members of the **worker caste** are embryogenically suppressed males and females; they are pale-colored, generally blind and with strong biting jaws. In most species they make up the majority of the population in a colony, performing all functions except reproduction and defense, including feeding the royal couple, the soldiers and the very young nymphs (larvae), caring for the eggs, grooming the queen and foraging for food. Normal immatures—that is, those not structurally specialized—supplement the labors of the definitive worker castes; in primitive families (Kalotermididae) there are no true workers and the immatures function in their place.

During the first year of a new colony the founding queen lays only a few eggs, some of which the royal couple eat. As workers and soldiers develop and take over the work load, the queen retires to become an egg-laying machine. Her reproductive capacity increases with age and, in certain tropical species, the abdomen becomes distended to grotesque proportions. A fully developed *Macrotermes* queen is capable of laying 34,000 eggs a day, and the queen and her consort are housed in a special chamber attended by workers and guarded by soldiers; as the eggs are dropped, they are carried away by workers to be incubated in special parts of the nest. In more familiar temperate zone termites the primary queen does not achieve such a fantastic reproductive potential and is not housed in a special chamber, but varies her location in the nest.

Hatching occurs in from one to three months. First instar nymphs are active and all much alike, but differentiate after a few molts into small- and large-headed forms. Small-headed nymphs become reproductives after six to eleven instars and about two years. Large-headed nymphs become soldiers or workers in about a year and pass through fewer instars. The mechanisms involved in the differentiation of castes are not clear.

The diet of almost all termites includes cellulose obtained from wood or other plant material, yet no species is known to secrete cellulose-digesting enzymes. Frequently the problem is solved by the presence in the termite gut of symbiotic protozoans able to break down cellulose, the by-products then being available for use by the host. Nymphs harbor these intestinal symbionts within a few hours after hatching, probably passed on to them by attendant workers by way of regurgitated or fecal material. The higher termites (family Termitidae) lack this obliging intestinal fauna, but nevertheless feed on and digest wood by processes not yet understood. Not all members of a colony feed directly on wood, some relying upon predigested food furnished by secretions, excretions or regurgitations from other members. In many termites the diet is supplemented by such other materials as shed cuticle, the corpses of colony members and sometimes hides or skins.

Water is essential to termites. Nests are always built where moisture in some form is available. In dry open country, tropical mound-building species may dig down for many feet in order to come into contact with the water table. Desert-dwelling species obtain moisture from roots and stems of cacti and other plants. Nests are built in trees and aerial situations only where the atmosphere is normally humid. The unfortunately common *Reticulitermes flavipes* Kollar, notoriously destructive of buildings in the United States, nests beneath the surface of the soil where water is available, sending tunnels out to timbers in which the workers feed and thus wreak their havoc. These worker termites are unpigmented and cannot expose themselves to light. To reach timbers not in direct contact with the ground, they construct mud tunnels up concrete or stone walls and even through the air. Drywood termites like *Kalotermes* are essentially tropical and subtropical. They nest within the timbers themselves, leaving only an outer shell as protection against light, but cannot survive without available moisture. Termites that construct their nests on the trunks, limbs or in the forks of trees are confined to the humid tropics. Many of the drywood- and tree-nesting species attack the roots and shoots of living plants and must be included among the serious pests of crops like tea, cocoa, rubber, citrus fruit and sugar.

In Africa and Australia, termite mounds or hills are a prominent, characteristic feature of the landscape in vast areas. These hills are constructed of clay particles cemented together with excrement and secretions, may be up to forty feet high and sometimes are very numerous. Within the hard outer shell, the hill contains the runways used by the colony, the royal chamber and the brood chambers. The royal chamber houses the enormous queen (we found a *Macrotermes* queen in Liberia which weighed 35.5 grams, and doubtless there are larger), her consort and her attending soldiers and workers. In West Africa, the adobe walls of native houses are made by preparing mud from termite hills and plastering it over a framework. Some tribes also break into hills and use them as ovens in cooking. Both in Africa and in South America, termites, especially the swarming reproductive caste, are cooked in oil and eaten. To the very considerable extent that termites destroy dead wood and return its molecules to the soil, they must be regarded as beneficial. Their damage to man's property is only the consequence of our insistence upon using the termite's natural food for our own purposes.

Termites seem to be genial hosts, quite willing to share their nests and runs with other creatures. More than 500 species of other invertebrates are known to be termitophiles, including many beetles and flies, various spiders, mites, millipedes and centipedes, some Collembola and Thysanura, a few Orthoptera and some immature Lepidoptera.

The majority of the some 1600 species of Isoptera are tropical and subtropical, but some have invaded the warmer parts of the temperate zones and one species reaches 7000 feet above sea level in the Rocky Mountains. The fossil record of this order goes back only to the Tertiary, but they must be vastly older. Jeannel (1960) supposes that earlier termites were solitary or lived in small colonies and were not common enough to become fossilized until, at a comparatively recent geologic time, complex social colonies with their large numbers of individuals were developed.

Order 9. Zoraptera Silvestri, 1913
(From the Greek: *purely* and *wingless*)
No common name
(Fig. 13.3C)

Small, pale, soft-bodied insects somewhat resembling tiny termites. Head hypognathous, free and relatively large. Moniliform 9-segmented antennae. Ectognathous biting mouthparts. All species dimorphic in both sexes. A few males and females with compound eyes, ocelli and membranous wings with reduced venation, the forewing larger, provided with basal suture to facilitate shedding; most males and females without eyes, ocelli or wings. Prothorax prominent. Legs short with 2-segmented tarsi and paired post-tarsal claws. Abdomen with 10 evident segments and a modified, fused eleventh. Short cerci. No ovipositor in female; male genitalia specialized. Oviparous; paurometabolous with terrestrial nymphs.

Five years after Silvestri named the order on the basis of the wingless forms he discovered, winged individuals were found.

Little is known of the life history of these rare, infrequently noticed insects. They are found under loose bark, in sawdust piles or in decaying humus, apparently feeding on fungus mycelia and on mites, and require warmth and humidity. Although they are gregarious and live in colonies, no caste system appears to have developed. Eggs have been found glued to the undersides of wood chips and bark. Two types of nymphs hatch, corresponding respectively to the winged and wingless adults.

About twenty species are now known, all included in the genus *Zorotypus*, distributed in the tropical and subtropical belts: southeastern United States, Jamaica, Central America, Brazil, Bolivia, Hawaii, Philippines, southeastern Asia and the East Indies, West Africa and Madagascar. Further field work will undoubtedly reveal other species and fill in the geographic picture. No fossils have been found.

Order 10. Plecoptera Burmeister, 1839
(From the Greek: *pleated* and *wing*)
Stoneflies, Salmonflies, Perlids
(Figs. 4.1A, 13.3D)

Medium to large insects with long, semiflat, lightly sclerotized bodies usually somber-colored. Prognathous head. Small or moderate compound eyes; ocelli 3, 2 or absent. Long filiform antennae. Weak ectognathous chewing mouthparts often reduced. Transparent net-veined wings with anal lobes, hindwing broader, folded flat over body at rest. Coxae small; tarsi 2- or 3-segmented with two post-tarsal claws and an empodium.

11 abdominal segments, the last reduced. Cerci long and filiform or with a maximum of 10 segments. Males of some species have a disc-like percussion hammer on the ninth abdominal segment with which they can produce a drumming sound. Oviparous; hemimetabolous with aquatic naiads greatly resembling the adult.

A female lays 1000 or more eggs on or close to water. The naiads hatch in one to two months and cling to the undersides of stones. They are flat and elongated with long cerci and antennae. The carnivorous species have strong mouthparts, while in the herbivorous groups they are somewhat reduced. Respiration is either cutaneous or by means of tracheal gills located behind each leg and on the first two abdominal segments.

After a number of ecdyses—as many as thirty-three have been recorded—the naiad leaves the water to undergo its final ecdysis on land. In some species this final molt occurs in winter, the naiad crawling out through cracks in the ice; others emerge during the summer. The entire cycle takes from one to four or more years.

Plecoptera develop in lakes or in cold, rapidly flowing streams. Many adults do not feed, though some eat the buds of young fruit trees. In contrast many naiads are voraciously predaceous on small aquatic animals. All furnish valuable fish food and are harmless to man.

Some 1500 species are known with world-wide distribution, but they are concentrated in the temperate, Arctic and Antarctic zones and are especially characteristic of icy torrents. The precursors of Plecoptera have been found in the Lower Permian beds of Kansas and Russia; living groups appeared during the Jurassic period.

Order 11. Grylloblattodea Brues and Melander, 1932
(From the Latin: *cricket* and *cockroach*)
No common name
(Fig. 13.3E)

Medium-sized, light-colored insects with small compound eyes and no ocelli. Long multisegmented filiform antennae. Ectognathous chewing mouthparts. Secondarily wingless. Legs slender with 5-segmented tarsi and post-tarsal claws; males often with lobed tarsi. Abdomen with 10 evident segments, the eleventh vestigial; styli frequently present on ninth segment of males. Cerci long, segmented. Females with exserted sword-like ovipositor and eversible sacs on ninth and tenth sternites. Male genitalia asymmetric. Oviparous; paurometabolous with terrestrial larvae.

When first discovered, these insects were tentatively placed as a family of the inclusive order Orthoptera. Special interest attaches to them in that

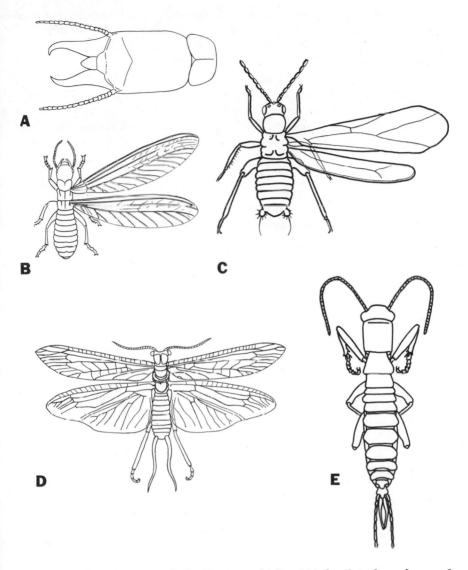

Figure 13.3. Isoptera, *Reticulitermes tibialis:* (A) head and prothorax of soldier and (B) winged adult; (C) Zoraptera; (D) Plecoptera; (E) Grylloblattodea. (A and B after Banks and Snyder, 1920; C after Caudell, 1920; E from specimen in Carnegie Museum; F after Walker, 1914)

they are relics of the primitive orthopteran stock from which crickets and roaches were derived. The formation of the legs is especially primitive, all three pairs being similar and the tarsi retaining the full five joints.

When the female is about a year old, she lays her black eggs singly in soil or moss. Incubation requires a full year. There are eight or more nymphal instars and maturity is reached in about five years. This unusually long, slow life cycle probably results from the characteristically cold environment, for these insects are found only in mountainous country at altitudes up to 9000 feet above sea level. They keep hidden under debris and in moss and appear to be nocturnal. The diet includes vegetable material and dead insects. Grylloblattids are active at the margins of melting snow fields and ice caves.

The score of species are found distributed in the mountains of western North America, Russia and Japan. No fossils are known.

Order 12. Phasmida Leach, 1815
(From the Greek: a *spectre* or *ghost*)
Walking sticks, Leaf insects
(Figs. 3.6K, 13.4A)

Large insects with well-sclerotized bodies either elongate and cylindrical or flattened and leaf-like, cryptically colored, usually brown or green. Prognathous head with small compound eyes, 2 or 3 ocelli in winged species. Long filiform antennae. Ectognathous chewing mouthparts. Prothorax small. Forewings reduced and thickened, forming leaf-like tegmina; hindwing membranous; wings flat over the body at rest; many species brachypterous or apterous. Legs similar with small coxae, 3- to 5-segmented tarsi with post-tarsal claws and terminal pad. Abdomen with 11 segments, the first closely attached to metathorax, the eleventh represented only by epiproct and paraprocts. Short unsegmented cerci. External genitalia or ovipositor concealed. Legs of some species provided with leaf-like expansions. Repugnatorial glands sometimes present in thorax. Nymphal legs with abscission suture between femur and trochanter; regeneration after loss results in 4-segmented tarsus. Oviparous; paurometabolous with terrestrial nymphs.

The phasmids have been variously included in the Orthoptera or the Dictyoptera or given separate ordinal status. Because they seem to represent a distinctive phylogenetic line of ancient origin, current specialists separate them from other orthopteroids. Among characters distinguishing them from Orthoptera proper are the concealed ovipositor (in females) or external genitalia (in males), the similarity of all three pairs of legs and the absence of both auditory and stridulatory organs.

The female lays about a hundred eggs, scattering them more or less at random over the ground. They look much like seeds and may take from a season to several years to hatch. The young closely resemble the adults, but the time required to reach maturity varies greatly with the species. Males develop more rapidly than females, undergo one or two fewer molts and do not live as long in the adult instar. Parthenogenesis is not uncommon; in a certain number of species no males have ever been discovered.

Phasmids are basically tropical phytophagous insects. In general, they are harmless to man, but a few species sometimes become sufficiently numerous that serious economic loss results from their depredations on tree crops.

They walk awkwardly, fly clumsily and reluctantly and have neither sting nor bite, though some emit an offensive, irritating substance. For protection the phasmids rely primarily on superb mimicry of their background. A walking stick at rest is convincingly a twig; a leaf insect just *is* a leaf, complete with bird droppings in many cases. A phasmid in its natural environment is impossible to recognize unless it happens to move. This is true mimicry, not to be confused with the convergent and parallel evolutionary processes which, in other orders, lead to close similarity between unrelated species. Many of the brown phasmids have integumental chromatophores which confer on them the chameleon-like ability to change color from dark to pale in response to light intensity.

The longest insect now living is the giant Australian walking stick, which may reach thirteen inches not including the antennae.

About 2000 species have been described, the majority from the Oriental tropics. The order is also found in the Neotropic, Ethiopian and Australian regions and twelve species inhabit North America, of which only one has wings.

Fragmentary fossil remains have been found in Mesozoic strata and the order apparently flourished during Jurassic times. Many specimens have been recovered from Baltic amber and from the Florissant bed of Colorado.

Order 13. Orthoptera Olivier, 1789
(From the Greek: *straight* and *wing*)
Grasshoppers, Locusts, Crickets
(Figs. 3.6B, H, 3.8B, 4.5, 6.5D, 8.2, 13.B–D)

Medium to large, usually with elongate lightly sclerotized bodies, varied cryptic coloration. Large compound eyes; 2, 3 or no ocelli. Mouthparts ectognathous, biting, strong. Antennae moniliform, filiform or setaceous. Forewing narrow, thickened into a protective tegmina, the hindwing membranous with a large anal area, folded fanwise under the tegmina at rest and both pairs held over the abdomen; some species lacking one or both pairs. Legs with small coxae, 3- to 5-jointed tarsi, 2 post-tarsal claws and terminal pads; hindlegs longest; forelegs sometimes modified for digging. Abdomen with 11 segments, the sternum of the first somewhat reduced and the last segments modified, bearing genitalic structures. Cerci long or short, usually not segmented. Female with well-developed ovipositor; male genitalia asymmetric, concealed. Stridulating and auditory organs frequently present. Oviparous; paurometabolous with terrestrial nymphs.

For a long time the order Orthoptera was used to comprise all orthopteroid insects: phasmids, blattids, mantids, grylloblattids, grasshoppers and crickets. Handlirsch (1906–1908), Martynov (1938) and others have shown that the original orthopteroid stock developed, possibly as long ago as the Paleozoic, into a series of distinct phylogenetic lines, each with its characteristic ecologic and morphologic features, and that living orthopteroids must be placed into a series of distinct orders. As now limited, Orthoptera includes only the grasshoppers and crickets.

In many groups the female drills a hole in the soil in which she lays a mass of from twenty to a hundred eggs enclosed in an egg sac formed from hardened secretions. In other groups, the eggs are inserted into plant tissue. Ordinarily there is one generation each year and the egg overwinters in temperate climates, but in the tropics there may be several generations. Nymphs differ from adults only in size, color and lack of functional wings.

Structural characters useful in distinguishing the major families lie in the antennae, tarsal segments, ovipositor, wing carriage and method of sound production. The fifteen families may be grouped into four superfamilies as follows:

TETTIGONOIDEA—The long-horned grasshoppers, katydids (Fig. 13.4B), cave crickets and sand crickets have antennae longer than the head and thorax combined or even longer than the entire body. There are four tarsal segments. Females have a sword-shaped, laterally flattened, conspicuous ovipositor. The hindwings, when present, are folded fan-wise under the tegmina and along the sides of the abdomen. Stridulation is produced by a scraper on the tegmina.

Most of the 4000 species in this group are tropical, but there is a substantial representation in temperate zones. They are basically plant feeders, though a few are carnivorous. A number of wingless species are known, for example, the "shield-back" of the western United States, a pest on vegetation in arid places. One tiny species is a nuisance as a leaf

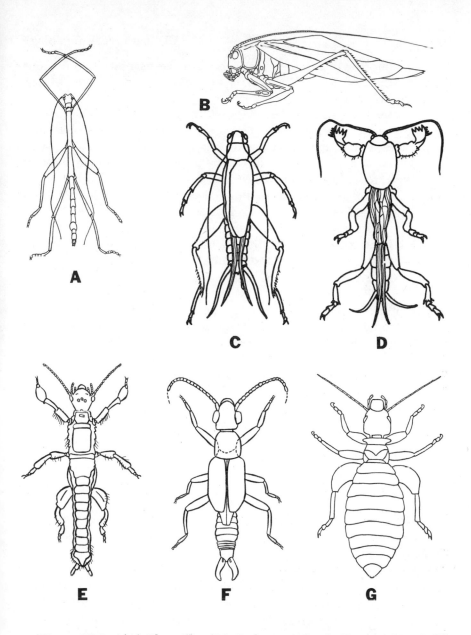

Figure 13.4. (A) Phasmida; (B) Orthoptera, family Tettigonidae, *Amblycorpha* species; (C) Orthoptera, family Gryllidae, *Gryllus* species; (D) Orthoptera, family Gryllotalpidae, *Gryllotalpa* species; (E) Embioptera; (F) Dermaptera; (G) Corrodentia. (A–D from specimens in Carnegie Museum; E redrawn from Ross *in* Essig, 1942, by permission of The Macmillan Company; F after Hebard, 1917a; G after Back, 1920)

roller, binding leaves together with silk to make its nest. The familiar green katydids, whose stridulation is so typical of midsummer nights, belong in this group.

GRYLLOIDEA—The true crickets (Fig. 13.4C) have long antennae and only three tarsal segments. The ovipositor is slender, needle-like and conspicuous. At rest, the wings are usually folded so that they embrace the abdomen. Stridulation is produced by a file and scraper on the tegmina. The cerci are extremely long.

Practically every country has its large black field crickets that are both phytophagous and predaceous, as well as smaller house crickets that are likely to be pestiferously omnivorous. The pale tree dwellers are the best musicians, but their habit of inserting their eggs into growing twigs makes them very destructive to trees and shrubs. One group, tiny both in size and numbers, are the "ant lovers" (Mymecophilinae), commensals in ant nests.

For centuries crickets have been a source of recreation in the Orient. Males of certain species of crickets are caged (females are mute) as highly prized songsters. The pugnacious male field crickets are caught and matched in fights. A good champion may sell for as much as $100 and there is an account of a cricket named Ghengis Khan, the Canton Battler, who went into the ring with $90,000 at stake among the spectators.

ACRIDOIDEA—The short-horned grasshoppers, true locusts and grouse locusts have the antennae shorter than the head and thorax. There are three tarsal segments; the ovipositor is short and inconspicuous. The wings are often brilliantly colored and at rest are folded fan-wise beneath the tegmina. Stridulation is produced by rubbing a scraper on the tegmina against a file on the femur, or by rubbing the hindwings against the thickened veins of the tegmina.

With about 5000 species, this is the largest and also the most destructive group of orthopterans. It includes the true locusts, the migratory grasshoppers so often described as Biblical plagues. The name "locust" is locally misapplied in some regions to the cicadas (Hemiptera), but is used correctly only for these grasshoppers. The "spur throat" (Melanoplus) has been a catastrophic crop pest in the United States; in the 1870's swarms destroyed every green thing in their path from Colorado to Texas. Around the Mediterranean, clouds of the desert locust (Schistocerca) from Africa are a menace; in 1881 the locust was so prolific that the people of Cyprus destroyed 1300 tons of egg cases. After a period of favorable environmental conditions the migratory locusts appear in literal millions, and then for a few years their numbers decrease, but a plague is always likely to recur.

In many uncivilized places they have been a standard diet item and now are available in our gourmet shops—french-fried or canned. A greater appreciation of these delicacies might lessen their depredations!

GRYLLOTALPOIDEA—The mole crickets (Fig. 13.4D) have short antennae and only two or three tarsal segments. The ovipositor is vestigial. The tegmina are short and the hindwings at rest are folded around the abdomen. Sound is produced only by wing vibration (hum) and there are no special stridulating structures. The forelegs have the tibia greatly modified to enable digging.

Although only forty-three species are known, these fascinating animals are found everywhere in the world, with the majority in the tropics. They live in burrows, generally near stream banks, and are rarely noticed but are not uncommon. The fore tibio-tarsus is highly modified and resembles a clumsy hand or the forepaw of a mole.

In all, the Orthoptera include about 15,000 species found in all parts of the world except in the polar regions. The fossil record indicates that the order probably originated in the Paleozoic era. Jurassic remains are of insects with stridulating organs and probably ancestral to the crickets. Acridoidea are plentifully represented in the Tertiary, but must have evolved during an earlier period.

Order 14. Embioptera Hagan, 1861
(From the Greek: *lively* and *wing*)
Web spinners
(Figs. 3.7B, 13.4A)

Small slender, cylindrical, soft-bodied insects with relatively large heads. Compound eyes large in male, smaller in female; no ocelli. Antenna filiform, medium length. Ectognathous chewing mouthparts. Wings, when present, membranous, similar in size and venation, held flat over the abdomen at rest; absent in some males and all females. Legs short and stout, the first segment of fore tarsi enlarged, containing silk glands; femur of hindlegs enlarged; tarsi 3-segmented, 2 post-tarsal claws. Thorax almost equal in length to the 11-segmented abdomen. Cerci 2-segmented, asymmetric in males. Oviparous; paurometabolous with terrestrial nymphs.

Embioptera pass their lives in unique protective silken tunnels which they busily and rapidly weave ahead of themselves to create routes to wherever they decide to go. The fairly large eggs are laid in groups, either uncovered or embedded in a cement of saliva and excrement and encased in silk. Females exhibit strong maternal care of eggs and nymphs. *Haploembia tarsalis* Ross is parthenogenetic, as probably are other species in which no males have ever been found. Most species are tropical or subtropical. Basically nocturnal, they are sometimes seen in the open on cloudy days. They live gregariously in their complex of tunnels under rocks, debris or loose bark. There is no evident social organization and there are no castes. They appear to be entirely phytophagous.

Despite their fragility, fossil specimens have been found in Lower Permian shales of Kansas, in Tertiary ambers and the Colorado Florissant bed.

Order 15. Dermaptera Leach, 1815
(From the Greek: *skin* and *wing*, probably referring
to texture of tegmina)
Earwigs
(Fig. 13.4F)

Small to medium-sized with narrow, elongate, dark, well-sclerotized bodies. Prognathous head broad or small; compound eyes well developed or absent; ocelli vestigial or absent. Filiform, segmented antennae, usually long. Ectognathous chewing mouthparts. Well-developed thorax, the metathorax fused with first abdominal segment. Forewings reduced to a short, truncated, leathery, elytra-like tegmina, hindwings membranous, semicircular, numerous weak veins, fan-folded and crossed at rest; some species wingless. Legs strong, with 3-segmented tarsi terminating with a pair of post-tarsal claws, with or without a median pad. Abdomen 11-segmented; only 9 evident in male in which first abdominal tergum is fused with metanotum, eleventh reduced to a tiny pygidium; in female seventh and eighth concealed under ninth, thus 7 evident segments. Cerci usually modified as heavily sclerotized forceps. Ovipositor reduced or absent. Oviparous; paurometabolous with terrestrial nymphs.

The female lays a group of twenty to eighty pale, smooth eggs in damp soil, manure or some similar place and exhibits unusual maternal care. She sits over the eggs like a brooding hen and keeps the young around her until they are able to look after themselves. Maturity is reached after six to eight instars; in temperate zones there is but one generation a year, but in the tropics proliferation is more rapid.

Earwigs are nocturnal, preferring moist, dark places of almost any sort —under stones, manure piles, in hollow plant stems or under bark. Temperate species are mostly herbivorous, but those in the tropics are frequently carnivorous and sometimes cannibalistic. Old superstitions hold that earwigs may enter the human ear during sleep and cause brain damage. There is no evidence that they are harmful to man except as an occasional pest on vegetation and fruit when they become too numerous.

About 1100 species have been described. The primitive precursors have been found as fossils in the oldest division of the Swiss Jurassic beds and true Dermaptera appear in the Tertiary Miocene and Oligocene with little deviation from forms living today.

Order 16. Corrodentia Burmeister, 1839
(From the Latin: *to gnaw*)
Psocids, Book lice, Bark lice
(Fig. 13.4G)

Minute to small with fragile, light-colored bodies, slender or slightly globose, smooth or hairy and dorso-ventrally flattened. Hypognathous head large, mobile. Compound eyes usually large; 3 ocelli in winged forms, absent in wingless. Antennae setiform or long and filiform. Ectognathous chewing mouthparts somewhat modified. Prothorax reduced and resembling a neck in winged forms. Membranous wings with simple venation and pterostigma, the forewing larger; held tent-like at rest; wingless forms more common; some brachypterous species. Slim legs with enlarged femora, tarsi of 1–3 segments with paired post-tarsal claws. Abdomen with 10 evident segments, the first reduced, and a vestigial eleventh. No cerci. Silk spinning tubes in labial palpi. Oviparous; paurometabolous with terrestrial nymphs.

Eggs, which vary greatly in appearance among the species, may be laid singly or in groups of over a hundred, usually covered with silk webbing or hardened secretions. At least six instars are required to reach maturity. Indoor species breed throughout the year, but others may have only two or three generations annually, particularly in colder zones. Some species are parthenogenetic.

The wingless "book lice" are probably the best known members of the order since they are serious pests everywhere indoors—granaries, libraries, entomology laboratories. They eat cereal products, debris or dead insects. Frequently they infest old papers and books from which they eat the paste and glue of the bindings. The majority of the order live outdoors among litter, where they consume all sorts of animal and vegetable debris, as well as bark and nuts.

The adults are able to make a substantial sound by striking their venters against loose wood or thin paper, which possibly contributes to the superstition about the "death watch ticking" in old, infested houses, although such noises are more likely to be caused by the Anobiid beetles.

There are over 1000 species with world-wide distribution. Because these insects are so delicate, only a few have been preserved as Tertiary fossils, mainly in Baltic amber, the copals and the Colorado White River beds.

Order 17. Mallophaga Nitzsch, 1818
(From the Greek: *to eat* and *wool*)
Biting lice, Bird lice
(Figs. 3.6I, 13.5A)

Small ectoparasitic insects, dorso-ventrally flattened with tough integument and large, distinct head. Antennae with 3–5 segments, either capitate and concealed or filiform and evident. Strongly modified chewing mouthparts tending to be endognathous. Compound eyes reduced and ocelli absent. Secondarily wingless. Short legs adapted for clinging; tarsi 1- or 2-segmented with 2, 1 or no post-tarsal claws; no empodium or pulvillus. Thorax narrow with prothorax free and well developed. 8–10 visible segments in abdomen resulting from fusion of first and second as well as eighth and ninth. Cerci absent. Ventral thoracic spiracles. No external genitalia; ovipositor frequently absent. Oviparous; paurometabolous, nymphs ectoparasitic.

Each female lays fewer than a hundred eggs (**nits**) attached separately by a gluey secretion to the base of the host's hair or feathers. Nymphs resembling the adults emerge in about four days and pass through three instars in a period of one to four weeks before reaching maturity; adult life lasts only a few months.

All Mallophaga are ectoparasites on birds or mammals and, because they have no personal means of transportation, tend to be rather host specific. Since the lice can transfer only when their hosts come in contact with each other, the presence of certain species often provides interesting correlation with the phylogeny of the host. They feed on feathers, hair, skin, scales and sometimes on dried blood around wounds. Those with claws run rapidly on the host's body and the claws are cunningly designed for clinging to hair or feathers. Species without claws cling with their jaws. The wingless condition is an adaptation to the parasitic life. In the intestinal tract of forms that feed on dried blood there are symbiotic bacteria which assist in digestion and which are passed on from generation to generation by transovarian transmission.

There is world-wide distribution of over 2000 known species. While they are not blood suckers or disease vectors, they can cause serious discomfort to their hosts. An infestation leads to constant scratching, sometimes to secondary infection along with loss of appetite and lowered egg production in fowl.

No fossils have been recorded for this order.

Order 18. Anoplura Leach, 1815
(From the Greek: *unarmed* and *tail*)
Sucking lice, Cooties
(Figs. 3.6J, 3.18C, 13.5B)

Small, pale or grey ectoparasites with hard body flattened dorso-ventrally, either elongated or crab-like. Head small, pointed. Eyes rudimentary or absent except in species attacking man; ocelli absent. Short setiform antennae with 3–5 segments. Cryptognathous mouthparts highly modified for piercing and sucking. Secondarily wingless. Short stout legs joined well to the side of thorax; tarsi 1-segmented with a long post-tarsal claw engaging a toothed tibial projection and adapted for clinging. Thorax small, broader than head, segments fused. Abdomen rounded or oval with 9 segments, no cerci. Oviparous; paurometabolous with ectoparasitic nymphs.

The Anoplura live as ectoparasites on mammalian hosts with relatively constant body temperatures and thus are spared the climatic fluctuations to which most insects must adapt. The life history is relatively simple. Several hundred eggs or nits are laid singly, attached to the hair or wool of the host. With optimum warmth automatically provided, they hatch within five days to two weeks. Larvae pass through four instars and in about ten days reach maturity. In the tropics reproduction continues throughout the year, but in cold regions it is sometimes retarded during winters.

All species are blood suckers on mammals, and most are host specific. Primates, ungulates, rodents and carnivores (except cats) are especially attacked. Only a few species attack man and domestic animals, but they produce large numbers of individuals. The irritation of a heavy infestation can imperil the health of the host, but the parasites are far more dangerous as vectors of various diseases. Lice transmit relapsing fever, trench fever and typhus (Chapter One). Under crowded or unsanitary conditions, epidemics result as the lice move from person to person.

There is world-wide distribution of the over 400 known species, but no fossils have been found.

Order 19. Hemiptera Linné, 1758
(From the Greek: *half* and *wing*)
Water striders, Bedbugs, Cicadas, Leafhoppers, Aphids
and bugs of all sorts
(Figs. 3.6D–F, 3.18B, 5.2D, E, 13.5C, D)

A large order of insects heterogeneous in size, shape, coloring and habits. Head prognathous or hypognathous. Compound eyes large; ocelli present or absent. Antennae various, with 2–10 segments, rarely more. Piercing, sucking mouthparts formed as a beak-like structure, sometimes pouched and retractable. Wings either long or short, venation simple; forewings thickened basally and carried flat over the back at rest, or membranous and held roof-like, or absent. Legs adapted for walking, running, digging, grasping or swimming; tarsi 1- to 3-segmented with 1 or 2 posttarsal claws, terminal pad present or absent. Abdomen with variable number of segments evident. Cerci absent. Oviparous, viviparous or both, dependent on species; most families paurometabolous, but Coccidae, Aleyrodidae and Phylloxeridae holometabolous. Immatures either terrestrial or aquatic.

Both the classification and the nomenclature of this large, very important group of insects have had a checkered history. When only the fauna of the temperate zone is considered, there is no difficulty in dividing them into two distinct orders. When the faunae of the entire world are taken into account, it is found that any attempt to define two orders is impossible; no matter on what basis a distinction is made, some of the numerous families are found to combine features of both supposed orders and no clear line can be drawn. It seems more logical to place them into a single order and students of classification have recognized one order as often as two. Four possible names are available and have been variously applied. Hemiptera of Linné is the prior name and must be used in any case. Homoptera and Heteroptera of Latreille have often been used when two orders have been recognized, though sometimes Hemiptera has been substituted for one or the other. A fourth name, Rhynchota of Burmeister, has also been used but there is no need for it.

Edith Patch (1920: 156) wrote delightfully that: "To attempt to epitomize the life cycle of the aphids is like trying to draw an orderly sketch of Chaos." Her remark is even more applicable to any effort to summarize life histories in the whole order Hemiptera. Aside from a few not always obvious morphological features, if any one characteristic is true of all Hemiptera, it is that they are evolutionarily plastic and opportunistically adaptive.

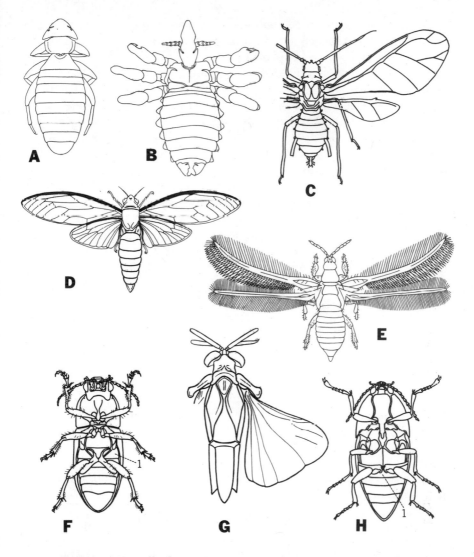

Figure 13.5. (A) Mallophaga; (B) Anoplura; (C) Hemiptera, family Aphididae; (D) Hemiptera, family Cicadidae; (E) Thysanoptera; (F) Coleoptera, suborder Adephaga, *Harpalus* species; (G) Strepsiptera; (H) Coleoptera, suborder Polyphaga. *1*, first abdominal segment. (A, B, D, F from specimens in Carnegie Museum; C after Gilette and Palmer, 1931; E after Foster and Jones, 1915; G after Pierce, 1909; H after Roache, 1960)

In oviparous groups the female may lay from a very few to many hundreds of diversely shaped and patterned eggs in almost every conceivable situation—on the ground, in plant tissue, on leaves or twigs, under stones, on or in water or within the tissues of living insects. Usually there are six immature instars, but there are only three for the neotenic females of scale insects (Coccidae), while the cicadas have seven. Like most insects, a great many of the Hemiptera have only one generation a year. The aphids, however, may have thirteen or more, while the famous seventeen-year cicada (incorrectly called "locust" by some) receives its name from the length of its immature life.

It has been estimated that in sexually reproducing leafhoppers, if a female lays only fifty eggs a day she would have 5 million descendants in six generations. In certain families parthenogenesis (see Chapter Seven) increases the reproductive capacity to staggering levels: the same statisticians estimate that the progeny of one stem mother aphid, who begins the annual cycle in temperate regions, would be 210^{15} in just 300 days! These figures assume no mortality, of course. Parthenogenesis is characteristic of the superfamily Aphidoidea (Adelgidae, Phylloxeridae, Eriosomatidae and Aphididae) and reaches its most complex level in the Aphididae, of which family certain tropical species apparently have no males at any time.

The vast majority of Hemiptera are paurometabolous, but in three families a holometabolous cycle has evolved, a development foreshadowed in many of the other families in which terminal embryogenesis tends to become concentrated in the last nymphal instar. Males of the Coccidae, Aleyrodidae and Phylloxeridae pass through a series of immature instars which are clearly larval (that they bear a superficial resemblance to the adults is beside the point, since the criteria for identifying a holometabolous larva are embryogenic), and then enter a typically pupal stage before becoming adult. When larval and pupal stages are present, the cycle is, by definition, holometabolous. In these three families the situation is made more difficult to comprehend at a glance by the fact that most of the females are neotenic, reaching sexual maturity while still morphologically larvae and without entering pupation. It has been frequently said that in these families the females are paurometabolous, whereas the males are holometabolous, a conclusion which obviously cannot be true.

The discovery (Hinton, 1948) that holometabolism has evolved polyphyletically in insects has upset a long-cherished notion that the holometabolous orders constitute a natural taxon and should clear the way for a better understanding of the major evolutional lines in the higher insects.

The numerous families of Hemiptera are divided into two suborders for convenience, the Heteroptera and Homoptera, in general distinguished by the following characterizations:

HETEROPTERA	HOMOPTERA
1. Forewings heavily sclerotized at the base, only the apical half membranous.	1. Forewings, when present, entirely membranous and of uniform texture.
2. Wings at rest held flat over the back.	2. Wings at rest held tent-like over the back.
3. Beak appears to arise at the anterior end of the head.	3. Beak appears to arise at the posterior end of the head and extends back between the legs.
4. Gular region of head well defined.	4. Gular region not clearly defined.
5. Pronotum usually greatly enlarged.	5. Pronotum usually not especially prominent.
6. Odiferous glands present.	6. Wax glands usually present.
7. Tarsi usually 3-segmented.	7. Tarsi 1-to 3-segmented.
8. Exlusively paurometabolous.	8. Either pauro- or holometabolous.
9. Terrestrial or aquatic nymphs.	9. Terrestrial nymphs or larvae.
10. Herbivorous, predaceous or blood-sucking.	10. Herbivorous only.

The HETEROPTERA include many familiar bugs, both noxious and beneficial. Aquatic families include the graceful water striders (Gerridae), the water boatmen (Corexidae) and the giant water bugs (Belostomidae). Bedbugs (Cimicidae) may be all too familiar. The delicate, exquisite lace bugs (Tingidae) unfortunately feed on foliage. Among the more serious pests are the cinch bugs (Lygaeidae), so destructive to grain, and the plant bugs (Miridae) which attack many kinds of crops—garden vegetables, rice, sugar cane, tea, fruit and shade trees. Not only do they weaken their host plants by sucking out the sap, but they also transmit a variety of fungal and viral diseases to them. Other Miridae, however, are predaceous species serving as a valuable control of aphids and similar pests. Among the common stink bugs (Pentatomidae) a number of species attack crop pests and can only be counted as beneficial, but the harlequin cabbage bug is a serious pest. The flower bugs (Anthocoridae) all are useful because of their regular diet of mites, thrips, phylloxerans and other harmful groups.

Very few HOMOPTERA are beneficial insects; all attack vegetation and because of their incredible reproductive capacity include many serious pests. Virtually no plant species is free of their depredations. The cicadas (Cicadidae), whose shrill mating song is the familiar background music of an August afternoon, weaken trees and shrubs by inserting eggs into growing twigs. Of the plant lice, the Chermidae (psyllids) particularly attack fruit trees, while the Phylloxeridae and Aphididae feed on the juices of a wide variety of plants. Since these and related families frequently alternate host plants during the course of a season, their potential for damage is increased. Certain plant lice are known as "ant cows" because they are protected and cared for by ants in return for "honey dew," secreted by the aphid and eaten by the ant. This unusual relationship serves to add to both their survival and their destructive ability. Many scale insects (Coccoidea) and leafhoppers (Cicadoidea) are exceedingly pestiferous and destructive.

The Hemiptera are the only insects properly called "bugs." The more than 48,000 species are distributed in every part of the world except the polar regions and, as a whole, are a most destructive order. The annual damage to useful vegetation as a result of their feeding on sap is enormous, but worse, perhaps, is the fact that they are major vectors of plant disease. While all this injury is only indirectly harmful to man, certain species feed on human blood and are directly harmful. In Mexico and southern United States and throughout Central and South America various species in the family Reduviidae transmit Chagas disease both to man and to rodents. Although the bedbug has not yet been conclusively indicted as a disease vector, an infestation of them is a severe and weakening annoyance, with which an estimated eighty per cent of the people in the world must cope. Most aquatic species bite viciously if touched and some attack fowl and small animals, but all also contribute to maintaining the balance of stream biota.

Some predaceous species help to control other arthropods and a few species are commercially useful. The dye cochineal is obtained from a scale insect, as are lac and Chinese wax. The shells of certain scale insects are used in some countries as jewelry. But these few contributions do not balance the depredations wrought by other Hemiptera.

The fossil record of this order is quite rich and begins in the lower Permian with the ancestral suborder Palaeorrhyncha, from which numerous lines evolved. In some Permian and Triassic strata the Homoptera are the commonest fossils present. As the ages of insect orders go, the Homoptera appear to be somewhat younger than most. By the Tertiary the living forms had evolved and fossils from the ambers are referred to modern genera or species.

Order 20. Thysanoptera Haliday, 1836
(From the Greek: *fringe* and *wing*)
Thrips
(Figs. 3.18A, 8.8A, B, 13.5E)

Minute or small insects with slender bodies and tough integument. Hypognathous head without obvious neck. Conspicuous compound eyes; winged forms with 3 ocelli. Antennae with 6–10 short segments. Asymmetric ectognathous cone-like mouthparts adapted for rasping and sucking. Wings long, narrow with few veins, fringed prominently with hairs, folded over the abdomen at rest; brachypterous and apterous species. Short legs with 1- or 2-segmented tarsi, post-tarsi with paired or single claws and a protrusible vesicle. Abdomen with 11 segments, the first usually reduced and the last often modified in connection with external genitalia. Cerci absent. Ovipositor and male genitalia present or absent. Oviparous; holometabolous with oligopod terrestrial larvae and adecticous exarate pupae.

Most thrips are bisexual, but others are wholly or partly parthenogenetic. A few species are viviparous. Oviparous species lay large numbers of eggs scattered at random on the ground, grouped in cracks or crevices, hidden under debris or inserted directly into plant tissue. Larvae hatch within about a week and require three or four instars to reach maturity. The pear thrips, larvae of which hibernate during summer and fall, produce one generation a year, but some other species may have as many as seven generations annually. The first several instars are oligopod larvae, lacking wing pads and with fewer antennal segments than the adult, but occupying the same ecological niche. Wings appear externally in the prepupal (last larval) instar; the pupa is essentially a resting stage, but is capable of limited locomotion (see Chapter Eight). Females of most species are neotenic and do not reach pupation.

There are two suborders. The Terebrantia are characterized by the presence of at least one complete longitudinal vein in the wings and a saw-like ovipositor in females. In the Tubulifera the wings are almost entirely devoid of venation and females, lacking an ovipositor, have the terminal segments of the abdomen formed as an extensible tube with which to deposit eggs.

A few species are scavengers on decaying vegetable matter, and a certain number are predators on small insects such as aphids or mites or attack the eggs and young larvae of larger insects. Most thrips, however, suck plant juices. When present in sufficient numbers, these phytophagous species may become pests to be reckoned with. The egg-laying habits of the Terebrantia cause destruction to growing shoots, and their feeding habits may be destructive to a crop. To compound the felony, they serve as vectors for virus and bacterial plant diseases.

The approximately 2500 known species are distributed throughout the tropical and temperate zones. Fossil species have been found in Tertiary shales, ambers and copal, but thus far not from earlier horizons.

Order 21. Coleoptera Linné, 1758
(From the Greek: *sheath* and *wings*)
Beetles, Weevils
(Figs. 3.6C, 3.8C–E, G, H, 5.2F, 5.7A–D, 6.5C, 6.6D,
8.6A, 8.10A, 13.5F, H)

Minute to large insects with heavily sclerotized integument, body of varied shapes and colors. Head free, hypo- or prognathous. Compound eyes well developed; ocelli usually lacking, but sometimes either lateral pair or median ocellus present. Antennae 9-, 10- or 11-segmented, variously developed. Ectognathous chewing mouthparts strong. Prothorax distinct; meso- and metathorax united, broadly joined with abdomen. Forewings heavily sclerotized (elytra), thickened, apparently veinless; hindwings membranous with reduced venation; at rest, hindwings usually folded under elytra, which form a protective shield and generally meet on a straight mid-dorsal line; wings sometimes reduced or hindwings absent. Legs strong, variously adapted; coxae sometimes immobile, tarsi 5-segmented in primitive, reduced to 3 or 4 segments in others; post-tarsi with claws paired or single. Abdomen basically with 10 segments, the first usually vestigial or atrophied, the others often reduced. Cerci absent. Mostly oviparous; holometabolous metamorphosis; larvae campodeiform (oligopod) or eruciform, often with urogomphi (polypod), usually terrestrial, sometimes aquatic; pupae decticous.

With some 300,000 species identified, this is the largest order in the animal kingdom. Something like 200 families are currently recognized on a world-wide basis, grouped into three to six suborders according to various authorities. In general, the beetles are structurally homogenous. The simplest division into suborders places the carabid-like families in Adephaga, all other beetles in Polyphaga, except a score of rare and problematic species assigned to Archostemata.

ADEPHAGA (Fig. 13.5F)	POLYPHAGA (Fig. 13.5H)
1. Fixed hind coxal cavities divide first visible abdominal sternite.	1. Hind coxal cavities not dividing first abdominal sternite.
2. Hindwings with 2 m–cu cross veins.	2. Hindwings without cross veins.
3. Prothorax with pleural sutures.	3. No clear pleural sutures on prothorax.
4. Larval thoracic legs with tarsi and 2 claws.	4. Larval thoracic legs without tarsi and only 1 claw.

Adephaga and many families of Polyphaga are predators and are regarded as beneficial natural controls of many noxious arthropods. Some are parasitic or semiparasitic. Phytophagous groups include a great many serious pests.

Most beetles are oviparous, but viviparity occurs in some species of three different families and a few species are parthenogenetic. Ordinarily the eggs are laid in or near the larval food and habitat. Several main types of larvae occur (see Figs. 8.6A and 8.10A), as well as many variations of each. The oligopod (including campodeiform, caraboid and scarabaeoid) larvae have antennae, eyes, cerci and thoracic legs but no abdominal legs. The caraboid type has long, strong legs and mouthparts well adapted for predaceous habits and is very active; in aquatic species, the hairy legs are suited for swimming as in Dytiscidae. Most phytophagous oligopod larvae are the scarabaeoid type—fatter and less active and with the appendages and eyes not so well formed. Eruciform larvae are the familiar "grubs," found concealed in protected places; they have reduced eyes, both antennae and thoracic legs are poorly developed and the cerci are modified into anal prolegs (**urogomphi**); this type of larva is less advanced in ontogeny and is the equivalent of the polypod embryogenic stage. The aquatic polypod larvae of the Gyrinidae bear on each abdominal segment a pair of articulated plumose lateral gills which develop from limb rudiments (Snodgrass, 1935). Certain apodous larvae lacking even the thoracic legs are sometimes thought to be modified from the polypod stage, but in most cases are probably modified oligopod. In parasitic Meloidae, for example, the first instar larva is oligopod (triungulin) and very active; subsequent instars are apodous. It seems most unlikely that ontogeny would be reversed.

Pupation occurs in sheltered places such as earthen cells, in larval mines, burrows or borings and sometimes on the surface of the ground beneath rubble. A cocoon, when it is present, is formed from silk produced from the malpighian tubules.

The majority of beetles have a single generation each year, but a number of species have as many as five. Certain wood-boring species are said to require twenty-five to thirty years to reach maturity.

ADEPHAGA

CICINDELIDAE—The tiger beetles are rapidly running hunters with somewhat depressed, often brightly colored bodies and prominent mandibles. The oligopod larvae live in earthen burrows, from the mouths of which they ambush passing prey.

CARABIDAE—The ground beetles are active predators, though a few also eat seeds and grain. About 21,000 species are known, distributed in every part of the world including the Arctic, with the greatest number in the tropics. Certain genera have elongated heads and narrow thoraces and attack land snails. Many tropical species climb trees in search of prey and fly well. Adults produce offensive odors from anal glands. The oligopod larvae are actively predaceous.

DYTISCIDAE—Predaceous water beetles and diving beetles are medium to large with oval depressed bodies. They are aquatic and predaceous in both immature and mature stages; the larvae have caudal gills, but adults must come to the surface to replenish their supply of air.

GYRINIDAE—The whirligig beetles are shiny, flattened and oval and have a habit of gyrating wildly or "figure skating" on the surface of the water. Adults are carnivorous and may dive for prey or for protection, but must return to the surface for air; their eyes are divided, with a lower part especially adapted for underwater vision. Larvae are aquatic and have a series of lateral abdominal gills; they, too, are predators.

POLYPHAGA

HYDROPHILIDAE—The water scavenger beetles are elongated oval, compact, heavily sclerotized forms. Despite the name, the family includes many semiaquatic and terrestrial species. Most feed on decaying plant matter, fungi or dung, and a few are predaceous. The adults readily fly and are strongly attracted to lights. Aquatic and semiaquatic larvae have lateral abdominal gills. Females of many species carry their eggs in cocoon-like cases until hatching.

SILPHIDAE—The carrion beetles are a small family with diverse habits. The most famous members are the sexton or burying beetles (*Necrophorus*). Several adults work together to undermine a corpse of a small mammal; after burying it they deposit their eggs in a gallery leading to the burial. Most Silphidae feed on carrion; a few are predaceous and some eat decomposing plant material.

STAPHYLINIDAE—The rove beetles have somewhat cylindrical bodies, prominent mandibles and very short elytra covering only the anterior part of the abdomen. Most adults are carnivorous or saprophagous; many species inhabit the nests of ants or termites. The oligopod larvae are almost all predaceous. A few parasitic species approach the "hypermetamorphosis" of Meloidae and Strepsiptera. The active triungulin-like first instar larva seeks out pupae of cyclorraphous flies, gnaws into the puparium and after molting becomes a degenerate apodous form. More than 20,000 species are known.

LAMPYRIDAE—The fireflies and glowworms are elongated, soft-bodied nocturnal beetles and some have light-producing organs on the abdomens of both adults and larvae. In many species the female is larviform, lacks wings and apparently is neotenic. Adults feed little or not at all; larvae are predaceous on soft-bodied arthropods.

CANTHARIDAE—Soldier beetles are narrow, elongated beetles frequently noticed around flowers. Both larvae and adults are predaceous and some species are particularly valuable because they feed on aphids and scale insects.

CLERIDAE—This essentially tropical family has representatives in temperate zones, including useful species, in which both larvae and adults are predaceous, attacking a wide variety of wood-boring and bark beetles, locusts and grasshoppers, bees, wasps and hornets. Several species are, however, pests in beehives. Adults are small to medium, cylindrical and frequently brightly colored.

ELATERIDAE—The click beetles include some 8000 species and are of world-wide distribution. Adults are elongated and flattened. When turned on their backs, they flip up and over with a sharp click. Some larvae are carnivorous, but the majority of species are phytophagous at all stages. The very destructive "wireworms," pests feeding on the roots of grass and cereal crops, are the larvae of certain genera.

BUPRESTIDAE—This large family of brilliantly colored beetles, the larvae of which are root, trunk, stem or bark borers, are found in forests and orchards everywhere, especially in the tropics. Adults are sometimes used as jewelry and are very popular with certain collectors, who pay high prices for gaudy tropical specimens. Larvae are very unpopular with tree farmers and foresters who pay even higher prices to destroy them.

DERMESTIDAE—The carpet, skin or larder beetles are small to medium in size and dull-colored. Adults fly readily and feed on flower pollen. The larvae are fuzzy or hairy, grey or reddish-brown. A number of species are cosmopolitan pests in stores, warehouses, homes, museums and wherever dead animals, animal products or cereals are stored or used. Larvae attack hides, furs, horn, wool, woolen goods, cheese, cured meats and cereal products.

COCCINELLIDAE—The ladybird beetles are small to medium-sized with oval or rounded bodies and are often brightly colored and spotted. The majority are predaceous in both larval and adult stages on aphids and similar plant pests. The larvae are active caraboid forms, usually spiny and orange-colored. Those of certain *Coccinella* species are known to destroy about twenty aphids a day, while the larva of *Hyperaspis* may destroy about ninety adults and 3000 immature scale insects in the same period. For this reason certain species are cultivated and commercially distributed for use in pest control. A few of the more than 3000 species are phytophagous. The genus *Epilachna* includes the Mexican bean beetle, a major agricultural pest, but on the whole the family is a beneficial one.

MELOIDAE—The blister beetles are medium-sized with somewhat elongated, soft bodies. Several species are of economic importance as pests on tomatoes, potatoes and other crops. *Lytta vesicatoria* (Linné), known as the "Spanish fly," has for centuries been the source of the notorious but dangerous aphrodisiac cantharidin, a drug now limited to use in certain urogenital disorders. The life cycle includes a series of different larval forms (hypermetamorphosis). Eggs are laid in the soil; the active first instar larvae (triungulins) of some species actively seek out their food, usually the eggs of grasshoppers, mantids or certain hymenoptera; at this stage the larval mortality is exceedingly high. Successful triungulins pass through seven instars and are apodous in the last immature (prepupal) stage. A few species feed on honey or on bee larvae and in the triungulin stage attach themselves to an adult bee, hitchhiking to her nest or hive— suggestive of the Strepsiptera.

TENEBRIONIDAE—The darkling beetles include about 10,000 species, many of them injurious to vegetation or to stored foods. Adults are most diverse in appearance and habits. The black or drab ground beetles generally have aborted hindwings or have immovable elytra and cannot fly. They walk clumsily and, when disturbed, feign death or emit horrible odors. They propagate so efficiently that their large numbers sometimes devastate crops and natural vegetation. They are plentiful in dry or desert situations. Mealworms and flour beetles are cosmopolitan pests in granaries and find their way into warehouses and homes. The mealworm, *Tenebrio molitor* (Linné), is commercially cultivated as food for laboratory and other animals.

SUPERFAMILY PTINOIDEA—Four small families of pestiferous beetles are included. The powder post beetles (Lyctidae) bore into dried hard-wood and are destructive to furniture, structural timbers and lumber piles. Bostrichidae larvae infest both dead and living tree branches, barrels and corks or feed on stored grains; one undiscriminating species in California gnaws into lead cables, allowing moisture to enter and causing short circuits in utility lines. The Anobiidae include the wood-boring furniture beetle and the death watch beetle, as well as the drugstore beetle and the cigarette beetle. These last two, and all Ptinidae, feed on stored, dried plant products.

SUPERFAMILY SCARABAEOIDEA—About 30,000 species of closely related beetles with distinctive appearance and habits in both adult and larva are included. On a world-wide basis it is divided into from six to more than twenty families, depending upon the viewpoint of the authority concerned. Larvae are scavengers on decaying animal or plant matter such as rotten wood, dead roots, dung and the like. Certain families feed on living plants and include some very serious pests. Melolonthidae, or May or June beetles and chafers, are almost all injurious. Adults feed on flowers and foliage, the larvae on roots. Rutelidae have similar habits and include the Japanese beetle, which was accidentally introduced into New Jersey in 1916 and, in the absence of the natural enemies of its native habitat, has spread over most of temperate North America and at times is a scourge. Scarabaeidae (= Copridae) are mostly dung feeders; they roll balls of fecal material and bury them, the females depositing a large egg in each. The sacred scarab of ancient Egypt belongs to this group. Dynastidae include the spectacular Hercules beetle of the American tropics, the Atlas and Goliath beetles of Africa and rhinoceros beetles of tropical Asia. Stag beetles and pinching bugs belong in the Lucanidae. The males of both families often are equipped with grotesque mandibles and wonderful horns on the head, thorax or both; such projections are reduced and small in the females. It has been widely held that these horns are used by the males in combat to secure mates, a belief not supported by facts; Beebe (1947) observed combats between males of the Hercules beetle in Venezuela and noted that as often as not the lady went off with the vanquished instead of the victor.

CERAMBYCIDAE—The long-horned beetles are easily recognized because the antennae are so unusually long, often longer than the slender, flattened bodies. Many of the 20,000 species are attractively colored and all are phytophagous, associated with woody vegetation. Adults feed on pollen, fungi and leaves, or do not feed at all. A number of species that frequent flowers are quite similar to wasps in shape, coloring and even behavior. Larvae burrow into dead or living wood or pith and although injurious to standing trees or to cut logs, only a few species are sufficiently numerous to be serious pests in forests or orchards.

CHRYSOMELIDAE—The leaf beetles and flea beetles are small or minute, often globular. More than 25,000 species are known. A few are scavengers in termite nests, but the vast majority feed on living plant tissue, many being pests or potential pests. One subfamily is aquatic or semiaquatic in all stages. Viviparity has been observed in several genera. The Colorado potato beetle, the several cucumber beetles infesting vine and other crops and the numerous flea beetles that attack vegetables are members of the family.

BRUCHIDAE—The pea and bean weevils are small, oval beetles that feed on beans, peas and other leguminous seeds or on palm seeds such as coconuts. They are widespread and universally destructive pests. Gregor

Mendel wrote a friend that these beetles, by destroying his sweet peas, freed him to discontinue his studies on inheritance.

CURCULIONIDAE—The weevils or snout beetles include 40,000 often destructive species. They are readily recognized by the fact that the head is prolonged into a proboscis with the tiny mouthparts on its tip, the palpi concealed. All are phytophagous, feeding on living or dried plant material. *Scylotus multistriatus* (Marsham) has been established as the vector of Dutch elm disease. Almost every species of plant and every sort of grain or stored food of plant origin are attacked by one or another weevil. The cotton boll weevil, the granary weevil and the rice weevil are most notorious examples. Parthenogenesis is known in several genera.

SCOLYTIDAE—The bark or engraver beetles lack the snout, but otherwise are structurally similar to weevils. All are borers, mostly in living or dead wood, and the family is responsible for very heavy timber losses in temperate forests.

FOSSIL RECORD

Imprints of elytra in Upper Permian strata demonstrate that the Coleoptera differentiated very early. Many younger horizons abound in beetle remains and Tertiary specimens belong to modern genera. The best paleontologic clue to the origin of Coleoptera is found in the nature of some of the Permian elytra, which resemble orthopteroid tegmina and retain a simplified venation. Derivation from an early orthopteroid line appears more plausible than from the mecopteroid stock; placing Coleoptera in the "panorpoid complex" is probably based on a traditional reluctance to admit the polyphyletic development of holometabolism.

Order 22. Strepsiptera Kirby, 1813
(From the Greek: *twisted* and *wing*)
Stylopids
(Figs. 8.6D, 13.5G)

Tiny (1.5–4.5 mm.) insects with sexual dimorphism and endoparasitic larvae. Males: robust, thinly sclerotized. Head prognathous, free, relatively large. Compound eyes stalked; no ocelli. Short flabellate antennae with 4–7 segments. Chewing mouthparts weak or vestigial. Pro- and mesothorax reduced, metathorax enlarged to half the body length. Forewings long, narrow, reduced, elytron-like; hindwings membranous, broad, fan-shaped with reduced venation, folded longitudinally at rest. Legs long; fore and middle coxae elongated, hind coxae fixed and covering first abdominal sternum; trochanter present only on forelegs; tarsi with 2–5 segments; post-tarsi with empodium, with or without claws. Abdomen

10-segmented, ninth segment reduced, tenth vestigial. Females: wingless, incompletely developed, neotenic; in Mengidae free-living with eyes, antennae, legs and mouthparts strongly reduced; in other families, larviform, parasitic, head vestigial, fused with thorax, abdominal segmentation obscured. Viviparous; holometabolous; first instar larvae oligopod (triungulin), terrestrial, subsequent instars apodous, endoparasitic; adecticous exarate pupae.

The dozen or so species of the family Mengidae are the most primitive existing strepsipterans, retaining a five-segmented tarsus and the female having true adult structures. The biology of one of the species, *Eoxenos laboulebenei* of southern France, has been pieced together from field observations. Two kinds of females exist—those that leave the larval exuviae and move about and those that remain entrapped within the exuviae. Both have the same level of development, with the eyes, antennae, legs and mouthparts present, though reduced by comparison with the male. The role played by the truly free-living females is uncertain. It is thought that the males fertilize them, but neither copulation nor their progeny have been observed. The entrapped females viviparously produce active first instar triungulin larvae; parthenogenesis is suspected but not proved. Triungulins find their way into the bodies of *Lepisma aurea* (Thysanura), a commensal in an ant's nest. How they enter the host is problematic, since their mouthparts are aborted. The second instar larva is a typically endoparasitic apodous form. The number of instars is uncertain, but the prepupal instar has been found under stones on the ground where pupation occurs. Males complete terminal embryogenesis, molting to become imagos. Females develop only partially and are in fact reproductive pupae.

The greater number of strepsipterans compose the family Stylopidae, with about 300 known species. The family sometimes is subdivided into six or more families. Many species are known only from males which sometimes are attracted to light. Others are known only from females and larvae discovered in host insects. Both sexes have been discovered for a substantial number of species and some life histories have been worked out more or less completely despite the great difficulty of rearing and observing all stages. Viviparity and polyembryony appear to be universal. Parthenogenesis probably occurs in those species of which no males have been found.

In *Xenos vesparum* (Rossi), a parasite of the wasp *Polistes gallicus* (Linné), the female becomes reproductive in the seventh instar (prepupa or last stage larva) and develops no further. She produces thousands of triungulin larvae, some of which find new host wasps. Boring in, they become endoparasitic. The second to sixth instars are apodous larval stages during which males differentiate from females. Males pass through the prepupal instar, pupate and finally emerge as winged imagos. These males apparently live but a short time, barely long enough to locate a larviform female to fertilize.

The effect on the hosts of stylopid parasitization has been widely studied. The first instar stylopids enter the hosts while the latter are still larvae, as a rule. Host tissues are not destroyed, merely displaced, but suffer from lack of nutrition and the net result is that the host, when it becomes adult, may have a somewhat altered body shape and coloring and incompletely developed appendages and reproductive system. Stylopids parasitize bees, wasps, ants, crickets and various homopteran Hemiptera.

A fossil species, *Mengea tertiaria* Grote, has been found in Tertiary Baltic amber and represents the living family Mengeidae. There is thus no paleontologic evidence on the age or the origin of Strepsiptera. Their phylogenetic relationships have been much debated. Jeannel (1944) listed a series of morphologic similarities with the Hymenoptera, at the same time dismissing the even longer list of similarities with Coleoptera as being coincidence, the result of convergent evolution. Most entomologists recognize the strepsipterans as aberrant coleopterans and some recent classifications of Coleoptera place the stylopids as a superfamily of that order.

Order 23. Neuroptera Linné, 1758
(From the Greek: *nerve* and *wing*)
Lacewings, Ant lions, Dobsonflies, Hellgrammites, Alderflies
(Figs. 8.7A, 8.10B, 13.6A)

Minute, medium-sized or large, usually with slender fragile bodies, smooth, hairy or covered with powdery wax. Small prognathous head free. Large compound eyes well separated; 3 ocelli or none. Antennae basically filiform, variable in length. Ectognathous chewing mouthparts. Prothorax often elongated. Membranous wings with network venation, similar in size and development, held roof-like at rest. Legs short, slender, tarsi 5-segmented, post-tarsi with paired claws. Abdomen with 10 segments, the first and last reduced; no cerci. Many species with specialized glands secreting wax, scent, stink or cement for eggs. Malpighian tubules may produce silk. Oviparous; holometabolous; larvae terrestrial oligopod or aquatic polypod with mouthparts adapted for biting or sucking; adecticous pupae.

The insects here included are sometimes termed the "neuropteroid complex." Living species are readily divided into three groups differing from each other to a considerable degree in general appearance, size and shape and to some extent in ecological adaptation. Accordingly, three orders are sometimes recognized—Megaloptera, Raphidoidea and Neuroptera, in the more restricted sense. Despite the superficial diversity, all these insects are remarkably similar in their internal structures, their developmental patterns and their skeletal organizations; it seems best to keep them together as a single order. As a whole, the Neuroptera includes many archaic types justly regarded as "living fossils."

The oviparous females lay eggs of diverse size, shape and color, placing them singly or massed in various places. Eggs of Nemopteridae are hidden in dust; those of Mantispidae are cemented on long, slender stalks to the ground, where they look somewhat like fungal fruiting bodies; Chrysopidae fasten similar stalked eggs to green leaves; Sialidae lay egg masses on rocks.

Larvae are predaceous with biting mouthparts often adapted for sucking by the presence of a ventral groove on the mandible, so that when the maxilla is pressed against the mandible, the groove becomes a tube. Several families have polypod aquatic larvae (see Fig. 8.10B) provided with appendicular tracheal gills (Snodgrass, 1935). Pupae lie in a silken cocoon and have their appendages free and the mandibles well developed. The Mantispidae are said to undergo hypermetamorphosis because the early larvae are active, whereas later stages are quiescent; these quiescent stages are more correctly viewed as modified oligopods. Development is comparatively slow, the insect requiring a year or more to reach maturity. The complete life cycle of the dobsonfly (Corydalidae) takes three years.

As adults the Mantispidae, Myrmeleontidae and Ascalaphidae are often mistaken for members of other orders; all can be identified as neuropterans by the absence of cerci and the reduced abdominal segmentation. The last two families resemble Odonata, but may be distinguished by their prominent antennae and terrestrial larvae.

The larvae of the lovely green lacewings (Chrysopidae) are the valuable "aphis lions." Larvae of the brown lacewings (Hemerobiidae) are also predaceous and vary their diet with mealy bugs, psyllids, mites and other pests. The funnel-shaped traps of the ant lions (Myrmeleontidae) are a familiar sight in dusty or sandy areas. Dobsonfly (Corydalidae) larvae are the "hellgrammites" so prized as bait by stream fishermen.

Most of the 4000 species in this order are found in temperate and subtropical regions and are rarely abundant. They attack man neither directly nor indirectly and many contribute to biological control of pest species.

Fossils from the Permian beds of Australia represent ancestral groups.

Direct precursors of living families have been found in Triassic and Jurassic strata. Tertiary ambers have yielded specimens of contemporary groups.

Order 24. Mecoptera Packard, 1886
(From the Greek: *long* and *wings*)
Scorpion flies, Panorpids
(Figs. 4.4E, 13.6B)

Small to medium insects with slender bodies, coloring cryptic or vivid. Hypognathous head elongated into a beak tipped with biting mouthparts. Large compound eyes; 3 ocelli or none. Antennae long, jointed, filiform. Wings membranous and long, held tent-like at rest, venation primitive; some apterous species. Long legs with 5-segmented tarsi, post-tarsal claws paired or single. Long, cylindrical abdomen with 11 segments, the last segment vestigial in males and some females. Cerci short. Oviparous; holometabolous with polypod terrestrial larvae and decticous pupae.

The life history of only a few species is fully known. The eggs are laid in a mass on the ground; larvae live in burrows and may emerge only occasionally. Pupation takes place either in an underground cell or among damp debris. The Mecoptera are principally carnivorous at all stages, feeding both on living and dead insects, but fungi, flowers and fruit are also eaten. They are neither beneficial nor harmful to man.

The family Panorpidae contains the true scorpion flies, so called because the bulb-like male genitalia are carried erect and forward over the back much like the tail of a scorpion. The Bittacidae, sometimes mistaken for crane flies (Diptera), have an interesting habit of clinging to a twig with their forelegs and using the prehensile hind tarsi to catch living prey. The Boreidae are brachypterous or apterous and are associated with the Arctic ecologies of winter in the northern temperate zone. The adults resemble tiny grasshoppers when they leap, sometimes in large numbers, on or near the snow in midwinter. The several other families all contain few species with discontinuous distribution and represent relics of very ancient faunae.

Fewer than 500 living species are known, principally found in the temperate and subtropical regions. The Mecoptera are regarded as an ancient group and as the phylogenetic key to the higher holometabolous orders. Fossil species closely allied to the four living Australian species constituting the family Choristidae have been found in Kansas beds of Permian age. Both the Panorpidae and the Bitticidae are represented in British Liassic strata. Tertiary fossils from the Florissant bed and from Baltic amber are closely related to surviving species.

Order 25. Trichoptera Kirby, 1813
(From the Greek: *hair* and *wing*)
Caddis flies, Water moths
(Figs. 4.4B–D, 13.6C)

Small to medium, cryptically colored insects with soft bodies. Hypognathous head small and free. Large compound eyes, 3 or no ocelli. Antennae filiform, long and many-segmented. Poorly developed ectognathous chewing mouthparts. Wings hairy or scaly with primitive venation and few cross veins; forewing longer, hindwings with well-developed anal area; wings held roof-like in repose; some females brachypterous. Long, slender legs with spurred tibia and elongated coxae; tarsi 5-segmented, post-tarsi with paired claws and terminal pad. Abdomen 10-segmented, the terminal segment greatly reduced. Cerci with 1 or 2 segments. Salivary glands of larvae secrete silk. Oviparous; holometabolous with aquatic larvae often provided with tracheal or caudal gills; decticous pupae.

These insects were originally included in the Linnean order Neuroptera because of their more or less transparent wings. They are closely related to the Lepidoptera, being set apart chiefly because of their aquatic larvae and mandibulate mouthparts, but wing venation and genitalia are essentially similar and the primitive mandibulated moths connect the two orders, which might well be placed together.

Females deposit eggs in gelatinous masses or strings attached to some plant or other object on or beneath the water surface. Hatching occurs in from one to three weeks. Many species have one generation a year and the five larval instars require eleven months. The usual larval ecology is fresh running water, but some species prefer a brackish or even a salty environment.

All larvae have powerful mouthparts, a cluster of six stemmata on each side of the head, short antennae, well-developed thoracic legs and a pair of short appendages (prolegs), jointed in a few species, on the last abdominal segment. Embryogenically they may be regarded as being either at a very late polypod stage or at an early oligopod stage, but the former interpretation probably is more precise in view of the general level of development, particularly of the eyes. Two general types of larvae occur: eruciform, with hypognathous head and three sucker-like papillae (two lateral, one median) on the first abdominal segment, and campodeoid, with prognathous head and without papillae.

The eruciform caddis worms, familiar to fishermen as excellent bait, construct portable cases from selected debris bound together with silk, each species using a characteristic group of materials and having a char-

acteristic form. That case making as an art was evolved within the order
is demonstrated by the fact that the campodeoid larvae generally live
free, seeking protection beneath stones or similar objects, and only certain species construct cases. In four of these families with campodeoid
larvae stationary shelters are constructed. In the Hydroptilidae, a case
is constructed only by the last instar larva. In the Rhyacophilidae, only
one genus is known to build a case, actually a silken tunnel. The groups
with stationary cases sometimes build funnel-like traps of silken webbing
to snare their prey. Case-building larvae fasten their cases to fixed objects
and pupate within the case; free-living pupae construct a case-like cocoon
for pupation. Pupae have free appendages and strong mandibles used to
cut through the pupal shelter. At final ecdysis the pupa swims or crawls
to the surface of the water and transforms in the air, resting on some
floating object or on the bank. The moth-like adults have reduced mouthparts and probably feed on flower nectar or not at all. Most are nocturnal
and strongly phototropic.

The importance of this, the largest order of aquatic insects, rests primarily in their contribution to the biological balance of water environments. The larvae are either carnivorous or phytophagous, respectively
helping to control small aquatic animals or plants, while in turn they make
up an important element in the diet of fish and other aquatic forms.
About 3600 species are known.

The earliest representatives of living families were fossils from the
Triassic horizons in Europe. Permian fossils from Australia (Paramecop-
tera) were believed by Tillyard (1926) to be ancestral both to Trichoptera and to Lepidoptera.

Order 26. Lepidoptera Linné, 1758
(From the Greek: *scale* and *wing*)
Moths, Butterflies
(Frontispiece, Figs. 3.5, 3.6A, 3.15A, 3.21, 4.2, 4.4A, 4.6C,
5.3B, 5.9, 6.4B, 6.6C, 8.4)

Minute to very large insects with soft cylindrical bodies. Body, wings
and appendages generally covered densely with pigmented scales providing color patterns characteristic of species. Hypognathous, relatively small
head free on a slender neck. Large compound eyes well separated; 2 or no
ocelli. Antennae slim, the numerous variations characteristic of major
groups. Ectognathous mouthparts mandibulate in several primitive families; in all others, mouthparts with vestigial mandibles and the maxillae
modified to form a sucking proboscis coiled in repose or maxillae vestigial.

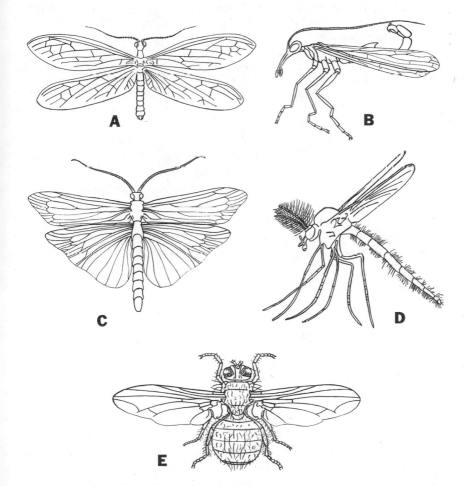

Figure 13.6. (A) Neuroptera, family Sialidae, *Sialis* species; (B) Mecoptera, *Panorpa* species; (C) Trichoptera; (D) Diptera, family Culicidae (male); (E) Diptera, family Tachinidae. (A–C, E drawn from specimens in Carnegie museum; D after Roback, 1959)

Thoracic segments strongly fused. Wings well developed, proportionately large, the hindwing smaller, longitudinal venation strong with few cross veins, in repose held in various positions; few apterous forms. Legs with large coxae fixed; tarsi basically 5-segmented, post-tarsi with paired claws. 10-segmented abdomen frequently partly fused or telescoped, not all segments usually evident. Cerci absent. Oviparous; holometabolous, polypod larvae generally terrestrial (a few aquatic), pupae decticous or (more often) adecticous.

With more than 105,000 known species, the Lepidoptera is one of the four largest insect orders. Because of the delicate beauty of so many moths and butterflies they have been exceedingly popular with nature lovers. Interest in collecting, studying and arranging Lepidoptera has initiated the careers of many professional scientists of all kinds.

It is difficult to divide the order into sound, manageable groups. Two popular approaches have had wide currency, but are quite without scientific validity. The distinction between Micro- and Macrolepidoptera is artificial: the latter "suborder" may be defined as including species large enough to be pinned conveniently into the collector's cabinet, the former includes all Lepidoptera too small for the average collector to bother with. The concepts of Rhopalocera and Heterocera are merely latinized expressions of the distinction between butterfly and moth respectively. It is true that butterflies probably are compact phylogenetically, but to obtain equivalent grouping of the moth families would require a whole series of categories. Many plausible systems based on structural and phylogenetic considerations have been proposed by a variety of able workers, who do not fully agree among themselves, though progress is being made.

Comstock divided Lepidoptera into two suborders. The Jugatae comprise a small group of very primitive families having a jugum or fibula (see Fig. 4.4B) at the base of the posterior margin of the forewing by which the wings are coupled. Some are mandibulate and have sometimes been placed in Trichoptera. All other families constitute the Frenatae, the wings being coupled by a frenulum (see Fig. 4.4F) or by overlapping alone where the frenulum is absent because of (presumed) loss. The numerous families—up to 170, depending upon the reference consulted— are best grouped into about twenty-one superfamilies, each roughly the equivalent of a family as conceived some years ago.

Eggs are normally provided with a tough chorion which is variously colored and shaped, often quite beautifully. Butterflies generally lay their eggs singly, gluing them to the larval food plant; a single female probably produces at most only a few hundred. Some of the leopard moths

(Zeuzeridae) are known to lay more than 1000 each. Tent caterpillar adults (Lasiocampidae) form egg cases ringing the twigs of food plants. Ovarian embryogeny proceeds fairly rapidly and eclosion occurs in a week or less except where interrupted by a suspension of activity attendant on overwintering or similar hibernation.

Larvae can be identified to family and species, so various are their structures and so characteristic the variations. In general, they are protectively colored and shaped to blend in with their normal background as a defense against macropredators; in some cases they are provided with urticating spines or with glands secreting unpleasant odors. Some, however, are brightly colored—interpreted as a "warning" to birds, monkeys and lizards that these caterpillars are distasteful dietary items. It should be remembered, however, that no matter what the taste or the mechanical protection, every species is certain to be eaten by some other species (stinging bees are the standard diet of certain birds) and that there is no such thing as universal distastefulness. Recent research suggests that the more important cause of larval mortality is bacterial and other disease, against which color, pattern and shape provide no protection.

Most larvae are phytophagous, feeding on leaves or sprouts. Many are quite destructive and Lepidoptera includes a large number of major agricultural pests. Some (Cossidae, Aegeriidae) bore within stems, trunks or roots of plants; the tiny larvae of many families mine leaves. Psychidae (bagworms) and several other families build portable cases reminiscent of those of Trichoptera. Some members of the large family Pyralidae are aquatic, feeding on or mining within aquatic plants; the larvae of a few of these species have gills and some of the winged adults swim.

Many moth families and some of the Lycaenidae (a butterfly family) have carnivorous larvae that attack aphids, scale insects or mites. But the carnivorous habit is not always beneficial; clothes moths (Tineidae) feed on various dry animal material and some species are noteworthy household pests in stored woolens.

The pupae of the most primitive families are decticous exarate, able to move about with comparative ease; the typical and more familiar lepidopterous pupa is adecticous and almost immobile. Pupation is passed in a silken cocoon or in a silk-lined chamber beneath the ground. The silken button or button-and-girdle arrangement of butterfly pupae is a vestigial cocoon.

Adults feed little or not at all and in some families the mouthparts are atrophied. Those that do feed take various liquids, especially flower nectar. Usually the imago lives only a short time, though a few overwinter in the northern temperate zone. A general trend in Lepidoptera is to reduce the activity and importance of the adult to a brief period of reproduction, and to prolong and to increase the importance of the larval instars.

A few of the more important or more familiar groups are:

MICROPTERYGERIDAE—These small, drab diurnal moths are of particular interest because their primitive structure demonstrates the relationship between Lepidoptera and Trichoptera. The mouthparts are mandibulate. With some related forms, they sometimes are placed in a separate order Zeugloptera.

COSSIDAE and ZEUZERIDAE—Goat or carpenter moths and leopard moths are two related families with boring larvae which attack the heartwood of many trees and shrubs; maturity requires two to three years. Because of their protected situation, boring larvae are generally difficult to control.

AEGERIIDAE—The clear-winged moths have slim bodies and narrow wings which often have transparent areas. In general appearance they resemble wasps. The larvae are borers and include some important pests of tree and shrub crops.

TORTRICIDAE—The leaf rollers are small to medium, nocturnal, drably colored moths with rather square-cut forewings. The larvae are sometimes present in large numbers and may be very destructive in forested areas.

TINEIDAE—This is a large family of small moths with fringed, pointed forewings. The larvae have diverse habits, some being case makers, many being phytophagous, others feeding on dried animal material. A few species attack woolens and similar material and are major household pests.

PYRALIDAE—This large and diverse family includes some aquatic species as well as many of the most important pests to agriculture. The European corn borer (*Pyrausta nubilalis* Hübner) has cost vast sums of money, both in direct destruction and in funds expended on research aimed at controlling this introduced species. Many native species also are crop pests.

PSYCHIDAE—The bagworm females are wingless neotenic larvae which remain in the larval cases. Males are drably colored, small to medium in size. Larvae feed on flowers, leaves or bark and almost all species are pests or potential pests.

ARCTIIDAE—The tiger moths are medium to large with stout furry bodies, the wings often beautifully and strikingly colored. The larvae of *Hyphantria* (fall webworm) are gregarious, living in unsightly webs spun loosely in the foliage of trees and shrubs in late summer and fall and often defoliating trees, though whether they are seriously harmful may be debatable. The well-known "woolly bear caterpillar" is a member of this family and it is popularly believed that the widths of the black and orange bands of its hairy body are reliable indicators of the severity of the forthcoming winter.

NOCTUIDAE—The cutworms, armyworms, millers and owlet moths are medium to large, usually drably colored moths whose long, naked larvae feed on foliage or seeds or bore into plant stems. A great many notorious pests belong in this family or to closely related ones, notably the army-worms and some of the cutworms. *Erebus odora* (Linné), a gigantic tropical species with a wingspread of 160 millimeters, migrates in great numbers and a few battered specimens are found as far north as New England every year after the early hurricanes. Local people on the south-ern tip of the desert peninsula of Baja California state that during late summer this species migrates from the Mexican mainland in vast num-bers, "darkening the sky." Related families (Notodontidae, Phalanidae, Plusiidae and others), all with the same general "mothmiller" appear-ance, include many pest species as well as the lovely and interesting genus *Catocala* (Plusiidae), called "underwings" because the forewings are cryp-tically colored to resemble tree bark and the hindwings are vividly striped.

LYMANTRIIDAE—The tussock and gypsy moths have caterpillars adorned with tufts of hairy bristles and almost all species of this comparatively small family are major pests. The brown-tail moth and the gypsy moth, both introduced accidentally from Europe, are especially destructive to ornamental and forest trees and have defied all efforts to eliminate them. The latter moth (*Lymantria*) has, however, proved to be an exceedingly valuable laboratory animal in the study of genetics and mutations. Females of many species are brachypterous.

SPHINGIDAE—The hawk moths, sphinx moths or hummingbird moths are mostly large and beautifully colored with long, slim forewings and a characteristic flight resembling that of hummingbirds. Most are nocturnal or crepuscular, though some are diurnal. The caterpillars are rather large and smooth and often bear a formidable but harmless anal horn. The larvae of a few species feeding on tobacco or tomatoes are sometimes pestiferous, but are easily controlled. The adult is provided with a very long proboscis and feeds on the nectar of flowers. For some plant species they are the principal pollinating agent.

SUPERFAMILY GEOMETROIDEA—The measuring worms or loopers and cankerworms are a complex of families with more than 12,000 species included. The adults have characteristic angled wings and relatively tiny bodies with long, slim legs. Larvae have prolegs only on the posterior abdominal segment and move by hitching their rear ends up to the thorax, then extending the front end ahead; they appear to be measuring. The females of many species have the wings vestigial or absent. Virtually any species may become troublesome if sufficiently numerous. The best known and most usual pests included are the cankerworms.

LASIOCAMPIDAE—Adult tent caterpillars are medium-sized, thick-bodied and mostly tan or reddish-brown. The hairy larvae are gregarious, producing the ugly tents all too familiar in the spring of the year, and may completely defoliate the trees they attack. The Syrian silk moth is a lasiocampid, and its cocoons were an important source of silk from ancient time until as recently as 1875, when it was supplanted by the Chinese silk moth (*Bombyx mori* Linné). The latter is a member of the small, closely related family Bombycidae. Its commercial advantage over the Syrian moth and other contenders lies in its shorter life cycle, producing many generations each year.

SUPERFAMILY SATURNIOIDEA—The giant silk moths are mostly large to very large moths with spectacular colors and patterns, feathery antennae. The larvae are large, often beset with formidable and fanciful spines and almost always brightly colored. They feed on the leaves of trees and shrubs, but are rarely common enough to become pests. Citheroniidae pupate beneath the ground. Saturniidae spin large, characteristic cocoons which have been unsuccessfully tried as sources of commercial silk. Every year a few people "discover" the luna moth, the cecropia or the polyphemus and plague museum curators with their efforts to capitalize on what they are sure are insects totally unknown to the scientific world. The hercules moth of Australia and Papua and the atlas moth of Malaysia attain wingspreads of nearly a foot and are among the largest insects living.

BUTTERFLIES—Mostly diurnal (the brassolids of tropical America are crepuscular), gaily colored creatures which are familiar to everyone. A small percentage of species are pests, particularly to tropical agriculture, and some, such as the cabbage worms (Pieridae), are troublesome in temperate zones. Aside from their aesthetic value, the principal importance of the butterflies resides in the wealth of material they afford for the study of evolution, phylogeny, ecologic associations and zoogeography. Roughly 20,000 species have been described and specialists agree only in a very general way as to the correct division into families and superfamilies. The Hesperioidea include the skippers, so named from their characteristic erratic, rapid flight. The lordly swallowtails, the cabbage butterflies, and their relatives form the Papilionoidea. The Nymphaloidea is a very large complex of generally brilliant butterflies of diverse form and habit but rather homogenous in structure, especially characterized by the reduction of the forelegs and the naked, suspended pupa. The Lycaenoidea include the blues, coppers, hairstreaks and the tropical riodinids; forelegs of males only are reduced. Several excellent accounts of North American butterflies are available and are mentioned in the bibliography.

Collectively, the Lepidoptera are rivaled only by Coleoptera and Hemiptera as a pestiferous group and the order is, in short, one of the most important for that reason. The fossil record is understandably sketchy. Only a handful of specimens known are incontestably Lepidoptera, all from the Tertiary. Certain Jurassic fossils are thought to be primitive moths.

Order 27. Diptera Linné, 1758
(From the Greek: *two* and *wing*)
Flies, Gnats, Mosquitoes, Midges
(Figs. 3.8F, I, J, 3.15B, 3.16, 5.2A, 6.7A, 8.6C, 13.6D, E)

Minute or small insects with compact or fragile bodies, often with metallic coloring, covered with bristles or scales. Large compound eyes, rarely reduced; 3 ocelli or none. Hypognathous head on slender neck. Ectognathous mouthparts modified for lapping (haustellate) or for piercing and sucking. Antennae variable. Thoracic segments firmly fused. Forewings membranous, elongated and triangular with strong longitudinal veins, few cross veins; hindwings reduced to vestigial knobs (halteres); forewings sometimes reduced or absent, but halteres almost never absent. Legs slender or stout, tarsi 5-segmented, post-tarsi with paired claws and both empodium and 1 or 2 pulvilli. Abdomen basically 11-segmented, sometimes only 4–5 segments evident. No cerci. Oviparous or viviparous; holometabolous; larvae terrestrial, aquatic or parasitic, variously modified oligopod (apodous), cephalic region often strongly reduced; pupae adecticous, exarate or obtect, sometimes enclosed in puparium, often free.

Since more than 75,000 species are known, the attendant problems of classification have been difficult. About 120 families are recognized. Brauer's arrangement into two suborders, based on the method employed by the imago to escape from the pupal shell, has been widely used. Certain recent systems divide the order into six suborders. The classification adopted in Imms (1957) seems logical and is used here. The suborder Nematocera includes the most primitive living Diptera, the Cyclorrhapha the most advanced; the Brachycera is an intermediate group. It must be recognized that even the most primitive of the living Diptera is already highly specialized.

NEMATOCERA	BRACHYCERA	CYCLORRHAPHA
1. Larval head capsule well developed, exerted, the mandibles with horizontal action.	1. Larval head capsule retracted, poorly developed, mandibles with vertical action.	1. Larval head capsule vestigial, no mandibles.
2. Pupa normally free.	2. Pupa free (except Stratiomyidae).	2. Puparium present (except Syrphidae).

Adults	*Adults*	*Adults*
3. Antennae usually longer than head and thorax, segments similar, no arista.	3. Antennae shorter than head and thorax, varied, usually 3-segmented, the last elongated and annulated, arista terminal if present.	3. Antennae 3-segmented, always with dorsal arista on last segment.
4. Palpi pendulous, 4- or 5-segmented.	4. Palpi porrect, 1- or 2-segmented.	4. Palpi 1-segmented or absent.
5. Discal cell absent; Cu cell open or absent.	5. Discal cell usually present, Cu cell contracted or closed.	5. Discal cell usually present, Cu cell contracted or closed.

Any effort toward a composite description of the dipterous life cycle results in a jumble resembling an abstract painting. More than any other group of insects, the Diptera have modified reproductive processes and evolved larval adaptations. Whole catalogs of variations in larval structures have been written. In the basic life cycle the egg is fertilized in the usual way and deposited on or near the larval food. An apodous larva hatches, feeds, passes through a series of molts, pupates in a protected situation and finally becomes adult.

Variations in reproduction include parthenogenesis in some midges (Chironomidae) and gall midges (Cecidomyiidae). In some genera of these families parthenogenesis is combined with neoteny and, in a few cases, with viviparity. Viviparity is best developed in the three highly evolved families Hippoboscidae, Streblidae and Nycteribiidae (Hagan, 1951). The larvae grow within the maternal reproductive system, are fed on special secretions and are deposited at the end of the last instar, ready to pupate. The same process occurs in tsetse flies (*Glossina*). Most of the muscoid and tachinoid flies exhibit a form of viviparity (ovoviviparity) in which the egg is retained until hatching; larvae are then deposited during the first to third instar and complete one to three more instars as free-living forms. Within each suborder the number of ecdyses is fairly consistent; four (most) to six (Simuliidae) for Nematocera; five to eight for Brachycera; three to five for Cyclorrhapha.

Larval diet and environment comprise almost the entire range of possibilities. Larvae may feed on plant or animal material—alive, dead or decaying—including plant juices, green leaves, blood, animal tissues, yeast, molds and fungi, mosses, debris and filth. A few are predators, some are external or internal parasites. The principal ecologic limitation appears to be the need for abundant moisture. Some larvae are aquatic, for example those of mosquitoes and midges, but there are many others. Nearly all terrestrial environments utilized by dipterous larvae are, in effect, semiaquatic: damp humus or decaying wood, mushrooms, moss, fresh excrement, living animal tissues. Some phytophagous larvae, such as the Hessian fly and other Cecidomyiidae, are serious agricultural pests.

Adults are usually efficient on the wing. They may not feed at all, or they may frequent plants for nectar, may suck blood or eat a great variety of things. Many are merely annoying, others inflict painful bites. Bloodsucking species are of primary importance as the vectors of pathogenic diseases to man and animals. In all fairness it must be stated that the majority of species have neither direct contact with man nor direct economic importance.

NEMATOCERA

MYCETOPHILIDAE—The fungus gnats are minute to small and varied in coloring. The larvae are abundant under loose, damp bark and in native fungi or leaf mold and may infest mushrooms, seed corn, potatoes and other vegetables.

TIPULIDAE—The crane flies are small to quite large. The common species look like oversized mosquitoes but are entirely harmless. They fly and walk awkwardly. Some larvae are aquatic and most feed on debris, but a few species ("leather-jackets") sometimes damage grass roots and corn. About 8500 species are known.

PSYCHODIDAE—The sandflies are tiny woolly-looking flies with broad bodies somewhat resembling moths. They are usually to be found in and around moist organic material such as sewage where the larvae live as scavengers; a few species are predaceous. Distribution is world-wide. In the tropics and subtropics the bloodsucking genus *Phlebotomus* acts as the vector for kala-azar, espundia, Oriental sore, Peruvian verruga, Oroya fever and pappataci fever (Chapter One).

CULICIDAE—The mosquitoes (Fig. 13.6D) have delicate, slender bodies, humped backs, long legs and the wings and sometimes the bodies are scaled. Larvae and pupae are aquatic, usually in still, somewhat stagnant or brackish water, and constitute an important dietary item for small fish. They feed on organic matter, yeasts, algae and other microscopic biota. The adult male feeds on pollen, but the female of many species must take a blood meal in order to mature her eggs. In doing so, she inadvertently acts as vector for malaria, yellow fever, filariasis, encephalitis and dengue. Only a few species are actively involved in transmitting disease to man; most mosquitoes feed on the blood of birds, monkeys and apes, ungulates or frogs, toads, snakes and lizards. Many of the man-biting mosquitoes are physiologically unable to act as the vectors for malaria or yellow fever. Animal-biting species may transmit animal diseases. A few species in the temperate zone feed on both bird and human blood and transmit encephalitis.

SIMULIIDAE—The black flies and buffalo gnats are tiny, stout, humpbacked insects with short wings. Adult females are avid bloodsuckers. They generally appear in hordes and can make life completely unbearable near the cold, swift streams which are their breeding places. At times they have been known to kill poultry and even cattle when inhaled in numbers. They are active only by day and do not enter habitations. In tropical Africa and in Central America, black flies transmit the filarial disease Onchocerciasis which sometimes leads to blindness.

CHIRONOMIDAE and CERATOPOGONIDAE—The midges and black gnats are minute or small, somewhat similar to mosquitoes but stouter and with broader wings. They incline to fly in swarms. Some species inflict painful bites and can make the woods or lakesides intolerable when they abound. Larvae are mostly scavengers and are aquatic.

CECIDOMYIIDAE—The gall gnats are frail creatures about half a millimeter long. The larvae of a few species are predaceous on pests and help control them; others feed on decaying vegetation. Most species attack living plants and may cause severe damage. To this family belongs the infamous Hessian fly, so named because it apparently was introduced into North America during the Revolutionary War in the straw imported as bedding for the horses of the Hessian troops.

BRACHYCERA

TABANIDAE—The horseflies and deer flies are medium-sized, compact, with strong legs and broad wings. The prominent eyes frequently are vivid green, purple or scarlet. During the summer tabanids are abundant in woods with streams and low, marshy areas and are most active on warm, sunny days. They fly rapidly and strongly, attacking any warm-blooded animal, including man, and inflicting a painful, slashing bite that feels like a hot needle. Their attacks on cattle have a debilitating effect; thirty or forty flies extract a quart of blood a week from their victim. Most species are tropical and subtropical. They transmit filariasis and tularemia to man and surra to horses. Undoubtedly they aid the spread of anthrax in cattle, the bacilli entering the wounds left by their bites. Larvae are aquatic, semiaquatic or subterranean, predaceous on small animals or insect larvae.

BOMBYLIIDAE—The bee flies are small to medium with stout, very hairy bodies and greatly resemble bees or wasps both in appearance and superficial behavior. Adults may be found frequenting flowers or around damp places. Larvae are parasitic or predaceous on an important variety of harmful insects: grasshoppers (including the migratory locust), beetles, bees and wasps, pupae of tsetse flies, cutworms and armyworms. This relatively small family of about 1800 species is decidedly beneficial.

ASILIDAE—The robber flies are medium to somewhat large, variously and often gaily colored. They are noticed in fields, in swampy areas or along stream banks resting in the sun, ready to swoop on passing insects which they attack on the wing. They rarely bite man, but are useful as predators on larvae and adults of other insects. Most of the larvae are subterranean predators on beetles and their larvae, though a few attack plant roots.

CYCLORRHAPHA

PHORIDAE—The humpbacked flies are tiny and dull-colored with a humped thorax. Adults fly actively, feeding on flower pollen and nectar. Larvae eat various decaying vegetable matter, are inquilines in termite or ant nests or parasitize eggs of spiders, millipedes, ants or other arthropods.

SYRPHIDAE—The flower, hover or sweat flies are medium to large, quite diversely colored. Some resemble bumblebees; others mimic wasps or honybees. They fly vigorously and are commonly seen in sunny areas hovering around flowers. Adults feed on nectar and pollen and are important pollenizing agents. Larvae are predators, especially on hemipterans such as aphids, are inquilines in termite or ant nests, or feed on living plants. Some of the last type are harmful to bulbs, while others attack cactus and still others feed on fungi beneath the dead bark of trees.

TRYPETIDAE—Fruit flies are small, dark or yellowish-brown with prominently banded wings. The phytophagous larvae feed on fleshy fruit, nuts, seeds, the flower heads of Compositae, or mine in leaves or stems. The family includes some of the most serious agricultural pests throughout the world. It has been specifically singled out by the United States Congress in a number of quarantine and control laws. The Metiterranean fruit fly, which attacks all sorts of tropical fruit crops, established a beachhead in Florida in 1929 and was eradicated at a cost of more than $6 million; it returned in 1959 but was again eliminated. Endemic species attacking most North American orchards, nut groves and garden crops are controlled (not eradicated) only at a tremendously large expenditure each year of effort and money. Their rapid growth and short cycle add much to their dangerousness and they are a constant threat to subtropical orchard crops in Florida and California.

EPHYDRIDAE—*Ephydra* species develop in strongly saline or alkaline pools and lakes in such great numbers that the aborigines of western North America used the larvae and pupae as food. *Psilopa petrolei* (Coquillet) lives in pools of crude oil in southern California, apparently subsisting on the insects that get stuck on the surface. Others abound in Great Salt Lake, Utah, living in a salinity of twenty-five to thirty per cent.

DROSOPHILIDAE—Vinegar or fruit flies are small to minute and are attracted to spoiling vegetables or fruits. The larvae feed on yeasts or the product of fermentation. Intrinsically, they have little importance. Since they are readily trapped and easily colonized in the laboratory, they have provided experimental material of the utmost value for genetics, cytology, physiology, embryology and population studies. Probably no member of the animal kingdom other than man himself has been the object of so much detailed observation and learned writing.

CHLOROPIDAE—Grass stem maggots are tiny, black or yellow flies. Adult eye gnats (*Hippelates*) often torment man and animals by flying into their eyes; in the process they may transmit pink eye and conjunctivitis. Larvae of some species are phytophagous and very destructive to crops such as wheat.

ANTHOMYIIDAE—Root maggots may feed either on bulbs, roots, stems or leaves and are very destructive; others develop in and eat all sorts of filth; a few are carnivorous and cause myasis in birds. Adults are small or medium in size, dark or dull buff, very hairy and look like ordinary houseflies.

GLOSSINIDAE—The tsetse flies include only the genus *Glossina* and about twenty-five species, all confined to tropical Africa. The manner of holding the wings at rest is distinctive—scissors-wise and flat over the abdomen. Larvae develop viviparously and pupate as soon as deposited. Adults are blood feeders and vectors of the trypanosome pathogens of sleeping sickness both to man and to domestic animals. Sleeping sickness has not only caused an untold number of deaths, but also has been one of the major barriers to opening up large regions in Africa.

MUSCIDAE—The common houseflies are familiar throughout the world. Larvae develop in garbage, lawn clippings, manure and other filth, maturing within four or five days; there may be from ten to twenty generations a year. Adults feed on any fluid or soluble material, frequent habitations and persistently crawl about on food. Their mouthparts, sticky feet and hairy bodies provide free transportation for a variety of pathogenic organisms. They have been implicated as carriers of sporadic typhoid, tuberculosis, dysentery, cholera, filariasis and, in the tropics, yaws and sores.

STOMOXYIDAE—The stable flies are similar to the houseflies in appearance, but are blood feeders and bite painfully. Larvae feed on dead or decaying animal or plant material.

GASTROPHILIDAE—Horse bot flies are small, very hairy and somewhat resemble bees. Eggs are laid on the lips, chin or legs of horses, mules, elephants, rabbits, and other animals, where they are likely to be licked off. The larvae, or bots, develop internally, eventually attaching themserves to the wall of the stomach or other part of the alimentary tract, by means of little hooks. Heavy infestations can be very serious to the host. The bots mature in about nine months, passing out with the feces and pupating in the ground.

HYPODERMATIDAE and OESTRIDAE—Warble flies, bot flies and gadflies are closely related; members of both families attack cattle, sheep, camels and many other warm-blooded animals. Larvae of warble flies develop deep in the dermis. Young oestrid larvae are deposited in the nostrils and develop in the nasopharyngeal region. Both parasites are extremely annoying to the hosts and a severe infestation of oestrids may be fatal. The warbles cause a loss of appetite in their victims; heavy infection of dairy herds lowers milk production. Even more serious is the loss caused to the meat and leather industries, estimated as high as $300 million a year. Meat around the larval "grub" holes is inedible, and punctured hides must be sold at a loss. Animals go to great lengths to avoid the adults, becoming extremely nervous in their presence, galloping about and attempting to evade the flies. Bots and oestrids sometimes accidentally infest man.

CALLIPHORIDAE and SARCOPHAGIDAE—Blowflies, bottle flies and flesh flies are medium to large. The larvae are scavengers or flesh eaters and attack most mammals and many cold-blooded groups. Many species will attack man, either occasionally or regularly. The maggots may cause severe cutaneous myasis. The larvae of many species such as *Calliphora augur* (Fabricius), *Cochliomyia americana* Cushing and Patton and *Phormia regina* (Meigen) are serious pests on sheep. Injury and even death result from their attacks. Screw-worms (Calliphoridae) feed on the flesh of the hosts and account for millions of dollars lost each year in the cattle industry. Some control has been achieved by releasing large numbers of radiation-sterilized males in infested areas. Because females mate only once, those that have copulated with sterilized males produce no progeny and, presumably, a certain percentage of the population of normal males have no opportunity to mate.

TACHINIDAE (Fig. 13.6E)—Though biologically similar to the foregoing families, these flies must be regarded as highly beneficial since the larvae parasitize a wide variety of other insects and are not known to attack mammals. Hosts, including larvae and pupae of Lepidoptera, Coleoptera, Orthoptera, Dermaptera, Hymenoptera, Diptera and Hemiptera, are killed or sterilized by the parasite. One species has been used in the control of the brown-tail moth in New England. Adults visit flowers and aid in pollination.

Three families, perhaps the most evolved in the order, are grouped as the "Pupipara." Larvae develop viviparously (Hagan, 1951) and are deposited ready to pupate. Hippoboscidae, the louse flies, are bloodsucking external parasites on birds and mammals, transmitting several pathogens. Many species are wingless in one or both sexes and resemble ticks. One of the widespread, most injurious species is *Melophagus ovina* (Linné), the sheep tick or ked, which infests sheep in all parts of the world and the alpaca and related animals in South America. In addition to annoying their hosts, they transmit some serious diseases. Streblidae and Nycteribiidae are parasitic on bats. The former family is winged, but the female sheds her wings and burrows beneath the skin upon finding a host. The latter have no forewings, though the halteres are present, and the compound eyes are reduced to a few facets. Both families are principally tropical.

FOSSIL RECORD

The earliest known fossil Diptera were found in Liassic strata. Many families are represented in Tertiary deposits. Tillyard thought that a four-winged fossil from the Upper Permian of Australia represented a mecopteran-like ancestral form. It is generally agreed that Diptera were derived from the mecopteran stock; nevertheless the possibility of a closer relationship with the hemipteran line has not been sufficiently explored.

Order 28. Siphonaptera Latreille, 1825
(From the Greek: *tube* and *wingless*)
Fleas
(Figs. 3.17, 8.7B, 13.7A)

Small, dark ectoparasites with strongly sclerotized, laterally compressed bodies. Hypognathous head usually with conspicuous row of spines. Compound eyes reduced to 1 facet or absent; ocelli absent. Antennae pectinate, short, stout, concealed in a groove with only 3 segments evident. Ectognathous mouthparts highly specialized for piercing and sucking. Secondarily wingless. Small thorax closely united with head. Strong, relatively long legs adapted for clinging, hindlegs longest, used for jumping; coxae flattened, femora stout, tarsi long, 5-jointed, post-tarsi with stout claws and basal pad. Abdomen 10-segmented, first sternum lacking, 3 terminal segments modified. Cerci vestigial. Body often with orderly rows of spines (ctenidia). Tenth tergite with sensory plate (pygidium) and, in females, dorsal stylets. Oviparous; holometabolous with terrestrial apodous oligopod larvae with biting mouthparts, adecticous exarate pupae.

Adult fleas are ectoparasites on mammals or birds. The female lays more than 500 eggs, scattering them among the host's hairs or feathers or in its nest. One to three weeks are required for incubation, depending on temperature. The larvae are apodous and blind, but have a well-developed head capsule and biting mouthparts; they resemble larval Nematocera (Diptera). They are nonparasitic scavengers, are very active and shun light. After two ecdyses, a cocoon is spun in which pupation takes place. Under favorable conditions a generation may be completed in twenty-one days; unfavorable conditions extend the length of time. Adults survive from one to three years and can fast for as long as six months. In general, fleas are noteworthy for their rapid development and prolific reproduction.

Fleas are not strongly host specific. *Pulex irritans* (Linné) particularly infests man in all parts of the world, but will also parasitize dogs, swine, poultry and many other animals. The various flea species that attack rats, squirrels and ground squirrels as well as man serve as the principal vectors of bubonic plague, the "Black Death" which destroyed a third of the population of Europe in the fifteenth century. Bubonic plague still is a danger in many parts of the world and is not confined to exotic places. It is a constant threat in western United States, where the pathogen is established in wild rodents. Epidemics are avoided only by controlling rats and other alternative hosts. Fleas may also serve as vectors for sylvatic plague, murine typhus and certain tapeworms (Chapter One).

The "jigger flea," *Tunga penetrans* (Linné), deviates from the usual life history. An impregnated female burrows into the flesh of some mammal, her legs disintegrate, her abdomen swells with eggs and severe local irritation or ulceration results. Walking barefooted in the tropics or subtropics is an excellent way to collect specimens, and they often burrow under the toe nails.

There are about 1000 species of fleas. Distribution of the order is world-wide, including the polar regions, though the majority of the species are tropical. Fossil specimens have been found in Tertiary ambers. Siphonaptera are undoubtedly related to the Diptera and probably derived from Nematocera-like ancestors.

Order 29. Hymenoptera Linné, 1758
(From the Greek: *membrane* and *wing*)
Sawflies, Wasps, Hornets, Ants, Bees
(Figs. 3.7A, 3.14, 3.20D, 5.2B, 5.3A, 8.6B, 13.7B–E)

Minute to medium size with well-sclerotized bodies naked or hairy. Hypognathous head prominent, free. Large compound eyes well developed, widely spaced, sometimes reduced or absent; 3 or no ocelli. Antennae various. Mouthparts mandibulate, biting and chewing in primitive groups, highly modified in some advanced groups. Wings stiff, narrow, membranous, with specialized venation; forewing usually with stigma; hindwing the smaller; coupling by hamuli; folded back over the abdomen at rest; wings sometimes absent. Legs slim, similar, often bearing modifications or special structures; femur often subdivided (proximal subdivision often called "second trochanter"); tarsi basically 5-segmented, fewer in some groups; post-tarsi with claws and pad. Abdomen with 10 segments but only 6–8 usually evident, first segment (**propodeum**) fused with metathorax, second broadly joined to first or strongly constricted (petiole). Cerci absent. Females with more or less prominent ovipositor. Oviparous; holometabolous; larvae polypod, often modified or apodous. Pupae adecticous, generally exarate, sometimes obtect. Parthenogenesis and polyembryony occur.

The evolution of Hymenoptera has emphasized ecological adaptation in the life cycle, but all are holometabolous and most are oviparous. The primitive sawflies cut into plant tissue and deposit their eggs singly. Their larvae fend for themselves and pupate in silken cocoons. The more

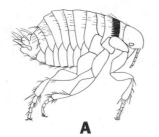
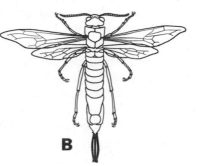

A

B

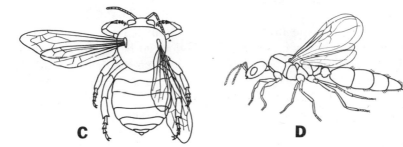

C

D

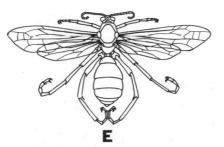

E

Figure 13.7. (A) Siphonaptera; (B) Hymenoptera, *Tremex* species; (C) Hymenoptera, *Bombus* species; (D) Hymenoptera, family Formicidae; (E) Hymenoptera, *Vespa* species. (A–C, E from specimens in Carnegie Museum; D after Marlatt, 1916)

advanced parasitic species lay eggs near, directly on or within host species, so that the larvae have an adequate supply of food at hand and need not forage. Among these parasites are found various modifications in structure and developmental attainment of the early larvae. Some are protopod, their precocious hatching from the egg made possible only because they are immediately bathed in the nutrient fluids of their hosts. Another variation provides the first instar larva, hatching from an egg near but not on or in the host, with locomotion so that it can find the host and bore into its tissues, where then it becomes apodous. It must be noted that these locomotory first instar larvae are polypod, bearing no homology with the oligopod triungulin types performing an analogous function among Strepsiptera and certain Coleoptera.

Solitary bees and wasps provide a burrow and a supply of food in the form of a stunned insect or spider for the future larva. A further step in maternal care is the reprovisioning of the burrow, noted in certain tropical wasps, after the larvae have eaten the initial supply. The ultimate is found among the highly organized ants and social bees. The reproductive female, the queen, has a staff of flunkies to whom she delegates all problems connected with child care, which reaches a degree of refinement surpassed only by higher vertebrates.

Unfertilized eggs become haploid males (Chapter Seven), fertilized eggs develop into diploid females. Aside from this male-producing parthenogenesis, another variety of the phenomenon sometimes occurs: diploid females may be produced without true fertilization, either by duplication of the oötid followed by fusion of the daughter cells or by fusion of a polar body with the oötid. Certain parasitic species have evolved polyembryony, enabling many larvae to form from a single zygote.

With 120,000 known species, Hymenoptera is the second largest order in the animal kingdom. More than 150 families are recognized, usually divided into two suborders distinguished on both structural and ecologic grounds. The names used for these two suborders have been inconsistent, about equally divided between Symphyta and Apocrita or Chalastogastra and Clistogastra in recent years. Choice of one or the other pair of names apparently has been decided on the basis of which name is thought to be the more aptly descriptive of the characteristics of its members. Because a name is only a name and its aptness has nothing to do with its use, the time seems ripe to apply strict priority—which results in Phytophaga and Apocrita. The former name, a century and a half old, was once widely used and is not unfamiliar.

PHYTOPHAGA LATREILLE, 1807
(= Symphyta Gehrstecker, 1867;
Chalastogastra Konow, 1897)

1. Abdomen without petiole, broadly joined to thorax.
2. Seemingly with 2 trochanters.
3. Hindwing with 3 or more basal cells.
4. Ovipositor adapted for sawing or boring, never for stinging.
5. Larvae caterpillar-like, head well developed, stemmata present, thoracic and abdominal prolegs (typically) present.
6. Larvae phytophagous except Orussidae.

APOCRITA GEHRSTECKER, 1867
(= Petiolata Bingham, 1897,
Clistogastra Konow, 1905)

1. Abdomen joined to thorax by the strongly constricted petiole.
2. Seemingly with 1 or 2 trochanters.
3. Hindwing with 2 or fewer basal cells.
4. Ovipositor sometimes adapted as a stinger.
5. Larvae grub-like, head and mouthparts reduced, no stemmata, apodous.
6. Larvae phytophagous, omnivorous, ecto- or endoparasitic.

PHYTOPHAGA

Except the obscure family Orussidae, ectoparasitic on beetle larvae, all members of this suborder are phytophagous and many are major agricultural pests.

TENTHREDINIDAE—Sawflies are small to medium in size, with hard bodies, often colored brown or brown and yellow. The female's saw-toothed ovipositor is not prominent. Eggs are usually inserted into plant tissues. Typical larvae resemble caterpillars, but have no crochets on the abdominal prolegs; some gall-making larvae are apodous slugs. Many spin extensive silken webs among boughs and leaves. All are injurious to vegetation, especially in forests.

SIRICIDAE—The horntails have slender cylindrical bodies and may be brilliantly colored (many are bright blue). Females have a stout, stiff ovipositor, often mistaken for a stinger, used to drill into tree bark or wood. The boring larvae may cause extensive damage in the heartwood of both coniferous and deciduous trees.

APOCRITA

SUPERFAMILY ICHNEUMONOIDEA—The Ichneumonidae, Braconidae and some smaller, less well-known families are included. Distinguishing features among these groups rest primarily with differences in venational details; wingless species sometimes are difficult to assign correctly. Some 16,000 species are known at present and many more undoubtedly await discovery. In general, the Ichneumonoidea are among the most beneficial of insects, serving as invaluable natural controls of their hosts, for all are parasitic and some are narrowly host specific. Some species have been cultivated in the laboratory and released in numbers to help destroy the noxious insects they parasitize. Hosts include a long list of Lepidoptera, Coleoptera, Diptera and Hymenoptera, while a subfamily of Braconids parasitize aphids (Hemiptera). Parasitized host insects are almost invariably killed at or before pupation. Adult Ichneumonoidea commonly frequent flowers, are active in warm sunlight. Females of many species overwinter. Eggs, depending on species, are inserted into a host, glued to its cuticle or deposited near it. *Thalessa,* a large ichneumonid with a six-inch ovipositor, drills into a tree trunk to place her egg within the borings of the horntail *Tremex.* Larvae are ecto- or endoparasitic. Most endoparasitic species have modified first instar forms (above and Chapter Eight). The greater number of adult wasps are tiny to minute.

SUPERFAMILY CYNIPOIDEA—The gall-making Cynipidae and some small families of parasitic species with interesting life histories are included. Very few members of the superfamily are even of medium size and all the gall wasps are smaller than four millimeters, many only one millimeter long. Wing venation is strongly reduced and there are many wingless species. Eggs are laid on or, more usually, in plant tissue. After the larva hatches, a gall begins to form. Briefly, a gall is a mass of pathologic plant tissue apparently produced through the interaction of secretions from the larva with meristematic plant cells. Each cynipid species forms its characteristic gall and different species produce different kinds of galls on the same plant. The larva develops within the gall, feeding on its cells. A number of gall wasps have "alternation of generation" (**heterogony**). One generation includes both males and females which develop in a typical gall; the next generation is comprised of females only and both the insects and their galls are structurally different from the previous generation. Alternative generations have even been placed in separate genera before their true relationship was understood. It is clear that two kinds of parthenogenesis are involved in cynipid heterogony; males, as usual in the order, develop from unfertilized eggs; females are alternatively sexually or parthenogenetically produced but always are diploid. It is not clear why alternation occurs so regularly or what factors control the phenomenon. Of historical interest is the fact that long before he became the controversial cataloger of human sexual habits, Kinsey was noted for his brilliant studies of cynipid wasps and their evolution.

SUPERFAMILY CHALCIDOIDEA—This superfamily includes from twenty to thirty families. The adults have prominent eyes, three ocelli and the wing venation is strongly reduced. A few species are medium size (up to 16 mm.) but the majority are small or tiny; *Alaptus magnanimus* (Annandale), (only 0.21 mm. long) is said to be the smallest insect known. Some of the Eurytomidae are phytophagous, producing galls in grass and cereal stems, and are quite injurious. Larvae of Agaontidae feed on the fruit of figs, usually producing galls, but the adults are the sole pollinating agents of these trees. *Ficus carica* trees are either male or female. The male trees, known in horticulture as "caprifigs," produce no edible fruit but the agaontid *Blastophagus psenes* (Linné) oviposits exclusively in its staminate flowers; female trees produce the commercially important, edible Smyrna figs, but the wasp never attacks the flowers. Centuries ago, fig farmers in the Mediterranean learned to hang branches of the caprifig in the Smyrna trees, a ceremony viewed as an amusing superstition until entomologists discovered that the female wasp cannot discriminate externally between male and female flowers. Accordingly, she enters male and female flowers at random, ovipositing only in male flowers, and by this process of trial and error pollinates the Smyrnas. Without her services, there is no crop. Almost all other members of the superfamily are parasitic, some of them hyperparasites (parasitic on parasites). Hosts include most orders of insects, especially Lepidoptera, Hemiptera, Diptera, Hymenoptera and orthopteroids, as well as ticks. Many groups—Trichogrammatidae, for example—attack exclusively the eggs of the hosts. While the chalcids and their allies are among the most important natural controls of numerous insect pests, not all of them are beneficial, since some attack such useful insects as parasites of injurious species.

SUPERFAMILY SERPHOIDEA—About a dozen families of small or minute parasites that attack the eggs or larvae of insects, spiders and myriapods are included. Most species are rare or infrequently noticed. The largest family, Platygasteridae, includes some important natural enemies of some major agricultural pests. *Platygaster vernalis* (Meyers) and *P. hiemalis* Forbes parasitize the extremely destructive Hessian fly. As noted in Chapter Eight and elsewhere, this genus produces numerous larvae within a single host through polyembryony. Adult females of *Rielia manticida* Kieffer (Scelionidae) hitchhike on female praying mantids, shedding their wings for the journey. When the mantis oviposits, the wasp slips off and lays her eggs on the host's oötheca.

SUPERFAMILY FORMICOIDEA—The nearly 4000 known species of ants belong in this group. They range in size from the inch-long "bulldog" of Australia to tiny forms less than a millimeter in length and are drably colored—black, brown or rusty red. Primitive groups are carnivorous, while some of the more evolved ants are herbivorous and many are omnivorous. Ants are colonial and polymorphism and castes occur in all species. Males are haploid and usually winged. Reproductive females are commonly winged at first, but after mating and migration the wings break off at an abscission suture near the base or are nipped off by the mandibles. Workers (and "soldiers," when they occur) are suppressed diploid females and as many as twenty-nine varieties have been observed in some species, varying in size and structural detail. Whether the development of workers depends on genetic factors or is the result of diet is a moot question which already has produced a five-foot shelf of books and remains quite undecided. Recent experimental research tends to support the genetic explanation but fails to convince adherents of the environmental school. Ants are found throughout the world in a wide variety of situations with a wide variety of habits and organizations. The writings of W. M. Wheeler (see bibliography) are a "must" for all interested in these insects and should be consulted for further information.

SUPERFAMILY SPHECOIDEA—The solitary wasps of this superfamily exhibit a degree of maternal care by constructing special chambers for their larvae and provisioning them with food. Because so many of the species are large, common and frequently noticed, a host of popular names are applied to the various species—burrowing wasps, digger wasps, mud daubers, cicada killers. On the whole they are even tempered and unaggressive and will not sting a person who does not molest them; many species, even when molested, prefer flight to defense. Their nests are built in burrows in the ground, in holes in wood, in plant stems or are made of a series of mud cells placed in protected situations on rocks, trees or buildings. Insects or arachnoids, which the female paralyzes or kills by her sting, are provided as food in the chambers. The effect of stinging is to preserve the prey, either by immobilizing it or, even when lethal, by an antiseptic effect of the venom. In most cases a food supply sufficient to provide for the larval needs until pupation is placed in the chamber, which then is sealed. Some (*Bembix, Sphex*), however, do not seal their chambers but feed the larvae daily until they mature. A great many of these wasps are narrowly selective in their prey, attacking only one genus or even only one species. The collective diet of the sphecoid wasps includes nearly every kind of insect or spider and they are therefore regarded as being beneficial.

SUPERFAMILY VESPOIDEA—The true wasps, hornets, yellowjackets, velvet ants, potter wasps, paper wasps, tarantula hawks and their numerous relatives are distinguished from the sphecoid wasps mainly by details of the thoracic structures. Many of them unhesitatingly stand up for their rights and some are aggressively ill-tempered. In habit they range from solitary forms to some with well-developed social organization and polymorphic castes. The fuzzy velvet ants (Mutillidae) parasitize the larvae of bees, ants or other wasps and build no nest of their own. The Scoliidae excavate a primitive chamber in the earth around a beetle grub immobilized by the sting; their principal prey are scarabaeid beetles and they are useful in the control of such pests as June bugs and the Japanese beetle. Eumenidae build nests in the ground, in plant stems, in burrows in wood or (potter wasps) attach beautiful vase-like chambers to twigs; their prey are mostly lepidopterous larvae (cutworms for some species) or beetle grubs. *Pepsis* (Pompilidae) attack spiders and nest in a variety of situations; some of the species are large and spectacularly colored. Vespidae and Polistidae are social, constructing large nests of papery material elaborated from masticated wood and leaves. In both families a winged and well-armed worker caste (infertile females) is produced. At the end of the season haploid males and fertile females develop; after mating, the females hibernate. In the spring each female builds a small paper nest, consisting of a few cells in each of which she lays a diploid egg. The grub-like larvae are fed on bits of insects, pollen and honey by the queen. Throughout the summer only workers develop; they construct and provision new cells, the queen performing only the egg-laying function. Colonies must begin anew each year, but old nests may be used by young queens. Aerial nests are more or less spherical, suspended by a central cord. Many species nest in the ground and others utilize hollow trees. *Polistes* nests are typically pendant and discoid, consisting of a single horizontal layer of cells open at the bottom until the larvae pupate.

SUPERFAMILY APOIDEA—The bees, grouped into six families, are distinguished from wasps by the fact that some or most of the thoracic setae are branched or plumose. The majority are solitary, some are social and some are inquiline parasites in the nests of other bees. In all cases the larvae feed on stored pollen and nectar, never being carnivorous. Bees are the primary and most important pollinating agents; without them certain crops could not be grown and a great many other plant species would not exist. Colletidae are primitive, solitary bees that nest in burrows, hollow stems or other small holes, lining the larval chambers with a thin, translucent, plaster-like substance. Halicitidae (sweat bees) and Andrenidae (short-tongued bees) mine burrows in the soil; frequently a great many individuals will nest in the same area, forming large bee villages. Certain species of Halicitidae approximate a social organization and produce a worker caste, while other species are parasitic. Megachilidae (leaf-cutting bees) derive their name from the habit of some common genera of cutting circular pieces from leaves and using them as nest lining; other genera build mud cells and the family includes some parasites. Bumblebees (Bombidae) of the genus *Bombus* (Fig. 13.7C) are nest-building social insects with a worker caste and annual cycle similar to that of Vespidae; nests are generally underground, but some species build on the surface. Bumblebees of the genus *Psithyrus* have no workers and build no nests, but parasitize *Bombus* nests. True honeybees belong to the family Meliponidae, with about 250 species, and to Apidae with four. Honey produced by various meliponid bees is highly regarded by aboriginals in tropical America and several species were cultivated by pre-Columbian societies. The domestic bee, *Apis mellifera* Linné, probably originated in the Far East, but is no longer found as a natural wild species except where swarms have escaped. Bee cultivation goes back thousands of years; it was already a well-developed industry in the time of the Pharaohs. Literature on the common honeybee is voluminous.

FOSSIL RECORD

Hymenoptera appear rather late in geologic history. The earliest known fossil is a siricid (Phytophaga) from the Lower Liassic and others have been found in Jurassic strata. That certain cretaceous specimens are galls produced by hymenopterans is rather wild speculation. Amber and other Tertiary deposits have yielded many examples representing all living families and more than half of the ants in amber belong to species still living. The order probably is much older than the fossil record indicates, and its derivation and relationships remain obscure. It is usually placed with the "panorpoid complex," a decision probably conditioned more by a desire to put all the "Holometabola" on a single phylogenetic branch than by definitive evidence.

> *Gabriel.* How about cleanin' up de whole mess of 'em
> and sta'tin all over ag'in wid some new kind of animal?
> MARC CONNELLY, *Green Pastures*

SELECTED TOPICAL
REFERENCES

The following topical bibliography is intended only as a guide. Preference has been given to recent works in English having a broad general approach, rather than to specialized monographs. Further bibliographies on particular subjects will be found in many of the references. A few large, basic references have been cited, as well as a few foreign language references where nothing comparable exists in English.

Insecta. Barker, 1960. Berlese, 1909a; an important basic reference frequently overlooked; in Italian. Borrer and De Long, 1954; good general keys; emphasis on North American fauna and economic groups; collecting and preserving techniques. Carpenter, 1961. Carpenter, 1928. Comstock, 1940. Essig, 1942; good general keys; world fauna; morphology summaries. Frost, 1942; ecological approach. Grassé, 1949–1951; general discussion in volume 6; insect orders in volumes 9 and 10; the best modern encyclopedic treatment in any language; in French. Imms, 1957; most useful one-volume reference in English. Jeannel, 1960; summary of insect fossils and modern classification. Matheson, 1947. Metcalf, Flint and Metcalf, 1962; emphasizes economic entomology. Ross, 1948; general discussions and keys.

Collembola. Maynard, 1951. Mills, 1934.
Protura. Berlese, 1909b. Ewing. 1940.
Thysanura and Aptera. Delany, 1954. Denis, 1949a. Ewing, 1942. Hilton, 1932. MacGillivray, 1893.
Ephemerida. Needham and Claassen, 1925. Needham, Traver and Hsu, 1935.
Odonata. Munz, 1919. Needham and Westfall, 1955. Walker, 1953.
Dictyoptera. Blatchley, 1920. Chopard, 1949a. Hebard, 1917b. Morse, 1920. Rehn, 1951.
Isoptera. Banks and Snyder, 1920. Grassé, 1949. Kofoid, 1934. Richards, 1953. Snyder, 1948, 1949, 1954.
Zoraptera. Denis, 1949b. Gurney, 1938.
Plecoptera. Claassen, 1940. Frison, 1942. Needham and Claassen, 1925.

Grylloblattodea.   Gurney, 1948. Walker, 1914, 1937.

Phasmida.   Blatchley, 1920. Chopard, 1949b.

Orthoptera.   Blatchley, 1920. Chopard, 1949c. Morse, 1920.

Embioptera.   Ross, E. M., 1944.

Dermaptera.   Blatchley, 1920. Morse, 1920. Rehn and Rehn, 1936.

Corrodentia.   Chapman, 1930. Gurney, 1950. Roesler, 1944.

Mallophaga.   Ewing, 1929. Harrison, 1916.

Anoplura.   Ewing, 1929. Ferris, 1951.

Hemiptera.   Blatchley, 1926. Britton, 1916. Leach, 1940. Miller, 1956. Torre-Bueno, 1916, 1939–1946.

Thysanoptera.   Shull, 1914. Stannard, 1957. Watson, 1923.

Coleoptera.   Arnett, 1960. Balduf, 1935. Blatchley, 1910. Bradley, 1930. Edwards, 1949, 1950.

Strepsiptera.   Bohart, 1941. Jeannel, 1944. Pierce, 1909, 1918, 1936.

Neuroptera.   Carpenter, 1936, 1940. Froeschner, 1947. Wheeler, 1930.

Mecoptera.   Carpenter, 1931a, 1931b.

Trichoptera.   Betten, 1934. Ross, 1944b.

Lepidoptera.   Collins and Weast, 1961. Forbes, 1923–1960. Holland, 1905, 1931. Klots, 1951. Seitz, 1905–1939.

Diptera.   Carpenter and La Casse, 1955. Curran, 1934. Hall, 1948. Horsfall, 1955. James, 1947. Sturdivant, 1942. West, 1951.

Siphonaptera.   Fox and Ewing, 1943. Hopkins and Rothschild, 1953.

Hymenoptera.   Britton, 1916. Creighton, 1950. Krombein, 1958. Michener and Michener, 1951. Mitchell, 1960. Muesebeck, Krombein and Townes, 1951. Richards, 1953. Townes, 1944. Wheeler, 1910.

Myriapoda.   Chamberlin and Hoffman, 1958; checklist and synonymy of North American Diplopoda. Verhoeff, 1902–1934; world-wide; detailed morphologic and taxonomic data on Diplopoda, Chilopoda, Symphyla, Pauropoda; in German. Williams and Hefner, 1928.

Arachnida.   Baker and Wharton, 1952; order Acarida. Bristowe, 1939–1941; order Araneida. Comstock and Gertsch, 1940; order Araneida. Ewing, 1929; parasitic Acarida. Gertsch, 1949; introduction to morphology and habits of American Araneida. Grassé, 1949–1951; volume 6 contains detailed treatment of morphology and embryology of arachnoids and detailed discussions of each order on a world-wide basis; in French. Hoff, 1949; American Pseudoscorpionida. Hoogstraal, 1956; includes useful general information on ticks (Acarida). Wharton and Fuller, 1952.

Paleontology.   Carpenter, 1930. Handlirsch, 1906–1908, 1937–1939; basic comprehensive references on insect fossils; in German. Jeannel, 1949, 1960; the former, in French, is more detailed; the latter, in English, is a useful summary. Laurentiaux, 1953; myriapods. Martynov, 1938; in Russian; data included by Jeannel. Petrunkevitch, 1955; detailed treatment of arachnoids. Tillyard, 1926, 1937; chapter 26 of the former gives a summary of Australian fossil insects. Wardle, 1936.

Classification Procedures and Techniques. Chamberlain, 1946; useful suggestions. Ferris, 1928; concrete and valuable. International Code Zoological Nomenclature, 1961; supersedes all previous versions; the guide to legalistic and clerical procedures. Schenk and McMasters, 1936; still useful as a literature guide for beginners. Simpson, 1961; modern exposition of the philosophy of classification by a contemporary master.

Classification and Identification. Borrer and De Long, 1954; keys to orders and some common families. Brues, Melander and Carpenter, 1954; keys to families (some subfamilies) of world-wide recent and fossil Insecta, Myriapoda and Arachnida; an indispensable reference. Essig, 1942; keys to common families of insects. Jeannel, 1949; summarizes Martynov's classification of insects. Martynov, 1938; basis for modern classification of insects.

Terminology. Melander, 1940. Torre-Bueno, 1937.

Morphology. Imms, 1957; insects only. Grassé, 1949–1951; detailed descriptive morphology of classes, orders and many families of insects and arachnoids; in French. Huxley, 1897. Richards, 1951; cuticle. Snodgrass, 1935, 1952; see also other papers by same author. Verhoeff, 1902–1934; includes descriptive morphology of all major groups of myriapods; in German.

Physiology. Imms, 1957; insects only. Richards, 1951; physiological aspects of arthropod cuticle. Roeder, 1953; insects only. Wigglesworth, 1947; insects only; see also other papers by same author.

Embryology and Life Histories. Chu, 1949; general keys to immature insects, primarily North American. Clausen, 1940; life histories of parasitic insects. Dawydoff, 1949; arachnoid embryology; in French. Grassé, 1949–1951; life histories of arachnoids and insects; in French. Hagan, 1951; general account and detailed embryologies of viviparous insects. Johannsen and Butt, 1941; general embryology and descriptive embryologies of selected insects and myriapods. Peterson, 1948, 1951; immature insects of some orders. Roonwal, 1939.

Medical Entomology. Chandler, 1944; vector and pathogen cycles. Herms, 1939. Herms and James, 1961; a recent review with special emphasis on the vectors. Mackie, Hunter and Worth, 1945; entomology, parasitology and medical aspects of vectored diseases. Patton and Cragg, 1913; a classic. Smart, 1948, identification of vector insects, special emphasis on Africa.

Economic Entomology. Brues, 1947. Fernald, 1935. Graham, 1963. Metcalf, Flint and Metcalf, 1962. Pcairs, 1941. Pfadt, 1962. Steinhaus, 1949. Sweetman, 1936.

Recreational Reading. Cheesman, 1953. Disney, 1954. Fabre, 1876–1904. Imms, 1947. King and Pessels, 1938. Klots and Klots, 1961. Neider, 1954. Verrill, 1937.

REFERENCES CITED

André, M., 1949. Ordre des acariens. *In* Grassé, 1949–1951, 6: 794–905.

Arnett, R. H., Jr., 1960. The beetles of the United States. Catholic Univ. Amer. Press, Washington, D.C. 1110 pp., ill.

Back, E. A., 1920. Book-lice or psocids. U.S. Dept. Agr. Farmers Bull., 1104: 1–4.

Bacot, A., 1914. Plague supplement, II. Jour. Hygiene, 13: 447–654, ill.

Baker, E. W., and G. W. Wharton, 1952. An introduction to acarology. Macmillan, New York. 465 pp., ill.

Balduf, W. V., 1935. The bionomics of entomophagous Coleoptera. John S. Swift Co., St. Louis, Mo. 220 pp., ill.

Banks, N., and T. E. Snyder, 1920. A revision of the nearctic termites. Bull. U.S. Natl. Mus., 108: 1–228, ill.

Barker, W., 1960. Familiar insects of America. Harper, New York. 235 pp., ill.

Beebe, W., 1947. Notes on the Hercules Beetle, Dynastes hercule (Linn.), at Rancho Grande, Venezuela, with special reference to combat behavior. Zoologica, 32: 109–116, ill.

Berland, L., 1949. Ordre des opilions. *In* Grassé, 1949–1951, 6: 761–793.

Berlese, A., 1909a. Gli Insetti, vol. 1. Societa Editrice-Libraria, Milan, 1004 pp., ill.

Berlese, A., 1909b. Monografia dei Myrientomata. Redia, 6: 1–182, ill.

Berlese, A., 1913. Intorno alle metamorfosi degle insetti. Redia, 9: 121–138, ill.

Betten, C., 1934. The caddis flies or Trichoptera of New York State. New York State Mus. Bull., 292: 1–570, ill.

Bishopp, F. C., 1915. Fleas. U.S. Dept. Agr. Bull., 248: 1–10, ill.

Blatchley, W. S., 1910. Coleoptera of Indiana. Nature Publ. Co., Indianapolis, Ind. 1386 pp., ill.

Blatchley, W. S., 1920. Orthoptera of northeastern America. Nature Publ. Co., Indianapolis, Ind. 784 pp., ill.

Blatchley, W. S., 1926. Heteroptera or true bugs of eastern North America. Nature Publ. Co., Indianapolis, Ind. 1116 pp., ill.

Bodenheimer, F. S., 1951. Insects as human food. W. Junk, The Hague. 352 pp., ill.

Bodenstein, D., 1953. Postembryonic development. *In* Roeder, 1953: 822–865, ill.

Bohart, R. M., 1941. A revision of the Strepsiptera with special reference to the species of North America. Univ. California Publ. Ent., 7: 91–160, ill.

Börner, C., 1904. Zur Systematik der Hexapoden. Zool. Anz., 27: 511–533.

Borrer, D. J., and D. M. De Long, 1954. An introduction to the study of insects. Rinehart, New York. 1030 pp., ill.

Bradley, J. C., 1930. A manual of the genera of beetles of America north of Mexico. Daw, Illston & Co., Ithaca, N. Y. 360 pp., ill.

Brauer, F., 1885. Systematisch-zoologische Studien. Sitzber., K. Akad. Wissensch. (Vienna), 91: 237–413, ill.

Bray, R. S., 1958. Studies on malaria in chimpanzees, VI. Laverania falciparum. Amer. Jour. Trop. Med. Hygiene, 7: 20–24.

Bray, R. S., 1963. The exoerythrocytic phase of malaria parasites. Internatl. Rev. Trop. Med., 2: 41–74, ill.

Bristowe, W. S., 1939–1941. The comity of spiders. The Ray Society, London. 2 vols., 560 pp., ill.

Britton, W. E. (ed.), 1916. Guide to the insects of Connecticut, Part 3. The Hymenoptera or wasp-like insects. Connecticut State Geol. Nat. Hist. Surv. Bull., 22: 1–824, ill.

Britton, W. E. (ed.), 1923. Guide to the insects of Connecticut. The Hemiptera or sucking insects of Connecticut. Connecticut State Geol. Nat. Hist. Surv. Bull., 34: 1–807, ill.

Brocher, F., 1920. Étude expérimentale sur le fonctionnement du vaisseau dorsal et sur la circulation du sang chez les insectes, 3rd partie. Le Sphinx convolvuli. Arch. Zool. Exp. (Paris), 60: 1–45.

Brues, C. T., 1947. Insects and human welfare (rev. ed.). Harvard Univ. Press, Cambridge, Mass. 151 pp., ill.

Brues, C. T., A. L. Melander and F. M. Carpenter, 1954. Classification of insects. Bull. Mus. Comp. Zool., 108: 1–917.

Buck, J. B., 1953. Physical properties and chemical composition of insect blood. The internal environment in regulation and metamorphosis. *In* Roeder, 1953: 147–217, ill.

Carpenter, F. M., 1930. A review of our present knowledge of the geological history of the insects. Psyche, 37: 15–34.

Carpenter, F. M., 1931a. Revision of the nearctic Mecoptera. Bull. Mus. Comp. Zool., 72: 205–277, ill.

Carpenter, F. M., 1931b. The biology of the Mecoptera. Psyche, 38: 41–55.

Carpenter, F. M., 1936. Revision of the nearctic Raphidioidea (recent and fossil). Proc. Amer. Acad. Arts Sci., 71: 89–157, ill.

Carpenter, F. M., 1940. A revision of the nearctic Hemerobiidae, Berothidae, Sisyridae, Polystroechotidae and Nilaridae (Neuroptera). Proc. Amer. Acad. Arts Sci., 74: 193–280, ill.

Carpenter, F. M., 1961. Insecta. *In* Gray, 1961: 509–514.

Carpenter, G. H., 1928. The biology of insects. Sedgwick and Jackson Ltd., London. 473 pp., ill.

Carpenter, S. J., and W. J. La Casse, 1955. Mosquitoes of North America (North of Mexico). Univ. California Press, Berkeley and Los Angeles. 360 pp., ill.

Caudell, A. N., 1920. Zoraptera not an apterous order. Proc. Ent. Soc. Washington, 22: 84–97, ill.

Chadwick, L. E., 1953. The motion of the wings. *In* Roeder, 1953: 577–614, ill.

Chamberlin, R. V., and R. L. Hoffman, 1958. Checklist of the millipeds of North America. Bull. U.S. Natl. Mus., 212: 236 pp.

Chamberlin, W. J., 1946. Entomological nomenclature and literature (2nd ed.). Edwards Bros., Ann Arbor, Mich. 135 pp.

Chandler, A. C., 1944. Introduction to parasitology (7th ed.). Wiley, New York. 617 pp., ill.

Chapman, P. J., 1930. Corrodentia of the U.S.A., 1. Sub-order Isotecnomera. Jour. New York Ent. Soc., 38: 319–402, ill.

Cheesman, E.. 1953. Insects, their secret world. William Sloane Associates, New York. 233 pp., ill.

Chopard, L., 1949. *In* Grassé, 1949–1951, 9. ill. (a) Ordre des Dictyoptères, 355–407; (b) Ordre des Cheleuoptères, 594–616; (c) Ordre des Orthoptères, 617–722.

Chu, H. F., 1949. How to know the immature insects. W. C. Brown Co., Dubuque, Iowa. 234 pp., ill.

Claassen, P. W., 1940. A catalogue of the Plecoptera of the world. Cornell Univ. Agr. Exp. Sta. Mem., 232: 1–235.

Clausen, C. P., 1940. Entomophagous insects. McGraw-Hill, New York. 688 pp., ill.

Collins, M. M., and R. D. Weast, 1961. Wild silk moths of the United States. Collins Radio Co., Cedar Rapids, Iowa. 138 pp., ill.

Comstock, J. H., 1918a. Nymphs, naiads and larvae. Ann. Ent. Soc. Amer., 2: 222–224.

Comstock, J. H., 1918b. The wings of insects. Comstock Publ. Co., Ithaca, N. Y. 430 pp., ill. (A revision and expansion of Comstock and Needham, 1898–1899.)

Comstock, J. H., 1940. An introduction to entomology (9th ed., rev. by G. W. Herrick). Cornell Univ. Press, Ithaca, N. Y., 1064 pp., ill.

Comstock, J. H., and W. J. Gertsch, 1940. The spider book. Doubleday, New York. 729 pp., ill.

Comstock, J. H., and J. G. Needham, 1898–1899. The wings of insects. Amer. Nat., 32 and 33: (in 23 short parts). (Reprinted in book form, 1899, Comstock Publ. Co., Ithaca, N. Y. 124 pp., ill.)

Corbet, P. S., 1963. A biology of dragonflies. Quadrangle Books, Inc., Chicago, Ill. 247 pp., ill.

Creighton, W. S., 1950. The ants of North America. Bull. Mus. Comp. Zool., 104: 585 pp.. ill.

Cuénot, L., 1949. Les tardigrades. Les pentastomides. *In* Grassé, 1949–1951, 6: 39–75, ill.

Curran, C. H., 1934. The families and genera of North American Diptera. Ballou Co., New York. 312 pp., ill.

Dawydoff, C., 1949. Développement embryonnaire des arachnides. *In* Grassé, 1949–1951, 6: 320–385, ill.

Delany, M. J., 1954. Thysanura and Diplura. Roy. Ent. Soc. Handb. Identification British Insects, 1: 7 pp., ill.

Denis, J. R., 1949. *In* Grassé, 1949–1951, 9. ill. (a) Diploures, 160–185; (b) Ordre des Zoraptères, 545-555.

Disney, W., 1954. Living desert. Simon and Schuster, New York. 124 pp., ill.

Dobzhansky, T. G., 1937. Genetics and the origin of the species. Columbia Univ. Press, New York. (3rd ed., 1951).

Dodson, E. O., 1960. Evolution: process and product (rev. ed.). Reinhold, New York. 352 pp, ill.

DuPorte, E. M., 1957. The comparative morphology of the insect head. Ann. Rev. Ent. Palo Alto, 2: 55–70.

DuPorte, E. M., 1959. Manual of insect morphology. Reinhold, New York. 224 pp., ill.

Edwards, J. G., 1949. Coleoptera or beetles east of the Great Plains. Publ. by the author, Ann Arbor, Mich. 181 pp.. ill.

Edwards, J. G., 1950. A bibliographical supplement to Coleoptera or beetles east of the Great Plains, applying particularly to western United States. Publ. by the author, San Jose State College, San Jose, Calif. pp. 182–212.

Essig, E. O., 1942. College entomology. Macmillan, New York. 900 pp., ill.

Ewing, H. E., 1929. A manual of external parasites. Charles C Thomas, Springfield, Ill. 225 pp., ill.

Ewing, H. E., 1940. Protura of North America. Ann. Ent. Soc. Amer., 33: 495–551; ill.

Ewing, H. E., 1942. The origin and classification of the Apterygota. Proc. Ent. Soc. Washington, 44: 75–98, ill.

Exner, S., 1891. Die Physiologie der Facettirten Augen von Krebsen und Insecten. Franz Deuticke, Leipzig. 206 pp., ill.

Fabre, J. H., 1876–1904. Souvenirs Entomologiques. Delegrave, Paris. 11 vols. (Many parts have been translated into English; various titles.)

Fernald, H. T., 1935. Applied entomology (3rd ed.). McGraw-Hill, New York. 403 pp., ill.

Ferris, G. F., 1928. The principles of systematic entomology. Stanford Univ. Press, Calif. 169 pp., ill.

Ferris, G. F., 1947. The contradictions of the insect head. Microentomology, 12: 59–64.

Ferris, G. F., 1951. The sucking lice. Mem. Pacific Coast Ent. Soc., 1: 1–320, 124 figs.

Forbes, W. T. M., 1923–1960. Lepidoptera of New York and neighboring states. Cornell Univ. Agr. Exp. Sta. Mem., ill. Part 1, 68: 729 pp. (1923); Part 2, 274: 263 pp. (1948); Part 3, 329: 433 pp. (1954); Part 4, 371: 188 pp. (1960).

Foster, S. W., and P. R. Jones, 1915. Life history and habits of the pear thrip in California. U.S. Dept. Agr. Bull., 173: 1–51, ill

Fox, I., and H. E. Ewing, 1943. The fleas of North America. U.S. Dept. Agr. Misc. Publ., 500: 1–128, ill.

Fox, Jean W., 1956. Comments on Aphididae list in Makino's atlas of chromosome numbers in animals. Ent. News, 67: 189–190.

Fox, Jean W., 1957. Chromosome number in Rhopalosiphum prunifoliae (Fitch) and Rhopalosiphum pseudobrassicae (Davis) (Hemiptera: Aphididae). Trans. Amer. Micros. Soc., 76: 208–211.

Fox, R. M., 1956. A monograph of the Ithomiidae (Lepidoptera), Pt. I. Bull. Amer. Mus. Nat. Hist., 111: 7–76, ill.

Fox, R. M., 1960. A monograph of the Ithomiidae (Lepidoptera), Pt. II. The tribe Melinaeini Clark. Trans. Amer. Ent. Soc., 36; 109–171, ill.

Fox, R. M., and R. M. Stabler, 1953. Basilia calverti, a new species of bat-tick fly (Diptera: Nycteribiidae). Jour. Parasitology, 39: 22–27, ill.

Frison, T. H., 1942. Studies on North American Plecoptera with special reference to the fauna of Illinois. Bull. Illinois Nat. Hist. Surv., 22: 235–355, ill.

Froeschner, R. C., 1947. Notes and keys to the Neuroptera of Missouri. Ann. Ent. Soc. Amer., 40: 123–136, ill.

Frost, S. W., 1942. General entomology. McGraw-Hill, New York. 524 pp., ill.

Gertsch, W. J., 1949. American spiders. Van Nostrand, New York. 285 pp., ill.

Gilette, C. P., and M. A. Palmer, 1931. Aphididae of Colorado, Part I. Ann. Ent. Soc. Amer., 24: 829–934, ill.

Gilmour, D., 1953. The biochemistry of muscle. In Roeder, 1953: 404–422.

Goodrich, E. S., 1897. On the relation of the arthropod head to the annelid prostomium. Quart. Jour. Micros. Sci., 40: 259–268, ill.

Graham, K., 1963. Concepts of forest entomology. Reinhold, New York. 388 pp., ill.

Grassé, P.-P., 1949. Ordre des Isoptera ou termites. In Grassé, 1949–1951, 9: 408–544, ill.

Grassé, P.-P. (ed.), 1949–1951. Traité de Zoologie. Vol. 6 (arthropods in general, chelicerates), 1949; vol. 9 (insects), 1949; vol. 10 in 2 parts (insects), 1951. Masson et Cie, Paris.

Grassi, B., 1887. Anatomia comparata die Tisanuri e considerazioni generali sull organizzazione degli Insetti. Atti R. Accad. Lincei (Rome) Mem., (4)4: 543–606, ill.

Gray, Peter (ed.), 1961. The encyclopedia of the biological sciences. Reinhold, New York. 1119 pp., ill.

Gurney, A. B., 1938. A synopsis of the order Zoroptera with notes on the biology of Zorotypus hubbardi Caudell. Proc. Ent. Soc. Washington, 22: 98–106, ill.

Gurney, A. B., 1948. The taxonomy and distribution of the Grylloblattidae (Orthoptera). Proc. Ent. Soc. Washington, 50: 86–110, ill.

Gurney, A. B., 1950. Corrodentia. In Pest control technology: 129–163, 3 figs. Natl. Pest Control Assoc., Inc., New York.

Hagan, H. R., 1917. Observations on the embryonic development of the mantid Paratenodera sinensis. Jour. Morph., 30: 223–237, ill.

Hagan, H. R., 1951. Embryology of the viviparous insects. Ronald Press, New York. 472 pp., ill.

Hall, D. G., 1948. The blowflies of North America. Thomas Say Foundation, Springfield, Ill., 477 pp., ill.

Handlirsch, A., 1906–1908. Die Fossilen Insekten und die Phylogenie der Rezenten Formen. W. Engelman, Leipzig. 1430 pp., ill.

Handlirsch, A., 1937–1939. Neue Untersuchugen über die fossilen Insekten mit Ergänzungen and Nachträgen sowie Ausblicken auf phylogenetische, paläogeographische und allgemein biologische Probleme. Ann. Naturhist. Mus. Vienna, 48: 1–140; 49: 1–240; ill.

Hansen, H. J., 1903. In Austen, E. E., A monograph of the tse-tse flies (genus Glossina Westwood) based on the collection in the British Museum. British Museum, London. pp. 105–120, ill.

Hanström, B., 1927. Das zentrale und periphere Nervensystem des Kopflappens einiger Polychäten. Zeitschr. Morph. Ökol. Tiere, 7: 543–596.

Hanström, B., 1928. Die Beziehungen zwischen dem Gehirn der Polychaten und dem der Arthropoden. Zeitschr. Morph. Okol. Tiere, 11: 543–596.

Hanström, B., 1930. Über das Gehirn von Termopsis nevadensis und Phyllium pulcrifolium nebst Beiträgen zur Phylogenie der Corpora pedunculata der Arthropoden. Zeitschr. Morph. Ökol. Tiere, 19: 732–773.

Harrison, L., 1916. The genera and species of Mallophaga. Parasitology, 9: 1–156.

Hebard, M., 1917a. A contribution to the knowledge of the Dermaptera of Panama. Trans. Amer. Ent. Soc., 43: 301–333, ill.

Hebard, M. 1917b. The Blattidae of North America north of the Mexican boundary. Mem. Amer. Ent. Soc., 2: 1–284, ill.

Henry, L. M., 1947–1948. The nervous system and segmentation of the head in the Annulata. Microentomology, 12: 65–110; 13: 1–48; ill.

Herms, W. B., 1939. Medical entomology. Macmillan, New York. 582 pp., ill.

Herms, W. B., and M. T. James, 1961. Medical entomology. Macmillan, New York. 616 pp., ill.

Hess, W. N., 1917. The chorodontal organs and the pleural discs of Carambycid larvae. Ann. Ent. Soc. Amer., 10: 63–74, ill.

Hesse, R., W. C. Allee and K. P. Schmidt, 1937. Ecological animal geography. Wiley, New York. 597 pp., ill.

Hilton, W. A., 1932. The Campodea of California. Jour. Ent. Zool., 24: 47–51, ill.

Hinton, H. E., 1946. A new classification of insect pupae. Proc. Zool. Soc. London, 116: 282–328, ill.

Hinton, H. E., 1948. On the origin and function of the pupal stage. Trans. Roy. Ent. Soc. London, 99: 395–409, 1 fig.

Hoff, C. C., 1949. The pseudoscorpions of Illinois. Bull. Illinois Nat. Hist. Surv., 24: 1–874, ill.

Holland, W. J., 1905. The moth book. Doubleday, New York. 479 pp., ill.

Holland, W. J., 1929. Forum on problems of taxonomy: types. IV Internatl. Congr. Ent., Ithaca, 1928, 2: 688–693.

Holland, W. J., 1931. The butterfly book (rev. ed.). Doubleday, New York. 424 pp., ill.

Holmgren, N., 1896. Zur Kenntnis des Hautnervensystems der Arthropoden. Anat. Anz., 12: 449–457.

Hoogstraal, H., 1956. African Ixodoidea, I. Ticks of the Sudan. Dept. Navy, Bur. Med., Res. Rept. NM 005 050.29.07. 1101 pp., ill.

Hopkins, G. H. E., and M. Rothschild, 1953. An illustrated catalogue of the Rothschild collection of fleas (Siphonaptera) in the British Museum, vol. 1. Tungidae and Pulicidae. British Museum, London. 361 pp., ill.

Horsfall, W. R., 1955. Mosquitoes. their bionomics and relation to disease. Ronald Press, New York. 723 pp.

Horton, J. R., 1918. The citrus thrips. U.S. Dept. Agr. Bull., 616: 1–42, ill.

Hubbard, C. A., 1947. Fleas of western North America. Iowa State Coll. Press, Ames. 553 pp., ill.

Huff, C. G., 1931. A proposed classification of disease transmission by arthropods. Science, 74: 456.

Huxley, T. H., 1897. A manual of the anatomy of invertebrated animals. Appleton, New York. 596 pp., ill.

Imms, A. D., 1939. On the antennal musculature in insects and other arthropods. Quart. Jour. Micros. Sci., 81: 273–320, ill.

Imms, A. D., 1940. On growth-processes in the antennae of insects. Quart. Jour. Micros. Sci., 81: 585–593, 1 fig.

Imms, A. D., 1947. Insect natural history. Collins, London. 316 pp., ill.

Imms, A. D., 1957 (rev. by O. W. Richards and R. C. Davies). A general textbook of entomology. Dutton, New York. 866 pp., ill.

International Code of Zoological Nomenclature, 1961, adopted by the XV Internatl. Congr. Zool. Internatl. Trust Zool. Nomenclature, London. In parallel French and English. 176 pp.

James, M. T., 1947. The flies that cause myiasis in man. U.S. Dept. Agr. Misc. Publ., 651: 1–175, ill.

Jeannel, R., 1944. Sur la position systématique des Strepsiptères. Rev. Française Ent. (Paris), 11: 111–118.

Jeannel, R., 1949. Les insectes. Classification et phylogénie. Les insectes fossiles. Évolution et Géonémie. *In* Grassé, 1949–1951, 9: 3–110, ill.

Jeannel, R., 1960. Introduction to entomology (English translation by H. Oldroyd). Hutchinson & Co., Ltd., London. 344 pp., ill.

Johannsen, O. A., and F. H. Butt, 1941. Embryology of insects and myriapods. McGraw-Hill, New York. 462 pp., ill.

Jones, J. C., 1950. The normal hemocyte picture of the yellow mealworm, Tenebrio molitor Linnaeus. Iowa State Jour. Sci., 24: 355–361, 1 fig.

Jones, T., 1954. The external morphology of Chirothrips hamatus (Trybom) (Thysanoptera). Trans. Roy. Ent. Soc. London, 105: 163–187, ill.

Keeton, W. T., 1960. A taxonomic study of the milliped family Spirobolidae (Diplopoda: Spirobolida). Mem. Amer. Ent. Soc., 17: 1–146, ill.

Keilin, D., 1944. Respiratory systems and respiratory adaptations in larvae and pupae of Diptera. Parasitology, 36: 1–66, ill.

Kenyon, F. C., 1895. The morphology and classification of the Pauropoda. Tufts College Studies, 4: 77–146, ill.

King, E., and W. Pessels, 1938. Insect allies. Harper, New York. 45 pp., ill.

Klots, A. B., 1951. A field guide to the butterflies. Houghton Mifflin, Boston. 349 pp., ill.

Klots, A. B., and E. B. Klots, 1961. 1001 questions answered about insects. Dodd, Mead, New York. 260 pp., ill.

Kofoid, C. A. (ed.), 1934. Termites and termite control. Univ. California Press, Berkeley. 795 pp., ill.

Köhler, W., and W. Feldotto, 1937. Morphologische and experimentelle Untersuchungen über Farbe. Form und Struktur der Schuppen von Vanessa urticae und ihre gegenseitigen Beziehungen. Arch. Entwick. Mech. Org. (Berlin), 136: 313–399, ill.

Krombein, K. V. (ed.), 1958. Hymenoptera of America north of Mexico, synoptic catalogue, first supplement. U.S. Dept. Agr. Monogr., 2, first supplement: 305 pp. (see Muesebeck et al., 1951).

Latreille, P. A., 1825. Familles naturelles du régne animal. Baillière, Paris. 570 pp.

Latzel, R., 1884. Die Myriopoden der Osterreichisch-Ungarischen Monarchie . . . , vol. 2. Die Symphylen, Pauropoden und Diplopoden. Vienna. 414 pp., ill.

Laurentiaux, D., 1953. Classe des myriapodes. *In* Piveteau, 1952–1957, Traité de Paléontologie, 3: 397–527, ill. Masson et Cie, Paris.

Leach, J. G., 1940. Insect transmission of plant diseases. McGraw-Hill, New York. 615 pp., ill.

Lew, G. T., 1933. Head characters of the Odonata with special reference to the development of the compound eye. Ent. Amer., 14: 41–73, ill.

Linné, Carl von, 1758. Systema naturae . . . regnum animale (editio decima). Stockholm. 824 pp.

Lowne, B. T., 1890–1892. The anatomy, physiology, morphology, and development of the blow-fly (Calliphora erythrocephala). R. H. Porter, London. 350 pp., ill.

MacGillivray, A. D., 1893. North American Thysanura. Canadian Ent., 25: 173–174, 218–220.

Mackie, T. T., G. W. Hunter III and C. B. Worth, 1945. Manual of tropical medicine. Saunders, Philadelphia. 727 pp., ill.

Makino, S., 1951. An atlas of chromosome numbers in animals. Iowa State Coll. Press, Ames. 290 pp.

Mallis, A., 1960. Handbook of pest control. The behavior, life history, and control of household pests (3rd ed.). MacNair-Dorland Co., New York. 1132 pp., ill.

Manton, S. M., 1949. Studies on the Onychophora, VII. The early embryonic stages of Peripatopsis and some general considerations concerning the morphology and phylogeny of the Arthropoda. Phil. Trans., (B)233: 483–580, ill.

Marlatt, C. L., 1916. House ants: kinds and methods of control. U.S. Dept. Agr. Farmers Bull., 740: 12 pp., ill.

Martynov, A. B., 1938. Studies on the geological history and phylogeny of the orders of pterygote insects, I. Palaeoptera and Neoptera Polyneoptera (in Russian). Trav. Inst. Paleontol., Acad. Sci. U.S.S.R. (Leningrad), 7: 1–150.

Matheson, R., 1947. Entomology for introductory courses. Comstock Publ. Co., Ithaca, N. Y. 600 pp., ill.

Maynard, E. A., 1951. A monograph of the Collembola or springtail insects of New York State. Comstock Publ. Co., Ithaca, N. Y. 339 pp., ill.

Mayr, E., 1947. Systematics and the origin of species. Columbia Univ. Press, New York. 334 pp., ill.

Melander, A. L., 1940. Source book of biological terms. Dept. Biol., City Coll., New York. 157 pp.

Metcalf, C. L.. W. P. Flint and R. L. Metcalf, 1962. Destructive and useful insects (4th ed.). McGraw-Hill, New York. 1086 pp., ill.

Michener, C. D., and M. H. Michener, 1951. American social insects. Van Nostrand, New York. 267 pp., ill.

Miller, N. C. E., 1956. The biology of the Heteroptera. Leonard Hill Ltd., London. 162 pp., ill.

Millot, J., 1949. In Grassé, 1949–1951, 6. ill. (a) Classe des arachnides. I. Morphologie générale et anatomie interne, 263–319; (b) Ordre des palpigrades, 520–532; (c) Ordre des uropyges, 533–562; (d) Ordre des amblypyges, 563–588; (e) Ordre des araneides, 589–743; (f) Ordre des ricinuleides, 744–760.

Millot, J., and M. Vachon, 1949. In Grassé, 1949–1951, 6. ill. (a) Ordre des scorpions, 386–436; (b) Ordre des solfuges, 482–519.

Mills, H. B., 1934. A monograph of the Collembola of Iowa. Iowa State Coll. Monogr. 3: 1–143, ill.

Mitchell, T. B., 1960. Bees of the eastern United States, vol. 1. Families Colletidae, Andrenidae, Halictidae, Melittidae. North Carolina Agr. Exp. Sta. 538 pp., ill.

Moore, R. C. (ed.), 1953–1960. Treatise on invertebrate paleontology. Parts D (1954), E (1955), F (1956), G (1953), I (1960), L (1957), O (1959), P (1955), V (1955). Geological Soc. Amer. and Univ. Kansas Press, Lawrence.

Morse, A. P., 1920. Manual of the Orthoptera of New England. Proc. Boston Soc. Nat. Hist., 35: 197–556, ill.

Muesebeck, C. F. W., K. V. Krombein and H. K. Townes (eds.), 1951. Hymenoptera of America north of Mexico, synoptic catalogue. U.S. Dept. Agr. Monogr., 2: 1420 pp.

Müller, J., 1826. Zur vergleichenden Physiologie des Gesichtssinnes des Menschen und der Thiere. Leipzig.

Munz, P. A., 1919. Keys for the identification of genera of Zygoptera. Mem. Amer. Ent. Soc., 3: 1–78, ill.

Needham, J. G., and P. W. Claassen, 1925. A monograph of the Plecoptera or stoneflies of America north of Mexico. Thomas Say Foundation, Springfield, Ill. 397 pp., ill.

Needham, J. G., J. R. Traver and Yin-Chi Hsu, 1935. The biology of mayflies. Comstock Publ. Co., Ithaca, N. Y. 759 pp., ill.

Needham. J. G., and M. J. Westfall, Jr., 1955. A manual of the dragonflies of North America (Anisoptera). Univ. California Press, Berkeley and Los Angeles. 615 pp., ill.

Neider, C. (ed.), 1954. The fabulous insects. Harper, New York. 276 pp.

Nutting, W. L., 1951. A comparative anatomical study of the heart and accessory organs of the orthopteroid insects. Jour. Morph., 89: 501–553, ill.

Packard, A. S., 1898. A textbook of entomology. Macmillan, New York. 729 pp., ill.

Parker, H. L., and H. D. Smith, 1933. Additional notes on the strepsipteron Eoxenos laboubenei Peyerimhoff. Ann. Ent. Soc. Amer., 26: 217–231, ill.

Patch, E. M., 1920. The life cycle of the aphids and coccids. Ann. Ent. Soc. Amer., 13: 156–167.

Patton, W. S., and F. W. Cragg, 1913. A textbook of medical entomology. Christian Literature Society for India, London. 764 pp., ill.

Peacock, A. D., 1961. Parthenogenesis. In Gray, 1961: 739–741.

Peairs, L. M., 1941. Insect pests of farm, garden and orchard. Wiley, New York. 549 pp., ill.

Peterson, A., 1948. Larvae of insects, Part I. Lepidoptera and plant infesting Hymenoptera. Publ. by the author, Columbus, Ohio. 315 pp., ill.

Peterson, A., 1951. Larvae of insects, Part II. Coleoptera, Diptera, Neuroptera, Siphonaptera, Mecoptera, Trichoptera, Publ. by the author, Columbus, Ohio. 416 pp., ill.

Petrunkevitch, A., 1933. An inquiry into the natural classification of spiders, based on a study of their internal anatomy. Trans. Connecticut Acad. Arts Sci., 31: 299–389.

Petrunkevitch, A., 1955. Arachnida. In Moore, 1953–1960, Part P: 42–162.

Pfadt, R. E., (ed.), 1962. Fundamentals of applied entomology. Macmillan, New York. 668 pp., ill.

Pflugfelder, O., 1932. Über den Mechanisms der Segmentbildung bei der Embryonalentwicklung und Anamorphose von Platyrrhacus amauros Attems. Zeitschr. Wissensch. Zool., 140: 650–723, ill.

Pierce, W. D., 1909. A monographic revision of the twisted winged insects comprising the order Strepsiptera Kirby. Bull. U.S. Nat. Mus., 66: 1–232, ill.

Pierce, W. D., 1918. The comparative morphology of the order Strepsiptera together with records and descriptions of insects. Proc. U.S. Nat. Mus., 54: 391–501, ill.

Pierce, W. D., 1936. The position of the Strepsiptera in the classification of insects. Ent. News, 47: 257–263.

Pocock, J., 1887. On the classification of the tracheate Arthropoda. Zool. Anz., 423: 271–275.

Poyarkoff, E., 1914. Essai d'une théorie de la nymphe des insectes holométaboles. Arch. Zool. Exp. Gen., 54: 221–265.

Raymond, P. E., 1920. The appendages, anatomy, and relationships of trilobites. Mem. Connecticut Acad. Arts Sci. 7: 1–169, ill.

Rehn, J. W. H., 1951. Classification of the Blattaria as indicated by their wings. Mem. Amer. Ent. Soc., 14: 134 pp., ill.

Rehn, J. A. G., and J. W. H. Rehn, 1936. A study of the genus Hemimerus (Dermaptera). Proc. Acad. Nat. Sci. Philadelphia, 87: 457–508, ill.

Remy, P., 1931. Un nouveau type de Pauropode: Decapauropus cuenoti. Arch. Zool. Exp. Gen., 71: 67–83.

Richards, A. G., 1943. Lipid nerve sheaths and insecticide reaction. Jour. New York Ent. Soc., 51: 55–69.

Richards, A. G., 1944. Optical properties of nerves. Jour. New York Ent. Soc., 52: 285–310.

Richards, A. G., 1951. The integument of arthropods. Univ. Minnesota Press, Minneapolis. 411 pp., ill.

Richards, A. G., and F. H. Korda, 1950. Electron micrographs of tracheal intima. Ann. Ent. Soc. Amer., 43: 49–71.

Richards, O. W., 1953. The social insects. Harper, New York. 219 pp., ill. (Harper Torchbook Edition, 1961.)

Roache, L. C., 1960. A revision of the North American elaterid beetles of the tribe Elaterini (Coleoptera: Elateridae). Trans. Amer. Ent. Soc., 8: 275–324, ill.

Roback, S. S., 1959. The subgenus Ablobesmyia of Pentaneura (Diptera: Tentipedidae, Pelopiinae). Trans Amer. Ent. Soc., 85: 113–135, ill.

Roeder, K. D. (ed.), 1953. Insect physiology. Wiley, New York. 1100 pp., ill.

Roesler, R., 1944. Die Gattungen der Copeognathen. Stettiner Ent. Zeitg., 105: 117–166.

Roonwal, M. L., 1936–1937. Studies on the embryology of the African migratory locust, Locusta migratoria migratorioides, I, II. Phil. Trans., (B)226: 391–421; (B)227: 175–244; ill.

Roonwal, M. L., 1939. Some recent advances in insect embryology, with a complete bibliography on the subject. Jour. Roy. Asiatic Soc. Bengal, 4: 17–105.

Ross, E. M., 1944. A revision of the Embioptera, or webspinners, of the New World. Proc. U.S. Nat. Mus., 94: 401–504, ill.

Ross, H. H., 1944. The caddis flies or Trichoptera of Illinois. Illinois Nat. Hist. Surv. Bull., 23: 1–326, ill.

Ross, H. H., 1948. A textbook of entomology. Wiley, New York. 532 pp., ill. (2nd ed., 1956.)

Russell, P. F., L. West and R. Manwell, 1946. Practical malariology. Saunders, Philadelphia. 684 pp., ill.

Schenk, E. T., and J. H. McMasters, 1936. Procedure in taxonomy. Stanford Univ. Press, Calif. 72 pp.

Schimkewitsch, L., and V. Schimkewitsch, 1911. Ein Beiträge zur Entwicklungsgeschichte der Tetrapneumones. Bull. Acad. Sci. St. Petersburg, (6)1911: 637–654, 685–705, 775–790, ill.

Schwabe, J., 1906. Beiträge zur Morphologie und Histologie der tympanalen Sinnesapparate der Orthopteren. Zoologica (Stuttgart), 50: 1–154, ill.

Scott, H. G., 1959. Collembola from Colorado. Ent. News, 70: 13–16, ill.

Seitz, A., 1905–1939. Die Grossschmetterlinge der Erde. A. Kernen, Stuttgart. 16 quarto vols., ill. color. (Vols. 5–8 on fauna of Americas.)

Sharp, D., 1898. Some points in the classification of Insecta Hexapoda. IV Internatl. Congr. Zool.: 246–249.

Shull, A. F., 1914. Biology of the Thysanoptera. Amer. Nat., 48: 161–176, 236–247.

Sihler, H., 1924. Die Sinnesorgane an der cerci der Insecten. Zool. Jahrb. Anat., 45: 519–580.

Silvestri, F.. 1903. Acari, Myriapoda et Scorpiones hucusque in Italia reperta. Classis Diploda, vol. 1. Anatome. Portici, Naples. 272 pp., ill.

Simpson, G. G., 1945. The principles of classification of mammals. Bull. Amer. Mus. Nat. Hist., 85: 1–350.

Simpson, G. G., 1953. Life of the past. Yale Univ. Press, New Haven, Conn. 198 pp., ill.

Simpson, G. G., 1961. Principles of animal taxonomy. Columbia Univ. Press, New York. 247 pp., ill.

Smart, J., 1948. A handbook for the identification of insects of medical importance. British Museum, London. 295 pp., ill.

Snodgrass, R. E., 1909. The thorax of insects and the articulation of wings. Proc. U.S. Nat. Mus., 36: 511–595, ill.

Snodgrass, R. E., 1910. The thorax of the hymenoptera. Proc. U.S. Nat. Mus., 39: 37–91, ill.

Snodgrass, R. E., 1924. The morphology of insect sense organs and the sensory nervous system. Smithsonian Misc. Coll., 77(6): 1–180, ill.

Snodgrass, R. E., 1925. Anatomy and physiology of the honeybee. McGraw-Hill, New York. 327 pp., ill.

Snodgrass, R. E., 1929. The thoracic mechanism of a grasshopper and its antecedents. Smithsonian Misc. Coll., 82(2): 111 pp., ill.

Snodgrass, R. E., 1932a. Evolution of the insect head and the organs of feeding. Ann. Rept. Smithsonian Inst., 1931: 443–489; ill.

Snodgrass, R. E., 1932b. Morphology of the insect abdomen, Part 1. Smithsonian Misc. Coll., 85(6): 1–128, ill.

Snodgrass, R. E., 1933. Morphology of the insect abdomen, Part 2. Smithsonian Misc. Coll., 89(8): 1–148, ill.

Snodgrass, R. E., 1935. Principles of insect morphology. McGraw-Hill, New York. 667 pp., ill.

Snodgrass, R. E., 1936. Morphology of the insect abdomen, Part 3. The male genitalia. Smithsonian Misc. Coll., 95(4): 96 pp., ill.

Snodgrass, R. E., 1938. Evolution of the Annelida, Onychophora and Arthropoda. Smithsonian Misc. Coll., 97(6): 159 pp., ill.

Snodgrass, R. E., 1944. The feeding apparatus of biting and sucking insects affecting man and animals. Smithsonian Misc. Coll., 104(7): 1–113, ill.

Snodgrass, R. E., 1951. Comparative studies on the head of mandibulate arthropods. Comstock Publ. Co., Ithaca, N.Y. 118 pp., ill.

Snodgrass, R. E., 1952. A textbook of arthropod anatomy. Comstock Publ. Co., Ithaca, N.Y. 363 pp., ill.

Snodgrass, R. E., 1954. Insect metamorphosis. Smithsonian Misc. Coll., 122: 1–124, ill.

Snyder, T. E., 1948. Our enemy the termite (2nd ed.). Comstock Publ. Co., Ithaca, N.Y. 257 pp., ill.

Snyder, T. E., 1949. Catalog of the termites (Isoptera) of the world. Smithsonian Misc. Coll., 112: 1–490.

Snyder, T. E., 1954. Order Isoptera, the termites of the United States and Canada. Natl. Pest Control Assoc., New York. 64 pp., ill.

Stannard, L. J., 1957. The phylogeny and classification of the North American genera of the Tubulifera (Thysanoptera). Univ. Illinois Press, Urbana, Ill. 200 pp., ill.

Stefferud, A. (ed.), 1952. Insects, the yearbook of agriculture, 1952. Govt, Printing Office, Washington, D.C. 780 pp., ill.

Steinhaus, E. A., 1949. Principles of insect pathology. McGraw-Hill, New York. 757 pp., ill.

Störmer, L., 1933. Merostomata from the Downtonian sandstone of Ringerike, Norway. Skr. Norske Vidensk.-Akad., Oslo, 1933(10): 1–125, ill.

Störmer, L., 1959. Arthropoda—general features. In Moore, 1953–1960, Part O: 3–16.

Störmer, L., A. Petrunkevitch and J. W. Hedgpeth, 1955. Chelicerata. In Moore, 1953–1960, Part P: 1–3.

Sturdivant, A. H., 1942. Classification of the genus Drosophila. Univ. Texas Publ., 4213: 1–51.

Sweetman, H. L., 1936. Biological control of insects. Comstock Publ. Co., Ithaca, N.Y. 461 pp., ill.

Sweetman, H. L., 1938. Physical ecology of the firebrat Thermobia domestica (Packard). Ecol. Monogr., 8: 285–311, ill.

Tiegs, O. W., 1940. The embryology and affinities of the Symphyla, based on a study of Hanseniella agilis. Quart. Jour. Micros. Sci., 82: 1–225, ill.

Tillyard, R. J., 1926. Insects of Australia and New Zealand. Angus & Robertson, Sydney, Australia. 560 pp., ill.

Tillyard, R. J., 1937. Kansas Permian insects, Part 20. The cockroaches of order Blattaria, Part II. Amer. Jour. Sci., 34: 249–276, ill.

Torre-Bueno, J. R. de la, 1907. On Rhagovelia obesa Uhler. Canadian Ent., 39: 61–64, ill.

Torre-Bueno, J. R. de la, 1916. Aquatic Hemiptera. A study in the relation of structure to environment. Ann. Ent. Soc. Amer., 9: 353–365.

Torre-Bueno, J. R. de la, 1937. A glossary of entomology. Brooklyn Ent. Soc., Brooklyn, N.Y. 336 pp., ill.

Torre-Bueno, J. R. de la, 1939–1946. A synopsis of the Hemiptera Heteroptera of America north of Mexico. Ent. Amer., 19: 141–304; 21: 41–122; 26: 1–141.

Tower, D. G., 1914. The mechanism of the mouthparts of the squash bug, Anasa tristis Degeer. Psyche, 21: 99–108, ill.

Townes, H. K., Jr., 1944. A catalogue and reclassification of the nearctic Ichneumonidae. Mem. Amer. Ent. Soc., 11: 1–925.

Vachon, M., 1938. Recherches anatomiques et biologiques sur la reproduction et le développement des pseudoscorpions. Ann. Sci. Nat. Zool. (Paris), (11)1: 1–207, ill.

Vachon, M., 1949. Ordre des pseudoscorpions. In Grassé, 1949–1951, 6: 437–481, ill.

Vandel, A., 1949. Généralités, composition de l'embranchement Arthropoda. In Grassé, 1949–1951, 6: 79–158.

Van Name, W. G., 1936. The American land and fresh-water isopod Crustacea. Bull. Amer. Mus. Nat. Hist., 71: 1–535, ill.

Verhoeff, K. W., 1902–1934. Myriapoda: Chilopoda, Diplopoda, Symphyla, Pauropoda. *In* Bronns, Klassen und Ordnungen des Tier-Reichs, vol. 5, abt. 2. Buch 1 (Chilopoda): 1–626 (1902–1925). Buch 2 (Diplopoda): 1–2084 (1926–1932). Buch 3 (Symphyla, Pauropoda): 1–200 (1933–1934).

Verrill, A. H., 1937. Strange insects and their stories. Grosset & Dunlap, New York. 205 pp., ill.

Walker, E. M., 1914. A new species of Orthoptera forming a new genus and family. Canadian Ent., 46: 93–99, ill.

Walker, E. M., 1937. Grylloblatta, a living fossil. Trans. Roy. Soc. Canada, (3)31: 1–10.

Walker, E. M., 1953. The Odonata of Canada and Alaska. Univ. Toronto Press. 293 pp., ill.

Wardle, R. A., 1936. General entomology. Blakiston, Philadelphia. 311 pp., ill.

Waterlot, G., 1949. Les arachnides fossiles. *In* Grassé, 1949–1951, 6: 893–905.

Watson, J. R., 1923. Synopsis and catalogue of the Thysanoptera of North America. Univ. Florida Agr. Exp. Sta. Bull., 168: 1–100.

Weber, H., 1952. Morphologie, Histologie und Entwicklungsgeschichte der Articulaten. Forschr. Zool., 9: 18–231, ill.

West, L. S., 1951. The housefly, its natural history, medical importance, and control. Comstock Publ. Co., Ithaca, N.Y. 584 pp., ill.

Wharton, G. W., and H. S. Fuller, 1952. A manual of the chiggers. Mem. Ent. Soc. Washington, 4: 1–185, ill.

Wheeler, W. M., 1910. Ants, their structure, development and behavior. Columbia Univ. Press, New York. 663 pp., ill.

Wheeler, W. M., 1923. Social life among the insects. Harcourt, Brace, New York. 375 pp., ill.

Wheeler, W. M., 1930. Demons of the dust. Norton, New York. 378 pp., ill.

Wiesmann, R., 1926. *In* Leuzinger, Wiesmann and Lehmann, Zur Kenntnis der Anatomie und Entwicklungsgeschichte der Stabheuschrecke Carausius morosus Br. Jena. 414 pp., ill.

Wigglesworth, V. B., 1933. The effects of salts on the anal gills of the mosquito larva. The function of the anal gills of the mosquito larva. The adaptation of mosquito larva to salt water. Jour. Exp. Biol. (Cambridge), 10: 1–37, ill.

Wigglesworth, V. B., 1947. The principles of insect physiology (3rd ed.). Methuen & Co. Ltd., London. 434 pp., ill.

Wigglesworth, V. B., 1959. The control of growth and form. Cornell Univ. Press, Ithaca, N.Y. 140 pp., ill.

Williams, J., 1947. The anatomy of the internal genitalia of Fumea casta Pallas (Lep.: Psychidae). Trans. Amer. Ent. Soc., 73: 77–84, ill.

Williams, S. R., and R. A. Hefner, 1928. The millipedes and centipedes of Ohio. Ohio State Univ. Bull., 33: 93–146, ill.

Wilson, H. F., and M. H. Doner, 1937. The historical development of insect classification. John S. Swift Co., St. Louis, Mo. 133 pp., ill.

I N D E X

Illustrations are indicated by italicized page numbers.